A Baby Guide to Calgary

2ND EDITION

MAKING THE MOST OF YOUR PARENTAL LEAVE

Now including Cochrane, Airdrie,
Chestermere and Okotoks

By Paula McGarrigle

First edition of *A Baby Guide to Calgary*
was written by Paula McGarrigle and Elena Rhodes

Playgroup Books
Calgary, Alberta

Copyright © 2008 Paula McGarrigle
Edited by Elena Rhodes and Cindy Mintz.
Proofread by Ellen Groskorth.
Front and back cover design and illustrations by Corinna Maguire.
Internal artwork by Juanita McGarrigle.
Layout based on work by Corinna Maguire and updated by Erin Woodward.
Library and Archives Canada Cataloguing in Publication

McGarrigle, Paula, 1966-
    A Baby Guide to Calgary: making the most of your parental leave / by Paula McGarrigle. — 2nd ed.

Includes index.
ISBN 978-0-9739482-1-9

1. Parents—Services for—Alberta—Calgary—Directories.
2. Infants—Services for—Alberta—Calgary—Directories. 3. Infants—Care—Alberta—Calgary—Information resources. 4. Infants' supplies—Alberta—Calgary—Directories. 5. Calgary (Alta.)—Directories. 6. Calgary (Alta.)—Guidebooks. I. Title.

HQ774.M22 2008   649.122025712338   C2007-905013-1

Playgroup Books
Suite 119, 2137 33 Avenue S.W.
Calgary, Alberta, Canada, T2T 1Z7

info@babyguidetocalgary.com
www.babyguidetocalgary.com
Printed in Canada

TABLE OF CONTENTS

Acknowledgements vii

Introduction viii

Disclaimer xi

Chapter One: Administrative Issues I
    Baby Naming I
    Maternity and Parental Leave Rights and Benefits I
    Employment Insurance I
    Alberta Health Care 3
    Adding Baby to Work Benefit Plan 4
    Birth Certificate 4
    Social Insurance Number 5
    Registered Education Savings Plan 6
    Canada Learning Bond 7
    Children's Fitness Tax Credit. 8
    The Alberta Centennial Education Savings Plan 8
    Canada Child Tax Benefit, National Child Tax Benefit and Alberta Family
        Employment Tax Credit 8
    Universal Child Care Benefit (UCB). 10
    Passport for Baby 10
    The Alberta Stay-at-Home Parent, Child Care Subsidy 12
    The Alberta Child Care Subsidy Program 14
    Government of Alberta Services for Lower-Income Albertans 15

Chapter Two: Surviving the First Six Weeks. 16
    Installing Your Infant Car Seat. 16
    Postpartum Community Services 16
    Early Start Parent Information Line 17
    Early Start Drop-In Service. 17
    Finding a Doctor or Paediatrician 17
    24-Hour Pharmacies 18
    "Back to Sleep, Tummy to Play" Information Sessions 19
    Breastfeeding 19
    Nursing Bras 30
    Formula 33
    Postpartum Depression Support 34
    Personal Concierge Service 36
    What's for Dinner? 37
    Delivered Groceries 40

Chapter Three: Parenting Help 42
  Parenting Help Lines and Websites 42
  Parent Link Alberta Centres 43
  Baby Care Fair 45
  Healthy Families Calgary and Area 46
  Children's Cottage Society 46
  Post Natal Helpers Ltd. 47
  Support for Twins or Multiples 47
  Laughing Families 48
  Support for Single Parents 49
  Parenting Courses 50

Chapter Four: Health of Baby and Mom 56
  Health Helplines and Websites 56
  Growth Charts 57
  Alberta Children's Hospital 57
  Pelvic Floor Issues 59
  Immunizations 59
  Child and Infant Learning and Development Research Group (Ch.I.L.D.) . 62
  Caring for Your New Baby's Teeth 62
  Speech Therapy and Language Development 67
  Eye Checkups for Your Baby 69
  Gross Motor Development Resources in Calgary 70

Chapter Five: Healthy Eating for Baby and Toddler 74
  Calgary Health Region 74
  Dietitians 75
  Reference Books on Making Baby Food 75
  Useful Websites 76
  Buying Baby Food 76

Chapter Six: Baby Safety 80
  Babyproofing 80
  General Information on Keeping Baby Safe 85

Chapter Seven: Clothing, Accessories and other Sundry 89
  Baby Product Advice 89
  Baby Retail Stores 90
  Second-Hand Stores 96
  Community Sales 100
  Diapers 101
  Car Seats 103
  Baby's First Shoes 106
  Baby's First Haircut 107

Chapter Eight: Shopping with your Baby 109
  Grocery Shopping 109
  Malls and Baby Friendly Stores Around Calgary 110

Chapter Nine: Just For You! 115
  Dealing with Advice 115
  Simplifying Your Life 116
  The Holy Grail...Achieving Balance 119

Keeping your Mind Active During Your Parental Leave 119
Developing Your Own Parenting Style 121
Organizing Your Parents' Club 121
Ding Dong, A Masseuse at Your Door 122
Have Baby, Will Travel (to Spa)! 123
Outgrown Clothing and Equipment 124
Deciding to go Back to Work or Not 126
Just for Moms 127
Just for Dads 133

Chapter Ten: Traveling with Baby or Toddler 136
Before You Go 136
Travelling By Car 139
Travelling By Air 140
Baby-Friendly Getaways From Calgary 143
Helpful Websites 144

Chapter Eleven: Fitness and Getting Back Into Shape 145
Walks 145
Hiking 159
Running 160
Cycling 161
Ice-Skating 162
Cross-Country Skiing 163
Downhill Skiing 163
Fitness Classes For You With Your Baby 167
Personal Fitness Focused on Moms 175

Chapter Twelve: Activities 178
Sites in Calgary and Area 178
Playgroups 191
Drop-in Playcentres 298
Movies 203
Dining Out, If You Dare 204
Festivals and Special Events 205

Chapter Thirteen: Toys, Books and Games 209
Toys 209
Books 221
Games to Play With Your Little One 225

Chapter Fourteen: Courses 226
Courses on Getting Your Baby to Sleep 226
Courses on Baby Sign Language 228
Courses on Postnatal Yoga 230
Courses on Nutrition 231
Courses on Safety, First Aid and CPR 232
Courses on Infant Massage 233
Calgary Public Library Children's Programs 234
Music Classes 234
Art Classes with Your Baby 238
Swimming with your Your Baby 239

Chapter Fifteen: Mementos 246
   Baby Announcements 246
   Scrapbooking 247
   Time Capsule. 248
   Photography. 249
   BP BirthPlace Forest 251

Chapter Sixteen: Child Care Options 252
   Babysitting 252
   Looking for Child Care After Parental Leave 255
   Innovative Child Care Ideas 266

Chapter Seventeen: Birthday Parties 267
   First-Birthday Party Locations 267
   Second-Birthday Party Locations 270
   Birthday Cake 272

Chapter Eighteen: Preschools 274
   At What Age Does Preschool Start? 274
   When Should You Start Looking at Preschools? 274
   Regulation of Preschools 275
   What Kinds of Preschools Are Out There? 277
   Where Do I Find a List of Preschools? 278
   Typical Costs 278
   How to Choose a Preschool 279
   Selecting a Preschool 279

Chapter Nineteen: Afterword 282

Chapter Twenty: About the Author and Contributors 283

Appendix 1: Reference Sheets and Checklists 287

Appendix 2: Even More Organizations and Publications. 293

**Appendix 3: Activity Timeline and Reminders for the First
   and Second Years.** 300

Appendix 4: Free and Inexpensive Activities and Courses 305

Appendix 5: Activities and Courses Suitable to Baby's Age 309

Appendix 6: Activities by Season. 313

Appendix 7: Time and Money Saving Tips 315

Index 317

Quick Reference Contact Details 325

ACKNOWLEDGEMENTS

I would like to thank Elena Rhodes for her work with me on the first edition of this book. The first edition provided an excellent foundation for the second edition. She also provided many hours of help with the editing of this edition. I would also like to thank all the parents who made the first edition a bestseller and total success.

Dr. Wendy Street-Wadey graciously provided the chapter on caring for baby's teeth. Dr. Pat Tarr wrote her perspective on choosing a preschool for your child. Nicola Sadorra provided the section on gross motor development. Dr. Evelyn Jain provided us a great section on breastfeeding common sense despite a busy schedule! Jill Olson offered her comments regarding twins and multiples throughout the book, using thousands of sticky notes in an effort to help other moms of twins and multiples. (I owe you some Post-It notes, Jill!) My sincere thanks to each of them for their help!

Thanks to Tanya Nermerich who reviewed the section on speech development and language. Many thanks to my fabulous editors, Elena Rhodes and Cindy Mintz, for their hours of editing and invaluable comments. Thanks also to Mark McGarrigle and Angela Christoffel for helping with some research.

My focus group of experts and fellow parents has been a tremendous help by providing comments, ideas and support. The focus group included Lisa Brygidyr, Sarah Deveaux, Sheila Kelly, Jennifer Nichols, Britt Raposo, Sue Deyell, and Sonya Lee, as well as the moms listed above. They are an amazing group of women who managed to find time out of their incredibly busy days to provide feedback.

All facts were checked before going to print by an extraordinary team that set aside part of their summer days to sit at a computer while the weather was absolutely gorgeous. The team included Leslynn Heerema, Angela Christoffel, Sandra Paulgaard, Devon and Tallon Black (and their coach/mom Kerry Toll). Big thanks to you for your help.

Finally, a big thank you goes out to my husband Leonard and my children, Declan and Ailish. I could not have done it without you.

INTRODUCTION

Congratulations on becoming a new parent! I am thrilled for you and hope that you thoroughly enjoy your parental leave with your new addition to your family. This time is precious and there are so many changes ahead for both your baby and you.

Elena Rhodes and I wrote the first edition of this book. We met during a prenatal class offered by the Calgary Health Region. We both became mothers in January 2004; Elena to a little boy named Daniel and I to a little boy named Declan. After the initial hectic and mostly housebound period of figuring out our new lives, we wanted to make the most of the remainder of our year on parental leave. However, we found it difficult to discover what is available in Calgary for new parents. Our information came mostly by word-of-mouth from other parents, and sometimes we received it too late to take full advantage of it. We decided to create a handbook for other parents to provide information on what is available in Calgary during parental leave, focusing on babies under one year of age. We each had a second child just before the first edition was published. Elena decided to spend more time with her kids and I decided to carry the torch for new parents with a second edition. I hope that this book will help to keep your mind, body and spirit awake during this wonderful, exhausting and rewarding time.

The first book was more successful than I had ever imagined. Readers suggested that I could make it even better by providing information for parents of toddlers and about neighbouring communities. This second edition therefore expands on the first by covering areas such as Cochrane, Okotoks, Airdrie and Chestermere. I have also expanded the scope of the book to the first twenty-four months. In the three years since the original concept of this book was born, the number of businesses catering to babies in the Calgary region has also expanded tremendously. I am constantly amazed by the entrepreneurial spirit of the mothers in this city. My children have enjoyed testing the places reviewed in the book, especially the toy stores.

The cost of services in the Calgary area has also increased significantly since the writing of the first edition. Prices are up between twenty and thirty percent. Unfortunately, employment insurance payments for maternity leave have not increased that much, if at all. With a latte now costing about $5 and a coffee over $1.50, you appreciate services that provide good value for money. Hopefully, this book will help you to find some great-value services now that you have more time than money (and your time is in short supply, too!).

The first eight chapters of this book are filled with information needed for day-to-day life with children under the age of two. This includes administrative items, surviving the first six weeks after delivery, parenting support and health for you and your baby, as well as, feeding baby, buying clothing and shopping with your baby.

Chapters nine through eleven focus on you as a parent and the transition that you are going through. Chapters twelve through fifteen deal with the fun things that you can do with your baby including courses, and activities. Chapters sixteen through eighteen address the items that you will need towards the end of your parental leave and at the end of each of your baby's first and second year.

The appendices contain a number of useful reference sheets: a timeline of things to do during the first two years, lists of activities by appropriate age group and cost, and some money- and time-saving tips.

In this edition of the book, Jill Olson has provided tips and comments on dealing with multiples. I met Jill in a Baby & You class when our eldest children were babies. She became part of a troop of moms that met up for walks and play. A spontaneous snap taken during one of our walks placed Jill on the book's cover. Jill's twin girls were born a couple of months after my second child. Jill was quickly immersed in the world of multiples while also parenting a toddler. Jill's comments appear throughout the book as "Jill says..."

Elena, co-author of the first edition, graciously provided additional comments on the second edition. They appear throughout the book as "Elena says..."

Every effort has been made to ensure that prices, business names and contact information in this book are accurate at the time of printing, but please be aware that such information can change at any time. All dollar figures have been rounded to the nearest dollar. In most cases, GST is not included in the price listed.

Given the amount of information available on the Internet, I have included references to useful or interesting websites. I have also provided other sources of information for readers without ready access to computers.

I also had to make some decisions about the scope of this book. As a result, it does not address the following topics:

- Adoption and specific resources available to adoptive parents;
- specific resources and programs available to parents of children with special-needs; or
- religious ceremonies for babies.

Information on each of these topics is available from the appropriate support organizations, government departments and religious organizations.

My website, www.babyguidetocalgary.com, has information on the current community sales in Calgary and area. These sales are a great way to save money during the time that children use clothes for no more than six months at a time. I also offer an e-mail newsletter that provides updates when new business or government programs become available.

As I write this second edition, I am appreciative of the support that made the first book such a success. Your encouragement ignited the spark to write the second edition. Perhaps there will be a third! I hope you find this book a useful resource. Tuck one copy into your diaper bag and keep another in your glove compartment.

Enjoy!

Paula

DISCLAIMER

The author has researched and prepared this book with care. To the best of her knowledge, all information included is accurate and unbiased. However, she cannot and does not guarantee the accuracy or completeness of the information. The inclusion or reference to any product, service or facility in this book does not imply the author's or publisher's endorsement or recommendation thereof. Similarly, the exclusion of any product, service or facility that may be available does not imply any criticism thereof. No information contained in this book reflects the author's or publisher's personal opinion. The author and publisher do not accept responsibility for any problems, damage or injury that might arise in relation to your choice of services, programs or facilities, whether or not using this book influenced your choice.

There are numerous references to websites in this book. The author and publisher do not guarantee the accuracy of the information contained in these websites. By their nature, websites are in a constant state of change and therefore, the author cannot guarantee that they will continue to provide the information for which they were selected to be referenced in this book.

CHAPTER ONE:
ADMINISTRATIVE ISSUES

In the first few months of your baby's life, you will be inundated with paperwork. It is tough to remember the order of the forms and to get all of the necessary documentation in place, particularly when you are so sleep-deprived. This section is designed to help you out with the administrative side of having a new baby.

BABY NAMING

You can access local statistics on baby names through the Services Alberta website. Here, you can find out the most common names from the past few years. Not only does the website list the top twenty-five names, but it also shows the names of all children born in Alberta and the frequency of names used. The website can be found at: www.servicealberta.gov.ab.ca; look in the "Quick Links" box for Top Baby Names.

MATERNITY AND PARENTAL LEAVE RIGHTS AND BENEFITS

If you are approaching your first maternity and parental leave, you probably have a lot of unanswered questions about your rights and benefits. Alberta Human Rights publishes a booklet entitled "Becoming a Parent in Alberta: What you need to know about human rights, maternity and parental leave and benefits". This booklet is available at www.albertahumanrights.ab.ca under "Publications and Resources". You can also order a copy by calling the Employment Standards telephone information centre at (780) 427-3731 in Edmonton. Alternatively, you can order a hard copy online at the website above.

EMPLOYMENT INSURANCE

In Canada, Employment Insurance payments are available for fifty weeks total for both parents during your parental leave. You are entitled to employment protection for fifty-two weeks. The basic benefit rate is 55%

of your average insured earnings up to a maximum payment of $423 per week. This is considered taxable income and so your bi-weekly cheque will have applicable federal and provincial taxes deducted. If you have a lower income and receive the Canada Child Tax Benefit, then you may be entitled to a family supplement. Be sure to review the website (see below) for all the details.

Prerequisites:
* You need to finish working before you can apply. You cannot pre-apply while you are still working. (Yes, I tried to apply ahead of time!) It is best to apply as soon as you stop working, but no later than four weeks after you stop working.
* Record of Employment from your last employer.
* Your Social Insurance Number (SIN) and SIN of the other parent.
* Your banking information for direct deposit.

Where to get the forms:
* Application forms are online only. Go to www.servicecanada.gc.ca and click on your language preference. In the box entitled "All Canadians" click on "Employment Insurance". Scroll down to "Forms" and click on "How do I apply for Employment Insurance on-line?"
* You can use a computer at one of the Service Canada offices to apply. Look for the addresses in the Blue Pages of the phone book (see "Government of Canada", "Employment").

Cost:
* Free to apply.

Processing Time:
* The Service Canada website indicates that the first payment will typically be made within twenty-eight days, "assuming the application was properly completed". However, it can take longer due to backlogs in the system. At the time of writing, the processing time was twenty-eight days.

Special Notes:
* The Calgary Health Region's (CHR) free Budgeting for Baby course handout provides a great summary of this subject.
* A brochure with a lot of useful information is available at any of the Service Canada offices.
* The application is long and takes about an hour to complete.
* Employment Insurance is calculated on a Sunday to Saturday basis. If you return to work in the middle of the week, any income you make that week will be deducted from any Employment Insurance that was paid to you. So wait until Monday for your return!
* You may be called in for an interview to confirm information. Be sure to bring all supporting documentation with you.

Paula says...

"When doing our taxes, a year after maternity leave, we realized that my husband had not been paid his Employment Insurance. He had been approved for eight weeks' parental leave but the cheques had not arrived. During the first two months we were so sleep-deprived that we didn't notice it. So make sure you check your bank account to confirm that you are indeed receiving Employment Insurance. They did pay us, but it was a year later."

ALBERTA HEALTH CARE

Alberta Health Care coverage is provided to newborn babies from their date of birth if notification is received within three months. Otherwise, the effective date of coverage is determined when you register your baby.

If your baby was born in a hospital, the hospital will notify Alberta Health Care of your baby's birth so that they can submit a claim for the costs of the birth. This process will generate a personal health care number for your baby. However, it will not be active until you complete a "Notice of Change" form and submit it to Alberta Health Care. Some hospitals may provide you with this form, and some may even forward your completed form to Alberta Health Care. Contact Alberta Health and Wellness to obtain a "Notice of Change" form, if you think your baby has not been registered.

Prerequisites:
• None.

Where to get the forms:
There are three ways to obtain the forms:
1) To receive them by mail, contact Alberta Health and Wellness using the following contact information:

Alberta Health and Wellness

Address:	P.O. Box 1360, Station Main, Edmonton, T5J 2N3
Phone:	Toll free 310-0000 then (780) 427-1432
Fax:	(780) 422-0102 (Edmonton)
E-mail:	health.ahcipmail@gov.ab.ca

2) Forms are also available at www.health.gov.ab.ca. Follow the links to "Health Care Insurance Plan" and click on "Forms". Scroll down the page to find the "Notice of Change Form" under "Applying for Coverage or Change of Status".

3) Finally, it is possible to apply in person at the Calgary office of Alberta Health and Wellness:

Address: 727 7 Avenue S.W.
Hours: Monday to Friday: 8:15 a.m. – 4:30 p.m.

Cost:
• Family coverage is $88 per month for two or more persons.

Processing time:
• If you apply in person, you can expect to get your baby's personal health card within a few business days. If you apply by mail, add a week for processing.

Special notes:
• You may qualify for a premium subsidy based on your previous year's income. The form is available at www.health.gov.ab.ca. Follow the link to "Health Care Insurance Plan" and search under "Forms" for a form called "Application for Premium Subsidy".

ADDING BABY TO WORK BENEFIT PLAN

If you work outside the home and your company provides a benefit plan, you may want to extend your coverage to your newborn. Your company's benefits administrator can provide you with the required forms. The time frame during which you may add your child to your benefit plan is usually limited. Often this period is thirty days after the birth. I strongly recommend that you find out the rules and obtain application forms before you go on your parental leave. Don't rely on your benefits administrator to inform you, as he or she may forget to let you know about "unimportant little details" such as the deadline for adding your baby.

BIRTH CERTIFICATE

The Birth Certificate is probably the most important document in your child's paperwork requirements. You will need this document to apply for your baby's passport, bank account, and Social Insurance Number. There are two sizes available, wallet and wall size. The wall size document includes the full names of parents.

Prerequisites:
• Statement of Live Birth filled out at the hospital and submitted by the hospital to Alberta Vital Statistics. (You will have retained a copy when you signed it at the hospital.)
• Final name of child. If you have delayed naming your baby, you should only apply for your baby's Birth Certificate after you have finalized and changed your baby's name with Alberta Vital Statistics.

Where to get the forms:
- Pick up the application at your local licensing and registry office (or the Alberta Motor Association if you are a member). They will handle the application or you can mail it to Alberta Vital Statistics yourself.

Cost:
- About $36 per certificate depending on the licensing agency.

Processing time:
- About ten working days. Rush delivery is available for an additional charge.

Special notes:
- Don't apply for the first couple of weeks since it takes time for the information from the Statement of Live Birth form to be entered into Alberta Vital Statistics' computer system.
- You may want to order more than one certificate including one long form certificate to enable getting your child's Social Insurance Number. Keep one Birth Certificate in a safe place and the other with you if you are travelling.

SOCIAL INSURANCE NUMBER

You will need a Social Insurance Number (SIN) for your baby in order to set up a Registered Education Savings Plan.

Prerequisites:
- Birth Certificate; long form is best since it confirms legal guardianship.
- A parent's Social Insurance Number.
- Document confirming legal guardianship.
- If the parent was not born in Canada, documentation of citizenship or immigration status.

Where to get the forms:
- At Service Canada offices or go to www.servicecanada.gc.ca, look under "All Canadians" and click on "Social Insurance Number". Scroll down to "Application Information" and click on "How do I apply for someone else?"

Cost:
- No fee is charged for a first-time SIN application.

Processing time:
- You can actually receive a Social Insurance Number the same day if you apply in person. If you send the document by mail, expect up to six weeks until the SIN is sent in the mail to your address.

Special notes:
- Take an original Birth Certificate to your nearest Service Canada office. You can show Service Canada staff the Birth Certificate and

submit the application in person. Alternatively, you can mail the original Birth Certificate in the envelope provided with your SIN application. You will need to provide either your own Birth Certificate if born in Canada or forms indicating your immigration status.

- Service Canada offices are listed in the White Pages in the Government of Alberta section. Look under "Employment". The "Newborn Registration Service" is only available for residents of British Columbia or Ontario.
- Service Canada recommends using only your baby's middle initial rather than middle name on your application form to impede identity theft.

REGISTERED EDUCATION SAVINGS PLAN

A Registered Education Savings Plan (RESP) is a type of savings account that grows tax-free until your child is ready for post-secondary education. There is no longer an annual maximum contribution limit and the lifetime limit is now $50,000 per beneficiary. Unlike Registered Retirement Savings Plans, there are no tax deductions available for contributions made to RESPs.

RESPs are a good way to save for a number of reasons:
- The money grows tax-free until the child needs it for tuition, residence and other educational expenses.
- An RESP allows you to apply for the Canada Education Savings Grant on your child's behalf. Under the grant program, the federal government will contribute an amount equal to 20% up to a maximum of $400 per child. Over the life of the plan, this could add up to an extra $7,200. Your RESP provider will apply on your behalf for the federal grant.
- It is possible to start saving right away; you simply need a Social Insurance Number for your baby.
- It allows your child to receive a grant under the Alberta Centennial Education Savings Plan.

It is recommended that you speak to an advisor in this area prior to opening an RESP. You need to find out what happens if your child decides not to pursue post-secondary education.

You can open an RESP though a promoter of RESPs. The Canada Education Savings Grant (CESG) Program provides a list of promoters to assist in this regard. You can also set up a self-directed RESP. Check out the Canada Revenue Agency's website for more information at www.cra-arc.gc.ca (follow the links for "Individuals", then "Registered Education Savings Plans (RESP)").

A family RESP can be more effective than individual RESPs for each child. The main advantage is that if one child decides not to pursue higher education, you can either name an alternate beneficiary or split the funds among other children. The money does not need to be shared equally among your children. To qualify as members, beneficiaries must be related by blood or adoption.

Prerequisites:
• Social Insurance Number.

Where to get the forms:
• Any promoter of RESPs will gladly fill out the forms for you.

Cost:
• Your contribution plus potential upfront membership fees.

Processing time:
• Can be completed immediately if you have your baby's Social Insurance Number.

Special notes:
• Make sure you understand in detail the RESP for which you are registering. Many RESPs have membership fees that may dilute your returns compared to self-directed funds.
• Friends and relatives can set up their own RESP in your child's name. The total of all RESP contributions cannot exceed the allowable maximums for the child.
• An RESP also makes a good gift for new babies, so suggest this to your relatives.

Additional information:
• Royal Bank offers a useful overview explaining the RESP. Look for it on the bank's website at www.rbc.com. Follow the links for "Investments", and then look under "Personal", "Canada", "Financial Planning", "Investment planning", and finally "Saving for Education".
• If your baby is born late in the year, work to set up the RESP quickly or you will miss the opportunity to contribute and receive the federal government grant for your baby's first calendar year.

CANADA LEARNING BOND

This is a federal government program that could contribute $500 to your child's RESP and $100 per year for fifteen years to a maximum of $2,000 per child. Children must have been born after 2003. The Canada Learning Bond is only available to families who qualify for the National Child Benefit Supplement. Qualification for the National Child Benefit Supplement is assessed when you apply for Canada Child Tax Benefit. Your RESP provider will help you apply for the Canada Learning Bond.

CHILDREN'S FITNESS TAX CREDIT

Since January 2007, parents of children under sixteen will be eligible to claim a federal non-refundable tax credit of up to $500 to help cover the costs of certain physical activity programs. Qualifying programs must be supervised; be at least once a week for eight weeks (or five consecutive days); and be predominantly related to physical activity. The program provider will provide you with a receipt for your federal income tax. More information is available at www.cra-arc.gc.ca/fitness.

THE ALBERTA CENTENNIAL EDUCATION SAVINGS PLAN

This provincial government plan provides an initial grant of $500 for babies born to or adopted by Alberta residents in 2005 or later. You need to fill out an application form for the grant and open an RESP. The funds are deposited directly into the child's RESP. Service Canada administers this plan. Also, beginning in 2013, additional grants of $100 will be available to students enrolled in Alberta schools at ages eight, eleven and fourteen. You will need to have deposited at least $100 during the previous year into an RESP to be eligible.

Prerequisites:
• Social Insurance Number for your child.
• An RESP account.
• Alberta residency.

Where to get the forms:
• Your RESP provider will apply on your behalf.

Cost:
• Free.

Additional information:
• Go to www.gov.ab.ca and scroll down to "Programs and Services" and click on "People Services". Then click on "Children" and under "Financial Resources - Benefits and Assistance" you can finally click on "Alberta Centennial Education Savings Plan".

CANADA CHILD TAX BENEFIT, NATIONAL CHILD BENEFIT AND ALBERTA FAMILY EMPLOYMENT TAX CREDIT

The Canada Child Tax Benefit (CCTB) is a federal benefit paid to lower-income families to help with the cost of raising children. It is administered by the Canada Revenue Agency (CRA). CRA also administers the National Child Benefit (NCB) program, which is a joint program of the federal and provincial governments. In Alberta, NCB provides the Alberta Family Employment Tax Credit (AFETC). There is a single application form for all of these benefits.

The calculation of benefit amounts is quite complicated. You can use an online "Benefits Calculator" on CRA's website at www.cra-arc.gc.ca/benefits to estimate the amount you are eligible to receive. The CRA booklet "Your Canada Child Tax Benefit" provides a summary of how the benefits are calculated. You can download the booklet from the same website or, click on "Canada Child Tax Benefit (CCBT)" and then "Forms and publications - Child and Family Benefits". The guide is called "T4114 Your Canada Child Tax Benefit". You can order a printed copy by calling 1-800-959-2221.

It is highly recommended that you apply even if you think you may not qualify to receive any benefits. The CCTB application form will determine your eligibility for the National Child Benefit Program, the Alberta Family Employment Tax Credit, the Universal Child Care Benefit program and the Canada Learning Bond. CRA automatically recalculates your benefits every year based on your filed returns, so if your income situation changes you won't have to apply again. It doesn't take long, so go ahead and do it.

Prerequisites:
- Social Insurance Number for you and your spouse or common law partner.
- Proof of birth for your child if born outside Canada or if your child is over one year of age.

Where to get the forms:
- You can get the application form online at www.cra-arc.gc.ca/benefits (you will need to follow a few obvious links to get to the printable document).
- A printed application form can be ordered by calling 1-800-959-2221.

Paula says...

"Make sure you fill out the Canada Child Tax Benefit application since this form is used to determine your applicability for the following programs:
- *National Child Benefit*
- *Alberta Family Employment Tax Credit*
- *Universal Child Care Benefit*
- *Canada learning Bond*

You only have to apply once and your eligibility is determined each year through Canada Revenue Agency."

Cost:
* None.

Processing time:
* Two months.

Special notes:
* The booklet "Your Canada Child Tax Benefit" and the application form are provided at the Calgary Health Region's "Budgeting for Baby" course. They may also be provided with the paperwork you get at the hospital after delivery. The "Budgeting for Baby" course also provides tips on filling out the application.

UNIVERSAL CHILD CARE BENEFIT (UCCB)

This is a federal initiative designed to help families by supporting their child care choices. The federal government pays $100 per child per month to provide financial support to families. This program is for children aged six and under. Enrollment for the Universal Child Care Benefit is through the Canada Child Tax Benefit program.

PASSPORT FOR BABY

If you plan on travelling outside Canada with your baby, you will need a passport for him. As of December 2001, all children who travel need their own travel document, including newborns. If your baby is not travelling with both parents, she also needs custody documentation and a parental consent letter from the other parent. It is recommended that this letter be notarized. There are sample consent letters for different situations on the Foreign Affairs Canada website at www.voyage.gc.ca, and the website also contains additional information on international travel with children. You can also call the Consular Affairs Bureau (Department of Foreign Affairs and International Trade) at 1-800-267-6788.

Prerequisites:
* You will need your baby's Birth Certificate, so plan ahead and get the certificate well before your travel date.

Where to get the forms:
* Print the application form from the Passport Office website (www.ppt.gc.ca); or
* Visit the Passport Office in the Harry Hayes Building (Suite 254, 220 4 Avenue S.E. or 14331 Macleod Trail S.W. Hours - Monday to Friday: 8:30 a.m. – 4:30 p.m.).

Cost:
* $22 for a child under three years of age.

Processing time:

- At the time or writing, Passport Canada was providing passports within two weeks. You can pay extra ($30) for a passport to be processed quickly and it will be ready in a few days. If you mail in the application, wait times are between two and four weeks excluding mailing time.

Special notes:

- Passport photos are required for even the littlest babies. Read the "Photo Specifications" on the application form carefully. Make sure the photographer follows all guidelines or your application will be rejected. I strongly recommend calling the photographer ahead of time to determine if they take passport photos of babies.

Elena says...

"I showed up at a photographer's where I had my own passport photograph taken only to find out that they don't take babies' photographs."

- If you are heading to the Harry Hayes Building to apply in person, make sure you park in a parking lot that allows you to stay longer than two hours. Also, when you are standing in line, pick up a ticket from the commissionaire.
- Plan to have your baby awake and in as good a mood as possible for his photo session. Be prepared for it to take quite a bit longer than your own passport photos did.
- This first passport will be valid for a maximum of three years. If it was issued in the first year of life, a replacement passport within the first three years, is free.

Additional information:

- See the Passport Office website (www.ppt.gc.ca) or the instruction pages of the application form for more information.
- As a bonus for all of this, you get quite a conversation piece. A baby's passport is a very cute thing to show around.

Elena says...

"The instructions say: 'The face must be square to the camera with a neutral expression and with the mouth closed'. This sounds a LOT easier than it is. When I took my then ten week old son, it took a while until I managed to have him look directly at the camera and not grin or gape or cry at it."

Paula says...

"A number of friends suggested the following places for
getting your baby's passport photos taken:
- Sears Photography at Chinook Centre, 6455 Macleod
  Trail S.W., Phone: 253-6511
- Black's at North Hill Mall, 1632 14 Avenue N.W.,
  Phone: 271-5353
- The Village Studio, 2580 Southland Drive S.W., Phone: 281-0444"

THE ALBERTA STAY-AT-HOME PARENT, CHILD CARE SUBSIDY

If you are a stay-at-home parent and your children attend an early
childhood development program, you may be eligible for a reimbursement
of fees up to $1,200 per year per child! That is certainly worth a little bit
of paper work.

This income-based program is run by Alberta Children's Services for
stay-at-home parents. It started in January, 2006.

For an updated list of approved Early Childhood Development (ECD)
programs, check the website: www.calgaryandareacfsa.gov.ab.ca. Check
under "Child Care" then "Stay-at-Home" and then "List of Approved
ECD programs".

ELIGIBLE PROGRAMS AS OF JULY, 2007 FOR CHILDREN UNDER TWENTY-FOUR MONTHS:

Music:
- Mount Royal Music Program www.mtroyal.ca/conservatory
- Creative Kids www.creativekidsclasses.ca
- Kindermusik with Linda www.kindermusik.ca
- Kodaly Preparatory School
- Sonata Yamaha School of Music
  www.yamaha.ca/content/musiceducation/findaschool

Preschool:
- Waldorf School www.calgarywaldorf.org
- Early Discovery Nursery School www.earlydiscoveries.ca
- Kinderhaus Montessori Preschool

Parenting Classes:
- Parents and Children Together (PACT) program www.pact.9f.com

Activities:
- Calgary Seeds of Discovery (Boundless Dance Studio)
- Creative Kids www.creativekidsclasses.ca
- Municipality of Cochrane courses (includes swimming)
- Town of Okotoks (includes a variety of activities, see website for details)
- YMCA www.ymcacalgary.org
- Dance Depot – Cochrane

Prerequisites:
- To be eligible, the working spouse must have a gross income of less than $6,225 per month depending on family size. This example amount assumes a two-parent family with two children and both children attending programs. There is an online calculator to determine gross income eligibility level. See website details below.
- One parent must be stay-at-home, not working or attending school for more than twenty hours per week. You can be eligible if you are on parental leave.
- Copies of identification for the children enrolled in a program. This can be their Birth Certificate or Alberta Health Care card. Identification must show your child's name and date of birth.
- Copies of the employed spouse's recent pay stubs for one month.
- Most recent Notice of Assessment (NOA) forms from the Canada Revenue Agency for both parents.
- Receipts for the qualified program showing start and end dates as well as your child's name.

Where to get the forms:
- Online forms are available at www.child.gov.ab.ca/whatwedo/childcaresubsidy. Click on "How to apply for subsidy" and scroll down and click on form CS2127.
- Go to Alberta Children's Services and ask for form CS2127 entitled "Information Sheet for Child Care Subsidy Application".
  Alberta Children's Services
  Address: #300; 1240 Kensington Road N.W.
  Phone: 297-6100
  Hours: Monday to Friday: 8:15 a.m. – 4:30 p.m. except holidays.

Cost:
- None.

Processing time:
- It can take from two to three weeks (or longer) for Alberta Children's Services to process your subsidy application. Alberta Children's Services provides funding to the Early Childhood Development Program. In turn, the Early Childhood Development program reimburses you directly.

Special notes:
- You cannot apply online; rather, you need to complete a hard copy application form.
- You do need to pay for the program ahead of time and then apply for the subsidy.
- You need to apply within one month of the start date of the program.

More Information:
- You can contact a Child Care Subsidy worker at 297-6469 or go online at www.child.gov.ab.ca/whatwedo/childcaresubsidy

THE ALBERTA CHILD CARE SUBSIDY PROGRAM

This subsidy program is intended to take the sting out of the costs of day care. It is available if both parents are working and your child is in daycare. The amount eligible depends on the age of the child but can be up to a maximum of $528 to $607 per month. This income-based program is run by Alberta Children's Services. They have an estimator tool on their website that helps estimate the amount of subsidy.

Prerequisites:
- To be eligible, both parents need to be Canadian citizens or permanent residents, and live in Alberta. You and your spouse need to be currently working, attending school, looking for work or have special needs. This subsidy is available for children under the age of seven years old and not yet attending grade one. Your child also needs to attend a licensed day care centre, an approved family day home, a licensed out of school care centre or be with a direct care provider.
- Copies of identification for each person in the family unit. For children, this can be their Birth Certificate or Alberta Health Care card. Identification must show your child's name and date of birth.
- Social Insurance Number for both parents.
- Your Child Care Subsidy Applicant ID if you have ever received Child Care subsidy in the past.
- Confirmation of employment, such as copies of recent pay stubs for one month.
- Most recent Notice of Assessment (NOA) forms from the Canada Revenue Agency for both parents.
- Name and address of the location that your child or children are attending.
- Verification of child or spousal support payments if applicable.

Where to get the forms:
- Online forms are available at www.child.gov.ab.ca/whatwedo/childcaresubsidy. Click on "How to apply for subsidy" and scroll down and click on form CS2127.
- Go to Alberta Children's Services and ask for form CS2127 entitled "Information Sheet for Child Care Subsidy Application".

Alberta Children's Services

Address: #300, 1240 Kensington Road N.W.
Phone: 297-6100
Hours: Monday to Friday: 8:15 a.m. – 4:30 p.m. except holidays.

Cost:
• None.

Processing time:
• It can take from two to three weeks (or longer) for Alberta Children's Services to process your subsidy application.

More Information:
• You can contact a Child Care Subsidy worker at 297-6469 or go online at www.child.gov.ab.ca/whatwedo/childcaresubsidy

GOVERNMENT OF ALBERTA SERVICES FOR LOWER-INCOME ALBERTANS

Phone: 1-866-644-5135
Website: www.gov.ab.ca/servicealberta/LowerIncomeGuide
Hours: Monday to Friday 8:15 a.m. – 4:30 p.m. The line is a 24/7, but is used as a crisis line after office hours.

The provincial government provides a number of programs to help lower-income Albertans. A booklet entitled "Guide to Services for Lower-Income Albertans" by the Government of Alberta covers a number of topics. Programs that target families with children include those for finding child care, helping with the costs of child care, support to care for someone else's child, and collecting child support. You can order a free copy of the guide by calling the number above, picking it up from your public health nurse or downloading it from the website listed above.

CHAPTER TWO
SURVIVING THE FIRST SIX WEEKS

The first six weeks as a parent are extremely hectic. Life for us as a family was a blur during this time, with so many appointments to keep and getting used to living without a lot of sleep. I hope that this section will help you cope during this period. There are many things in here that I wish I had known at the time. The next chapter talks about ways of getting assistance and support for parents, which is also very useful information to have in the immediate postpartum period.

INSTALLING YOUR INFANT CAR SEAT

You are required to bring your new baby home from the hospital in an infant car seat. See "Chapter Seven: Clothing, Accessories, and Other Sundry" – "Car Seats" for information on car seats and on the CHR's free car seat education class.

POSTPARTUM COMMUNITY SERVICES

Provider: Calgary Health Region
Phone: 944-7400 (North Office)
             943-9118 (South Office)
Hours: Monday to Friday: 8 a.m. – 4:30 p.m.
Age group: 0 – 2 months

This service provides information and support to families with babies from birth to two months of age. A public health nurse will contact you by phone within twenty-four hours after being discharged from the hospital and offer to visit your home. Be sure to say 'yes' to receive a follow up visit from the public health nurse.

EARLY START PARENT INFORMATION LINE

Provider: Calgary Health Region
Phone: 244-8351
Hours: 24 hours, 7 days a week
Age group: 0 – 2 months

This around-the-clock information line staffed by registered nurses is specifically for parents of babies under two months of age.

EARLY START DROP-IN SERVICE

Provider: Calgary Health Region
Phone: 244-8351
Hours: Call to confirm
Age group: 0 – 2 months

This drop-in service gives parents of infants from birth to two months old a chance to meet with a public health nurse and other parents. The service is offered weekly and provides information on infant feeding, jaundice, infant growth and development, adjusting to parenthood and safety.

BABY ANNOUNCEMENTS

See "Chapter Fifteen: Mementos" – "Baby Announcements".

Paula says...

"Make sure you book your own six-week follow-up with your doctor! We tend to forget about our own health checkups when baby comes along."

FINDING A DOCTOR OR PAEDIATRICIAN

Provider: Calgary Health Region
Phone: 943-5465 (LINK)
Website: www.calgaryhealthregion.ca/doctor/
Hours: Call to confirm
Age group: 0 – 2 months

You can look at the Calgary Health Region's website to find a family doctor who is accepting patients. This website is searchable by quadrant of Calgary, by town, by gender and specialty. Alternatively, you can call the

Health Link line at 943-LINK (5465) and the nurses on staff will let you know which family physicians in your area are accepting new patients.

A paediatrician is a physician who has extensive additional training and experience in child development and common childhood ailments and disabilities. A referral from your family doctor will allow you to see a paediatrician. Paediatricians are typically only available for children who are chronically or seriously ill or have developmental issues. There are often waiting lists to see a paediatrician, up to two to four months in some cases in Calgary, depending on the urgency of the situation.

Paula says...

"Ask your friends! Often doctors will take on new patients from referrals from their own patients."

24-HOUR PHARMACIES

During the first week after bringing our baby home I quickly found that few pharmacies are open at four in the morning. There are two 24-hour, 7 days a week pharmacies in Calgary:

Shoppers Drug Mart at North Hill Shopping Center
Address: 1790, 1632 14 Avenue N.W.
Phone: 289-6761

Shoppers Drug Mart at Chinook Center
Address: 6455 Macleod Trail S.W.
Phone: 253-2424

Paula says...

"I needed a breast pump early one morning, and was so relieved to find a 24-hour pharmacy open."

There is also a company in Calgary that will deliver your prescriptions to you. Ask your doctor's office to fax or call in your prescription and Pharmacy on Call will deliver it to your home. You will need to call the pharmacy to let them know your payment details and insurance details. They provide a 24-hour prescription service with free delivery:

Pharmacy on Call Limited
Address: 1905 20 Avenue N.W.
Phone: 289-2201
Fax: 289-8432

"BACK TO SLEEP, TUMMY TO PLAY" INFORMATION SESSIONS

Address: 2888 Shaganappi Trail N.W.
Provider: Alberta Children's Hospital
Phone: 955-7211
Website: www.calgaryhealthregion.ca/ACH
Age group: Newborns and older

Alberta Children's Hospital provides free information sessions on recommended ways to position your baby for both sleep and play. The sessions are offered once a month. There is no need to register, simply drop in. Contact the Alberta Children's Hospital to find out when and where the next session is being held. Sleep courses are available; see "Chapter Fourteen: Courses", "Courses on Getting Your Baby to Sleep".

For information on what you can do to reduce the risk of SIDS, visit www.phac-aspc.gc.ca. Click on "Health Promotion", scroll down under "Healthy Pregnancy and Infancy", "Sudden Infant Death Syndrome".

BREASTFEEDING

Breastfeeding can be a tremendous experience for both you and your baby. For some, it can also be frustrating. Should you have any difficulties breastfeeding there are significant resources in Calgary to help you, whether your difficulties are insufficient milk, excessive milk, latch or other issues. During your typically short hospital stay, you may be able to attend a breastfeeding information session or talk to a lactation consultant. Ask your nurse or doctor. After your discharge from the hospital, a Calgary Health Region nurse will stop by your house within twenty-four to forty-eight hours. Among other things, the nurse will be able to help you with your breastfeeding issues and can visit you several times if necessary. Be sure to ask the nurse lots of questions.

Calgary Health region has a free course available on the topic of breastfeeding. They also have a specific course on "Twins/Triplets Breastfeeding". Call their offices at 741-1450 or check their website at www.birthandbabies.com to register for the next available course. These courses review common breastfeeding problems.

Commonsense Breastfeeding

By Dr. Evelyn Jain, BSc, MD, CCFP, FCFP, IBCLC, Family Practitioner and Director, Lakeview Breastfeeding Clinic

Is breastfeeding best? Yes.
Is it natural? Yes.
Will I "just know" how to do it? Not necessarily!

There is plenty of advice (almost too much!) about breastfeeding. It is very important – and comforting – for you to know what part of the advice applies to you and your own baby. The timeliness of the advice will also vary greatly depending on whether your baby is one day, one week, or one month old (and everything in between). One of the biggest causes of distress is receiving so much conflicting advice. Determine if your current breastfeeding regime is working for you and your baby. If not, try to develop a different plan that provides enough nutrition for your baby and provides progress with any issues such as painful nipples, breasts, and your own exhaustion.

Remember, just about all breastfeeding problems can be solved, or at least understood and managed.

VISIT A BREASTFEEDING EXPERT BEFORE YOUR BABY ARRIVES

There are a number of situations in which a breastfeeding expert can help you even before your baby arrives.

- Flat or inverted nipples: Excellent positioning and latch and in some cases a nipple shield can help you greatly when your baby arrives (see below for more details on nipple shields). A niplette can be worn for between one to three months for inverted but not flat nipples to stretch the tissue and make breastfeeding a lot easier. These are available without prescription from www.avent.com or at Lakeview Breastfeeding Clinic.
- If you have previously had problems with either not enough or too much milk, then seek help from a breastfeeding expert before your baby arrives.

BREASTFEEDING

- Painful nipples and yeast infections can also be prevented by seeing a breastfeeding expert prior to your baby's arrival.
- If you have had breast reduction surgery you can probably nurse well but will need to supplement, pump and take Motilium to increase your supply.

BABY IS HERE! THE FIRST WEEK OF YOUR NEW JOB!

Most jobs require an interview, training, and a good night's sleep before your first day! Motherhood, on the other hand, requires you to plunge in! Some moms get off to a great start and receive help while they are at the hospital. Breastfeeding difficulties can be caused by baby factors such as: a small mouth, a tongue tie, a receding chin, sleepiness and many other reasons. You may have not had appropriate help in the hospital. The medical system is stretched to the limit. But all is not lost; don't quit – get help!

BABY'S NUTRITION

The most important thing you can do is to learn to recognize your baby's behaviour and her cues for seeking food: typically nuzzling, and mouthing anything near her face. When you see this, feed your baby!

Some numbers may help but don't be rigid. Just have your baby's weight checked in the first week:
- Between eight to twelve feeds each twenty-four hours on average.
- Feeds are irregular and not by the clock. Feed whenever your baby wants to be fed.
- A wide-awake baby or baby roused from a light sleep will feed better than one awoken from a deep sleep. So watch for these times.
- Feed with both breasts as much as possible at each feeding time. An exception would be an experienced mother who has previously had a huge milk supply.
- Feed your baby for about fifteen to twenty minutes with each breast. If your baby feeds faster than this and is gaining weight, well then no worries, just enjoy!
- On day one to three, your baby will have black sticky stools!
- On about day three to five, the stool will change to brown, to mustard and finally to yellow.
- Around day five, the stools will become thick, seedy and yellow.
- By day four or five, your baby will have at least six heavy wet diapers each day.
- Weight loss is normal in your baby's first few days but do seek help if there is greater than a seven percent loss of birth weight. Typically your baby will regain his birth weight by day seven to nine and continue to gain about 1 oz (30 grams) daily after that for first few weeks.

HOW DO YOU FEEL?

- Accept all offers of help.
- Don't let your time be taken up by visiting unless that is just what you need. Leave a nice newsy message on your phone and leave your bedroom ringer off.
- Sleep when your baby sleeps; nothing will help you cope as well as having some rest.
- If you are too wound-up to sleep – a small dose of a sedative from your doctor for a few days could do you a world of good without any harm to your baby.
- If you are feeling depressed, see your doctor or a postpartum group (See the section below on postpartum depression). The adjustment to parenthood is the biggest one you will ever make. If you need an antidepressant in addition to support and counseling, several medications are considered safe for breastfeeding and you and your baby will do much better if you properly treat your depression and anxiety.

OUCH! MY NIPPLES AND BREASTS!

A few days of tender nipples can be expected. Lanolin cream is routinely given to new mothers and is quite soothing. If, however, you have issues with your nipples such as major cracks, bleeding, pus, non-healing blisters, severe pain (causing toe curling, breath holding and dreading the next feed), tingling, itching, stabbing, jabbing in the nipples and or breasts, exceptional redness, flaking skin or cracks around the base of the nipple, use your lanolin as a hand cream rather than a nipple cream. At this stage, lanolin will not do much for your nipples! Seek medical help as soon as possible.

Latch is key to preventing nipple issues. See www.drjain.com for illustration of proper latch. Once your nipples are damaged, bacteria and yeast can settle in and cause you great discomfort and prevent healing. I have found that a fifty-fifty mixture of Canesten (anti-yeast) cream and Fucidin (a prescription antibiotic cream) used generously after every feeding or pumping, and left on until the next feed, works best. Will your baby ingest a bit? Yes. Will it do harm? No. If you need more treatment than this, your physician can prescribe you a prescription of Diflucan (fluconazole) pills (used for at least two weeks) to zap it.

See your family physician if your baby has a tongue-tie. Tongue-tie is a condition in which the free movement of the tongue is restricted due to abnormal attachment of the base of the tongue towards the tip of the tongue. The tongue tie should be released.

On day three or four it is common for your breasts to be very full. Try to rest during that day. Cover your entire breasts with cold refrigerated uncooked cabbage leaves to soothe your breasts. You could also consider taking ibuprofen after consultation with your physician. You may need to pump or express a little milk to soften the nipple area.

A nipple shield may be used while breastfeeding to allow your nipples to heal and protect them from more damage and to train your baby to open his mouth wider. Pumping milk and bottle-feeding for a couple of days can provide time to help your nipples heal from the damage.

Nipple shields are also used for breastfeeding babies who cannot latch or stay latched because of flat, inverted, extra small or stiff nipples or because it is "just the way it is".

Medela nipple shields are available without prescription at the Bowness Breastfeeding Centre, the Lakeview Breastfeeding Centre, and some pharmacies. The breastfeeding clinics can provide you some assistance with choice and use of a shield. Nipple shields come in three sizes: 24 mm, 20 mm and 16 mm and look like a Mexican hat. Generally the largest size that the baby can nurse well with will be the best for you. As a safety measure, a lactation professional should observe the feeding and follow up with you within a few days of using a nipple shield.

You will hear many strong opinions for or against a nipple shield. The bottom line is: Is it working for you and your baby?

HELP! MY BABY HAS NOT GAINED ENOUGH WEIGHT!

Seek a lactation consultation at one of the breastfeeding clinics indicated below.

a) Ways to Increase Your Milk Supply
- All moms need rest, hydration, nourishment and relaxation to maximize milk supply.
- Feed frequently using both breasts.
- Pump with a good brand pump, preferably electric (MEDELA, HOLLISTER (also known as EGNELL-AMEDA)
- Best pump times are typically just after morning breastfeeding. Try about ten minutes for each breast.
- See your physician for a prescription of Motilium (also known as domperidone – not a fine wine!). The usual dose is 30 mg, four times a day for at least two weeks and often longer.

b) Supplement Your Baby If Needed
Try to use expressed breast milk if possible and, if not, then use formula as a supplement. Give supplements after most breastfeedings rather than replacing entire feeds. However, you can replace entire feeds with formula, especially if Mom is exhausted and needs a long sleep. Catching up on sleep may also help her milk supply. If there is significant weight loss by the baby then see your doctor or a medical breastfeeding clinic.

JAUNDICE

If your baby's skin is yellow, check with your doctor as soon as possible. Often jaundice resolves itself after a few days with good feeding and the baby having yellow stools. It is vital that your physician follow up closely with blood tests to ensure that your baby's bilirubin level is dropping. Occasionally, your physician will recommend that your baby be placed under ultraviolet lights for a period of time at the hospital.

Remember, you can get through a night or a day, and help is at hand for you. Breastfeeding problems are really tough to have but they can be resolved, often quite quickly. Once you and your baby have settled, breastfeeding can be a wonderful experience for you both for many months.

General Breastfeeding Information

There are a number of books that are quite helpful for learning about breastfeeding. Here are two that you might want to take a look at:
- Jack Newman, *Dr. Jack Newman's Guide to Breastfeeding: Revised Edition* (Harper Collins, 2003)
- La Leche, *Womanly Art of Breastfeeding* (Plume, 2004)

Here is a summary of breastfeeding resources that are available.

La Leche League (Calgary)
Phone: 242-0277
Website: www.lalecheleaguecanada.ca

La Leche League is an international organization that provides mother-to-mother support, encouragement, information and education. It promotes a better understanding of breastfeeding as an important element in the healthy development of the baby and mother. The league organizes monthly meetings throughout Calgary and area. Locations vary by month. Phone to get up-to-date meeting dates and addresses. Fathers are welcome at some of the evening meetings.

Calgary Health Region
Website   www.calgaryhealthregion.ca

The Calgary Health Region (CHR) website has in-depth information on breastfeeding your baby. This is a comprehensive website with topics ranging from problems during breastfeeding to choosing a maternity bra. From the home page, click on the tab for "Programs and Services" and select "Women's Health". "Breastfeeding" is listed on the "Women's Health" page. The same information is also included in the CHR's "From Here through Maternity, A Resource for Families" provided by your health care provider.

Alberta Medical Association

Website: www.albertadoctors.org

On this website you can find the Alberta Breastfeeding Support Services Directory, which lists contact information for breastfeeding resources in Alberta communities. From the home page, select "Clinical Resources", "Women's Health", and then "Breastfeeding".

Motherisk

Phone: (416) 813-6780
Website: www.motherisk.org

If you are concerned about which medications are safe for you to use while breastfeeding, talk to your doctor or call the Motherisk Hotline. This is a Toronto-based organization. The telephone line operates Monday to Friday from 9 a.m. – 5 p.m. E.S.T. Outside of these hours you can hear recorded information on common drugs and household products. The website also has information about taking medication during pregnancy.

Breastfeeding.com

Website: www.breastfeeding.com

This website provides a lot of information on breastfeeding, from instructional videos and information on the benefits of breastfeeding to breastfeeding humor and more.

Paula says...

"After the birth of my second child I found breastfeeding even more difficult than the first time around. This was not because of any physical reason, but because my son Declan had significant jealousy issues and would tear the house apart while I breastfed. I felt I was being taken hostage by the situation. I then devised two tactics that helped. The first was having him sit beside me on the couch with his favourite book. He held the book and turned the pages while I read it to him and breastfed my daughter. I also made a "special box" containing interesting toys and occasionally a new book. He could only take it out when Ailish was being breastfed. Soon he was trying to convince me that my daughter was hungry all the time!"

Public Lactation Consultants

Lactation consultants are usually nurses who have had extra training in helping mothers to breastfeed. At the hospital, you may have met with a consultant who discussed any potential latch issues with you. It is possible to get in touch with a lactation consultant by contacting your public health unit. Public health units are listed in this book in "Chapter Four: Health of Baby and Mom" under "Immunizations". Lactation consultants cannot provide you with any prescriptions. They are often available on the weekends. There is no charge for this service. You can also contact a lactation consultant through the Infant Feeding Resource Centre. Leave your name and number at 943-4526 and they will get back to you.

Breastfeeding Clinics with Physicians

There are three clinics in Calgary (one in the North and two in the South) specializing in breastfeeding where physicians are International Board-Certified Lactation Consultants in breastfeeding consulting.

Bowness Breastfeeding Centre (Dr. Woolgar)
Location: Alex Community Health Centre
Address: Suite 101, 1318 Centre Street N.E.
Phone: 266-2622 (press 1)
Hours: Monday to Friday: 8:30 a.m. – 4:30 p.m. for appointment booking. Appointment hours depend on doctor availability.

Dr. Woolgar's office has a team of three female physicians specializing in lactation consulting. You do not need a referral to attend the clinic; merely call ahead and make an appointment. Try to have your baby ready to nurse for your appointment, but not starving. Bring Alberta Health Care cards for you and your baby. Bring any supplements that you are providing to your baby. At the time of printing, they were booking seven days in advance.

Copperfield Breastfeeding Clinic (Dr. Landy)
Location: Circle Medical
Address: 123, 15566 McIvor Boulevard S.E.
Phone: 726-0524
Hours: Monday, Wednesday, Friday: 8:30 a.m. – 4:30 p.m. for appointment booking. Appointment hours depend on doctor availability.

Dr. Landy provides assistance to any moms who are encountering difficulty with breastfeeding. A referral is preferred but you do not need a referral to attend the clinic; merely call ahead and make an appointment. Try to have your baby ready to nurse for your appointment, but not starving.

Bring Alberta Health Care cards for you and your baby. Bring any supplements that you are providing to your baby. At the time of printing, they were booking one to two days in advance.

Lakeview Breastfeeding Clinic at Mayfair (Dr. Jain)
Address: 211, 6707 Elbow Drive S.W.
Phone: 246-7076 (Call for appointment and hours of availability.)
Fax: 249-0156
Hours: Appointment hours depend on doctor availability.

Make sure you get a referral from your physician in order to attend Dr. Jain's clinic. Your baby must be with you unless you are prenatal or your baby is in the hospital. Try to have your child ready to nurse for your appointment (but not starving), and bring your Alberta Health Care card. Dr. Jain also requests that you refrain from wearing perfumes since she is allergic.

Jill says...

"The malls do have nursing rooms, but I found it easier to feed the twins one at a time while having lunch or a drink in the mall's food court. The chairs scattered through the mall also made nursing comfortable and the nursing bib was great for being discreet. Feeding both babies at the same time is near impossible to do discreetly and I found the nursing rooms better for this. My arms and hands got tired holding two babies up without the special feeding pillow. Try to save feeding both babies at the same time for when you are at home."

Tip! *If you are breastfeeding multiples, you can purchase a nursing pillow specifically for twin nursing or borrow one from the Twins, Triplets and More Association of Calgary.*

Private Lactation Consultants

Some doulas and midwives are also trained in lactation consulting. These private consultants will charge an hourly fee. They are not affiliated with any medical boards.

Breast Pumps

There are two main types of breast pumps: hand pumps and electric pumps.

HAND PUMPS

There are a few makes on the market and their cost ranges between $30 and $80. These are convenient and great for providing a bit of freedom for mom as well as for ensuring a "safety net" of extra milk in the freezer. You can purchase hand pumps at most pharmacies, Kacz' Kids, bo bébé, Toys "R" Us and other stores. Hand pumps made by Avent work very well.

ELECTRIC PUMPS

Electric pumps are available in two grades: domestic or hospital. Hospital grade electric pumps are the most powerful. They cost about $1,000. Domestic pumps can be purchased for about $350 or they can be rented. If you plan to, or need to, pump on a consistent basis, the $350 can be well worth it.

Many pharmacies in Calgary and breastfeeding clinics mentioned above rent or sell electric pumps. Typically, a deposit of about $100 is required. Costs vary, but daily, weekly and monthly rates are usually available and are approximately $70 per month or $3 per day. You will need to purchase a pump attachment kit for your rental, which costs about $35 for a single kit or $55 for a double kit.

In addition to the pharmacies and breastfeeding clinics, there is one company in Calgary that provides breast pump rentals and will deliver them to your home:

Wee Feed Inc.
Phone: 246-7008
Website: www.weefeed.com

Wee Feed offers domestic and hospital grade pumps. The domestic pumps are for sale or rent; the hospital grade pumps are for rent only. View their website or contact Wee Feed Inc. directly for the rates. Wee Feed also offers nursing pillows and breast pump accessories. There is free delivery on orders over $50 within Calgary and Okotoks. There is a charge for delivery to Cochrane, Airdrie and Chestermere. They offer very quick response times and sometimes can have the product delivered that same day.

There are two main manufacturers of electric breast pumps: Medela Inc. and Hollister Ltd. You can contact them as follows:

Medela Inc.
Phone: 1-800-435-8316
Website: www.medela.com
Hours: Monday to Friday: 7:30 a.m. – 8 p.m. C.S.T.
                      Saturday: 8 a.m. – 12 p.m. C.S.T.

Hollister Ltd.
Phone: 1-800-263-7400
Website: www.hollister.com
Hours: Monday to Friday: 8:30 a.m. – 5 p.m. E.S.T.

STERILIZER

You might also consider buying a sterilizer that can be used in the microwave for your breast pump and baby bottles since it is much more convenient than boiling all of the equipment for ten minutes each time. Sterilizers only take five to seven minutes depending on the power of your microwave and require a lot less fuss than saucepans with boiling water on the stove. Follow the sterilizer directions for what time is appropriate for your microwave. Sterilizers are sold in most stores that sell hand pumps.

Alternatively, Medela sells a Quick Clean Micro-Steam Bag which is convenient for travel. Each bag can be used up to twenty times and each box has five bags. Each bag holds two bottles and accessories. Simply add two ounces of water with your bottles and place it in the microwave for two minutes. Leave your sterilizer at home and use these for travelling.

TIP! *You may want to use distilled water for sterilizing your pump since Calgary water will leave mineral deposits on your pump, bottles and other equipment. Alternatively, adding some lemon juice to the water may help to reduce the formation of mineral deposits.*

STORING BREAST MILK

Routinely pumping extra milk allows a helper to feed the baby and give Mom a bit of a break. It also provides security in case Mom gets sick and has to take medication, or if Mom will be away from baby for a few feeds. If you would like to do this, aim to keep three to four feeds of breast milk in the freezer. For storage and thawing instructions, consult CHR's "From Here through Maternity, A Resource for Families" book given to you by your healthcare provider. Many books on baby care also provide this information.

You can find additional information on storing breast milk on the Alberta Government website: www.parentlinkalberta.ca (follow links for "After the Birth", then "Breastfeeding".)

Paula says...

"I used bags especially designed for breast milk storage that have a seal at the top of the bag and are self-standing. I liked them since I could thaw the milk right in the bag. Some brands don't have this feature. I also made sure I labeled and dated the bags."

Tip! *A lot of dads really enjoy bottle-feeding their baby! Try pumping so that Dad can help in the feeding, too.*

NURSING BRAS

In the first month of your baby's arrival you will need to choose a nursing bra if you are breastfeeding. It is probably best to wait a while before investing. You will probably have increased in size and a properly-fit nursing bra will help you feel more comfortable. Some women wear their bra at night for more comfort. You'll need at least two bras (wear one at a time!) so that you can wear one while the other is being washed. Remember, you are going to be wearing these bras for a long time so invest in comfortable bras.

Nursing bras typically range in price from $35 to $65, but can cost as much as $110 for a custom-fit bra. Your cup size will vary during the day and before and after feeds, so keep this in mind when you are trying on a bra. Try them on and try opening and closing the cup with one hand. If it takes two, it will be harder to be discreet in public!

Here are a few tips from the Calgary Health Region on choosing a nursing bra.

- Shop where you will get help with measurement and selection. It is difficult to properly fit yourself.
- Cup size should allow the addition of breast pads without being too tight. A bra that is too tight can inhibit milk supply. It is important that seams do not press into your breast. Pressure can lead to blocked ducts and breast infection (mastitis).
- Underwire bras are not recommended.
- Cotton bras will breathe better but may shrink. Lycra bras may offer more stretch when breasts are full but may not offer enough support for some women.

Some popular brands of bras include: Anita, Bravado (a Canadian-made bra), Bellamaterna, Jeunique, Emma Jane, Thyme Maternity and Warner Baby and Me soft cup nursing bra.

Thyme Maternity sells two nursing bras (without underwire): a sports nursing bra and a cotton nursing bra, each of which cost about $45. For locations, check out www.thymematernity.com.

There are two specialty bra boutiques in Calgary (by appointment only):

sportsbras.ca
Address: 11-A, 2219 35 Avenue N.E.
Phone: 270-4250
Website: www.sportsbras.ca

This store is a boutique by-appointment-only store which sells a Canadian-made nursing bra by Bravado (four different styles). It also sells Jeunique bras that are custom fit. Prices vary by size. It also sells expanders so that you can get more use out of your nursing bras. You can order your bra online.

thebralady.ca
Address: 606, 537 14 Avenue S.W.
Phone: 264-9377
Website: www.thebralady.ca

This store is another boutique that provides a personalized fit with Jeunique brand bras.

Many stores in Calgary and area offer nursing bras. Here is a list:

Baby & Me Maternity
Address: #105, 3400 14 Street N.W.
Phone: 283-3070
Website: www.babyandmematernity.com

The Bay (Lingerie Department)
Address: 200 8 Avenue S.W. (4th floor)
Phone: 262-0345
Website: www.hbc.com

bo bébé Fine Baby Products
Location: Market Mall N.W.
Phone: 288-5020
Website: www.bobebe.com

bo bébé Fine Baby Products
Location: 730, 20 Crowfoot Crescent N.W., Crowfoot Village
Phone: 252-0320
Website: www.bobebe.com

Cream Body & Bath
Location: 206, 304 Main Street S., Airdrie
Phone: 945-3114
Website: www.creambodyandbath.com
Note: A $5 coupon is available on their website.

Ella Bella Maternity Boutique
Location: 286, 10816 Macleod Trail S.E.
Phone: 271-0050
Website: www.ellabella.ca

Home Care Medical Supply
South Location
Address: 9309 Macleod Trail S.
Phone: 252-2266
Northwest Location
Address: 765 Northmount Drive N.W.
Phone: 283-7273
Northeast Location
Address: 470, 3545 32 Avenue N.E.
Phone: 291-1558
Website: www.homecaremedicalsupply.com

Knickers n' Lace
Address: #208, Willow Park Village, 10816 Macleod Trail South
Phone: 225-1413
Website: none

Posh Mommy
Address: 2120 Kensington Road, N.W.
Phone: 283-1654
Website: www.poshmommy.ca

SHE Apparel Inc.
Address: 602 17 Avenue S.W.
Phone: 299-1743
Website: www.sheapparel.com

Tip! *Nursing bibs allow you to feed your baby more discretely. They are available at most maternity stores.*

NURSING BRAS

FORMULA

There are a variety of brands of formula available, varying in caloric content, nutrients, taste and price. Baby formula comes in three basic formats: powdered, concentrated and ready-to-drink. All of these are available at grocery stores and pharmacies. Make sure that you read the labels carefully so that you prepare the formula exactly as specified by the manufacturer.

Available formulas include those based on cows' milk, soy-protein based formulas, formulas for premature infants and formulas for infants who have problems with their metabolism. Find out from your physician or paediatrician exactly what kinds of formula are suitable for your baby.

Additional information on formula-feeding your baby can be found in the "Feeding Your Baby" section of "From Here Through Maternity, A Resource for Families" published by Calgary Health Region.

The Alberta Government's Service Alberta website at www.servicealberta.gov.ab.ca has information on formula. Under "Life Events" section, follow the links for "Becoming a Parent", then "Healthy Baby", "Growing up Healthy" and "Infant Formula".

Most manufacturers of formula make information available on their websites. Some examples include the following:
- Enfamil/Enfalac at www.enfamil.ca. Search under "Products", then "Family of Formulas".
- Nestle Carnation/Good Start at www.verybestbaby.com. Click on "My Baby" followed by "Formula Feeding".
- Similac/Isomil at www.welcomeaddition.com. Look under "Product Info".

Paula says...

"Different concentrations of formulas may be packaged similarly. Concentrated formula that is not diluted properly can be harmful to your baby. Make sure you read the labels every time! "

Tip! *Consider buying the "ready to drink" baby formula for the first four or six weeks. Sleep-deprivation at this time is extraordinary and this may give you one less thing to worry about.*

> **Tip!** *If someone calls and asks what kind of gift would you like, get them to check out www.newbornessentials.ca. They have very pragmatic gift baskets (no stuffed animals, I promise!). Alternatively, ask your friend to give you the gift of a grocery run, or even drop by to help you with laundry, make a meal, or clean the kitchen. That's the sign of a true friend!*

POSTPARTUM DEPRESSION SUPPORT

According to the Askdrsears.com website, the "baby blues" are very common and occur in up to 85% of new mothers. Symptoms vary greatly and can start any time from a few hours to a few days after giving birth. If you have symptoms and feel that they aren't improving, contact your physician for an appointment.

Postpartum depression (PPD) is a more serious form of depression than the "baby blues" that, according to a 2005 University of New Brunswick study website, affects up to 30% of new mothers. A common misconception is that the "baby blues" are synonymous with PPD – this is not true. The "baby blues" are a short-lived, mild form of depression, whereas PPD is more severe and can last longer if it goes untreated. The popular book "Down Came the Rain" by Brooke Shields provides an excellent overview of her journey through PPD. It is a quick, funny and easy read. It is available at the Calgary Public Library as well as at most bookstores in Calgary.

Treatment of PPD usually involves a combination of medication, therapy, support programs exercise and proper nutrition.

In Calgary, you can find one-on-one counseling through the Calgary Regional Health Authority or through Numina Counseling Inc.:

Calgary Regional Health Authority
The Calgary Regional Health Authority has one specialist who provides one-on-one counseling for women with pre- and postpartum depression. This program is run out of the Rockyview Hospital in the Urgent Psychiatric Care department. You do need a referral from your doctor. The therapy includes ten sessions which are covered by Alberta Health Care.

Numina Counseling Inc.
Dr. Petra Spletzer PhD, R. Psych.
Address: Nielsen Homeopathic Medical Clinic,
                 220, 1919 Sirocco Drive S.W.
Phone: 819-5676
Website: www.numinacounselling.com

Dr. Petra Spletzer is a registered psychologist who provides counseling services specializing in prenatal and postpartum depression. Her services cost $125 per session (fifty minutes) and are not covered by Alberta Health Care. Your employer's extended health benefit plan may cover a portion of the cost. She counsels out of her clinic and will occasionally provide services at your home.

The following are some books that can be helpful in understanding and overcoming postpartum depression:
- Soshana Bennett, *Beyond the Blues: A Guide to Understanding and Treating Prenatal and Postpartum Depression* (Moodswings Press, 2003)
- Karen Kleiman, *This Isn't What I Expected: Overcoming Postpartum Depression* (Bantam Books, 1994)
- Natasha Mauthner, *The Darkest Days of My Life: Stories of Postpartum Depression* (Harvard University Press, 2002)
- Sandra Poulin, *The Mother-to-Mother Postpartum Depression Support Book* (Berkley Trade, 2006)
- Ronald Rosenberg, *Conquering Postpartum Depression: A Proven Plan for Recovery,*(Da Capo Press, 2004)
- Linda Sebastian, *Overcoming Postpartum Depression and Anxiety* (Addicus Books, 1998)
- Brooke Shields, *Down Came the Rain* (Hyperion, 2005)

The following websites provide additional information:
- www.askdrsears.com (click on "Pregnancy and Childbirth", "Tenth Month: Post Partum" and then "Postpartum Depression");
- www.cmha.ca (search under "postpartum depression");
- www.postpartum.net;
- www.postpartumdads.org;
- www.mooddisorderscanada.ca (click on "Understanding mood disorders", and then "Other types of depression" and then "Post Partum Depression");
- www.wellmother.com (click on "Postpartum").

Paula says...

"It is amazing to me how many mothers I meet that have postpartum depression, yet we don't speak openly about it to each other. It was only when I read 'Down Came the Rain' by Brooke Shields that I realized how many symptoms of PPD I had. Get help as soon as you can."

Here are a couple of programs in Calgary that provide support for PPD:

Families Matter Society – Postpartum Support Program
Phone: 205-5177
Website: www.familiesmatter.ca (click on "Register now")
Hours: Monday to Friday: 9 a.m. – 4 p.m.

This program provides support specifically to those suffering from postpartum depression. They offer free one-to-one telephone support with women who have "been there". Group support is offered where you can meet weekly with others going through PPD. The group is facilitated by trained leaders and professionals. They also provide an informative evening for couples; please register ahead of time. An extensive lending library of books, articles and videos are available. Please call the number above or visit the website to find out about the specific support services offered.

Parenting Resource Line
Phone: 205-5189
Hours: Monday to Friday: 9 a.m. – 3 p.m.

Support for parents with children of all ages who may be experiencing stress in their parenting, including PPD.

PERSONAL CONCIERGE SERVICE

Yes, this is the ultimate in luxury. If you can't find a local teenager to run your errands for you, this might be an alternative. A personal concierge service can provide everything from standing in line for you to doing your errands such as dry-cleaning and grocery shopping. They will even do your Christmas shopping and baby announcement cards for you! Here are a few Calgary-based services that you might be interested in. If you are looking for others, check out www.yellowpages.ca and look under Concierge Services.

Life Assistants
Phone: 990-3307
Website: www.calgaryconcierge.ca

If you need help on anything from organizing, personal shopping, cleaning, travel arrangements, errands or even event planning, Life Assistants could be your solution. Their services can be offered on a one-time basis or on a regular basis. Look at their website for information on the New Mom package which includes laundry, meal preparation, light cleaning, errands, grocery shopping and two hours of babysitting. Where was this company when I had my babies?

TimeOut Solutions Inc.
Phone: 827-7129
Website: www.timeout-inc.com

They have two levels of service: Level 1 covers general errands at $35 per hour and Level 2 provides wait service and more complicated services at $45 per hour. Evenings and weekends are extra. The main service area is south of 17 Avenue S. and within the Calgary city limits. Outside of this service area an extra 10% surcharge is applied. Some multiple-hour packages are available.

Time is Money Executive Concierge Inc.
Phone: 612-2993
Website: www.timeismoney.ca

This executive concierge service offers three levels of service: Level 1 is Easy Services ($65/hour), Level 2 is Essential Services ($80/hour) and Level 3 is Exceptional Services ($110/hour). Membership packages that reduce the hourly rate by about 15-20% are available.

WHAT'S FOR DINNER?
Prepared Meals

Even if you don't have a kindly neighbour who will drop off a tuna casserole big enough to last you the first week with your new baby, you can still eat well without having to cook during this hectic time.

BUYING PREPARED MEALS

Besides buying prepared meals at your local grocery store, there are a few other options in Calgary, including M&M Meat Shops and Sunterra Quality Food Markets. You can also head out to your local farmers' market and pick up precooked meals.

M&M Meat Shops
Address: Multiple locations
Website: www.mmmeatshops.com

M&M Meat Shops carry frozen prepared meals. Many of them can be warmed or cooked in the microwave. The website has a product catalogue with pictures, including listings of low-fat products.

Jill says...

"Work colleagues presented us with two shopping bags full of frozen M&M entrees as a 'baby gift' when our twin girls were born. We gratefully enjoyed every one of them."

Sunterra Quality Food Markets
Address: Multiple locations
Phone: See below
Website: www.sunterramarket.com

There are five Sunterra locations in Calgary. At each one, you can pick up prepared food at the deli counter. The main reason for mentioning Sunterra here is its Friday Night Feasts. You can pre-order these prepared complete dinners on Thursday by 3 p.m. and pick them up on Fridays. The cost is $15 per person (more for special holiday dinners). You can also pre-order for Mother's Day, Thanksgiving, Easter and Christmas meals and simply pick them up. To pre-order call one of these Sunterra locations: Britannia at 287-0553, Bankers Hall at 269-3610, Sunterra Village Marché at 262-8240, West Market Square at 266-3049 or Petit Marché at 263-9756.

Elena says...

"Sunterra's Friday Night Feasts make for a great stay-at-home date night."

DELIVERED PREPARED MEALS

Over the last two years, there has been a proliferation of prepared meal choices that are a long way from "TV dinners". Here are a few options beyond just ordering pizza or Chinese food:

CookingForYou.ca
Phone: COOKING (266-5464)
Website: www.cookingforyou.ca

This company has a regularly changing menu of healthy gourmet entrees or full meals (complete with pictures on the website). Some items are cooked and frozen, while others are prepared and ready to bake or barbeque. The food is prepared in a commercial kitchen in Calgary and is delivered once a week to your part of Calgary (e.g. delivery to North Calgary is on Mondays). You need to order by 3 p.m. the previous day. The prices are similar to a mid-range restaurant, plus approximately $5 for delivery and a refundable $5 deposit for the insulated delivery box. Minimum order is $50.

CopperPot Creations
Phone: 585-4717
Website: www.copperpotcreations.com

This company has healthy gourmet entrees, soups and side dishes. Meals are individually portioned, packaged, frozen and labeled. The food is prepared in a commercial kitchen in Calgary. You need to order by noon at least two days ahead. The prices are similar to a mid-range restaurant, plus delivery charges that vary by order and location. Within Calgary, delivery is offered on orders over $50. In neighbouring communities, delivery is offered on orders over $100. Check their website for more details on delivery charges. CopperPot Creations also offers gourmet organic baby food.

Entrees Express
Phone: 252-3801
Website: www.entreesexpress.ca

This company offers a "TLC package" for parents with babies under two months old. Choose your meals online, select TLC on the monthly calendar and place your order. They will call you to arrange delivery. Entrees are typically portioned for four people, but you can ask them to cut the entrees in half. The prices are similar to a mid-range restaurant. Delivery within 10 km of their kitchen is free. You can also pick up your order.

The Liberated Cook
Phone: 233-2665
Website: www.theliberatedcook.com

This company will assemble and deliver your meals for you. Meal packages start at $70. Simply register and choose your meals online. Delivery is on Saturdays and costs $25 if you are within their service region. You can also pick up your meals. Entrees are portioned for four people, however, you can also choose half-sized meals for two people. Packages contain either five or ten meals (each serving four people). You can also order over the phone. Alternatively, when you get a bit more time on your hands, you can assemble the meals yourself.

Waiters en Route
Phone: 229-DINE (229-3463)
Website: www.waitersenroute.ca

This is a Calgary restaurant delivery service. You may order from any of the Waiters en Route partner restaurants located within eight kilometers of your address. Orders can be placed by phone or online. The delivery charge is between $5 and $7 depending on the distance. The food usually arrives thirty to sixty minutes after you order, depending on factors such as traffic, weather and how busy the restaurant is. You are expected to tip the delivery person.

Personal Chef Services
One idea for a group gift from friends or co-workers to new parents is a gift certificate for a personal chef service. A personal chef will plan menus for a period of time, shop for groceries and prepare meals which can be stored and reheated later. Personal chefs are private entrepreneurs whose businesses tend to change over time, so I have decided not to list specific businesses here. One way to find out about personal chefs operating in Calgary and area is to do a search on the Internet. You can also try the www.chefsearch.ca website.

DELIVERED GROCERIES

When the thought of going grocery shopping seems daunting, it is handy to have groceries delivered to the door. There are two full-service grocery stores (Pic'N'Del and Sunterra) and an organic produce grocer (Small Potatoes Urban Delivery) who offer delivery in Calgary:

Pic'N'Del
Phone: 1-866-PICNDEL (742-6335)
Website: www.picndel.com

This online grocery shopping service provides deliveries from the Calgary Co-op stores but is a separate company. You do need to be a Calgary Co-op member. Not all products available at the Co-op are shown in the online store, but you have the option to ask for any specific item and it will be included in your order as long as it is available at the local Co-op. According to their website, the prices are the same as in the store except that Co-op flyer specials are not available. However, there are some specials on the website. The website is well organized, with pictures and detailed information for most products. You pay when the groceries are delivered so you don't have to give out your financial information over the Internet. The delivery charge is approximately $15. Multiple delivery times are available every day. At the time of writing, Pic'N'Del was not offering delivery outside Calgary.

Sunterra Quality Food Markets
Phone: 287-0553 (Sunterra Marketplace in Britannia Shopping
             Plaza)
Website: www.sunterramarket.com

As well as having a number of stores in Calgary, Sunterra Quality Food Markets provides an online or order-by-phone shopping service. The service is provided from the Sunterra Marketplace in Britannia Shopping Plaza.

The selection of non-food items (most importantly, baby products) was limited when I checked. On the other hand, you can order Sunterra's baked and prepared foods, which are not available in other stores. Delivery is available every day, excluding Christmas and New Year's Day, at a cost of approximately $8. There is a minimum order of $50. You can also order online and pick up your order at Sunterra Marketplace in Britannia at no charge and without the minimum purchase requirement. If an order is placed before 4 p.m., it can be delivered the same day. At the time of writing, Sunterra did not deliver outside the city of Calgary.

Small Potatoes Urban Delivery

Phone: 615-3663
Website: www.spud.ca

This online store offers certified organic groceries including bread and grains, dairy, nuts, pasta, beverages, household and personal care products. It also offers a weekly or bi-weekly delivery of customized boxes of organic fruits and vegetables. Delivery is on different days of the week for different parts of Calgary. There is no delivery charge on orders over $35. Refundable deposits are charged on ice packs, freezer bags, and items such as milk bottles.

CHAPTER THREE
PARENTING HELP

Becoming a parent for the first time (or even a second time) provokes feelings of uncertainty and anxiety. Fortunately, there is a lot of help available to new parents in Calgary.

PARENTING HELP LINES AND WEBSITES

211 in Calgary and Cochrane
Provider: The City of Calgary, the Distress Centre and United Way of Calgary and Area
Phone: 2-1-1
Website: www.211calgary.ca
Hours: 24 hours, 7 days a week

211 is a three-digit telephone number that connects callers to a full range of community, social and government services information. The calls are answered by Certified Information and Referral Specialists. It is free, confidential and multilingual. Among other things, this line provides information on free programs and available subsidies.

Children's Link Website
Provider: The Children's Link Society
Phone: 230-9158
Website: www.childrenslink.ca (select "Support Links")

This website lists resources available for families of children with special needs in the Calgary and Rockyview area.

Families Matter Society's Parent Resource Line
Provider: Families Matter Society
Phone: 205-5189
Website: www.familiesmatter.ca (select "Register Now")
Hours: Monday to Friday: 9 a.m. – 3 p.m.

This line is for parents, grandparents and guardians of children up to eighteen years of age. Parent Resource Line offers one-time phone support to family members under stress, in crisis or facing a challenge with their children.

Parent Information Line
Provider: Alberta Children's Services
Phone: 1-866-714-KIDS
Website: www.parentlinkalberta.ca
Hours: Monday to Saturday: 9 a.m. – 9 p.m.
               (Closed on Sundays and statutory holidays)

This help line provides information on early childhood development, child care programs and services. It also provides information on daycare subsidies.

PARENT LINK ALBERTA CENTRES

The Government of Alberta, through Alberta Children's Services, provides community-based Parent Link Centres. They provide support in the form of parent education, early childhood development and care, family support, information and referrals. The goals of these centres are to: build parents' and caregivers' skills and confidence; focus on play-based problem-solving experience; help parents be active in their children's development; and provide registries of child care providers, resource libraries and referrals to community programs and services. Their website at www.parentlinkalberta.ca is filled with information on developmental stages and how to interact with your child. There is a lot of information worth taking a look at.

The following is a list of Parent Link Centres for Calgary and area.

Calgary

Aboriginal Parent Link Centre
Address: 19 Erinwoods Drive
Phone: 240-4642
Website: none

Awo Taan Family Wellness - Parent Link Centre
Address: 100, 1603 10 Avenue S.W.
Phone: 531-1970 (extension 202)
Website: www.awotaan.org

The New Family Place - Parent Link Centre (Calgary Catholic Immigration Society)
Address: 1410 1 Street S.W.
Phone: 266-6686
Website: www.ccis-calgary.ab.ca

Family Pride - Parent Link Centre
Address: 4615 85 Street N.W.
Phone: 205-5193
Website: none

Hand in Hand - Parent Link Centre
Address: 2623 56 Street N.E.
Phone: 293-5467 Extension 27
Website: none

North Central Family Connections - Parent Link Centre
Address: 520 78 Avenue N.W.
Phone: 295-6666
Website: none

Parent Link Corridor - Parent Link Centre
Address: YWCA of Calgary, 320 5 Avenue S.E.
Phone: 232-1582
Website: none

Airdrie

Airdrie Family Services
Address: 125 Main Street N., Airdrie
Phone: 945-3900
Website: www.airdriefamilyservices.ca

North Rocky View Community Resource Centre
Address: 112 1 Avenue N.W., Airdrie
Phone: 948-0263
Website: www.yourcrc.com

Chestermere

East Region 3 - Parent Link Centre
Address: 105 Marina Road, Chestermere
Phone: 207-7060
Website: none

Cochrane

Western Rocky View PLC - Parent Link Centre
Address: #2, 209 2 Avenue W., Cochrane
Phone: 851-2250
Website: www.cochrane.ca

High River and District

High River
Address: 508 1 Street S.W., High River
Phone: 652-8633
Website: none

The City of Okotoks has a Family Resource Centre:

Okotoks Healthy Family Resource Centre
Phone: 995-2626
Address: 11 Cimarron Common, Okotoks
Website: www.ohfrc.org
Hours: Monday, Tuesday, Thursday and Friday: 8:30 a.m. – 4:30 p.m.
             Wednesday: 9 a.m. – 6 p.m.

This centre offers a variety of support and referral services to community resources. They have brochures and information on topics such as parenting, pregnancy and stress. They also offer events such as a children's clothing exchange.

BABY CARE FAIR

Provider: Calgary Health Region (Perinatal Education Office)
Location: Varies
Phone: 781-1450
Website: www.calgaryhealthregion.ca
             (Search under 'Baby Care Fair')

Calgary Health Region puts on at least two Baby Care Fairs each year. Parents, families, friends and caregivers of new babies are all welcome. Educators are on hand to answer questions and give advice on baby care. This fair is free.

HEALTHY FAMILIES CALGARY AND AREA

Phone: 204-0800
Hours: Monday to Friday, 8:30 a.m. – 4:30 p.m.
Website: www.healthyfamiliescalgaryregion.com

This is a free support service provided by the Calgary Regional Home Visitation Collaborative. Access to this program is provided to families with children less than three months of age through a referral from a public health nurse.

A Healthy Families Home Visitor can help new parents learn more about their baby, help them deal with the stress of having a new baby, and help them find other community support services.

CHILDREN'S COTTAGE SOCIETY

Location: 845 McDougall Road N.E.
Phone: 283-4200 (General Information Line) or 233-2273
Website: www.childrenscottage.ab.ca

The Children's Cottage provides the following crisis and respite support programs to families:
*   24-hour Crisis Nursery – the ten-bed Crisis Nursery provides up to three days of 24-hour child care. This is available to parents who are temporarily unable to care for their children because of stress, marital conflict, sudden illness, housing or financial crisis. The Crisis Nursery is available to children from birth to eight years of age.
*   Community Respite – this program consists of three components and offers a range of respite and crisis child care options to families with children, newborn to twelve years of age, when parents are experiencing personal or family stress and have no other support available. The program allows parents to receive assistance prior to reaching a crisis level. Parents of twins and triplets may qualify for respite care. The three components are:
    In-home Infant Respite Program – assists parents of infants, newborn to six months, when alternate respite options are not available. Respite care workers are available to come to your home and care for your child while you regain your energy by having a rest or attend to your household chores.
    Daycare Program – works with daycares throughout the city to provide space free of charge when registered children are absent. This program allows parents to attend appointments such as counseling, job interviews and hospital or doctor visits, to search for housing, to deal with a death in the family or to meet other crisis needs.
    Volunteer Respite Homes Program – screens volunteers throughout the city to provide respite care to children in the volunteers' homes. Families in need are matched for this program in situations similar to those requesting daycare.

POST NATAL HELPERS LTD.

Phone:	640-0844 (24-hour answering service)
Website:	None
Hours:	Try to accommodate all client requests, depending on staff availability.

This company employs mothers (about fifty at the time of writing) and has been operating in Calgary for over twenty years. Their staff provides both emotional and physical assistance in your home. They primarily provide in-home temporary child care services and miscellaneous help around the house. They also provide care for children with special needs and some emergency care for sick children. They have lots of experience with twins and multiples and provide night time assistance.

Jill says...

"I was not planning on night time help. During the first few days after the twins were born we were getting about one hour of sleep in every three on a good night. One time at 3 a.m. my husband peered at me with bleary eyes and asked, 'Who are those people who will come into your house and help you at night?' I'm not sure how we would have coped without a few nights of help during the first few weeks. Extra help is indeed expensive but keeping your health and sanity is more important."

SUPPORT FOR TWINS OR MULTIPLES

To parents of twins or more, multiple congratulations and hats off to you in this exciting year ahead! The Calgary Health Region Perinatal education has two courses to help you adjust to your new clan.
* Twins/Triples Breastfeeding (Free),
* Twins, Triplets, and More: Adjusting to Parenthood ($20)

You can register online at www.birthandbabies.com or call the Perinatal Education Office at 781-1450.

TIP! *When you have multiples it might seem as if someone is always crying. It is better if it is not you! If you need to, get help in the house for a couple of mornings or afternoons so that you can sleep or take a break.*

The main resource for parents of multiples in Calgary is the Twins, Triplets and More Association of Calgary. Get involved with this organization early and even before your multiples are born.

Twins, Triplets and More Association of Calgary (TTMAC)
Phone: 274-8703 (voicemail)
Website: www.ttmac.org

This non-profit association is membership-based and mostly run by volunteers. Currently, TTMAC includes over five hundred families with multiples in Calgary and area. Membership costs $35 for the year. TTMAC membership provides access to a specialized library and various support services, discounts from numerous Calgary stores and businesses, a ten-issue newsletter, playgroups and early access to TTMAC's semi-annual used toy and clothing sale. Their newsletter has a lot of twin and triplet equipment and clothing for sale. There are monthly coffee parties hosted by members and various events throughout the year. These gatherings provide a wonderful opportunity to meet other parents of multiples in the area.

Jill says...

"I found the TTMAC zone socials to be an incredible source of information and ideas. Before the birth of my twins, I attended a few socials and received some practical advice and a supportive network. I started making it out to the TTMAC Zone socials again when my twins were four months old. It offered one night out each month that was a real touchstone for the experiences I was going through as a mother of multiples. Some socials are for couples so that dads can get to meet their peers."

LAUGHING FAMILIES

As you embrace your new life with an addition to the family, you can enjoy it with a good laugh! Laughing families is a program that is put on by the Southern Alberta Child and Youth Health Network. It runs the first Thursday of every month from 6 p.m. – 7:30 p.m. at the Alberta Children's Hospital in room B2200 on the second floor. The entire family can come for a free giggle and belly laugh. No registration is needed. For more information please call 955-7420.

SUPPORT FOR SINGLE PARENTS

Single Parent Support Program

Provider: North Central Community Resource Centre
Address: Huntington Hills Community Association
           520 78 Avenue N.W.
Phone: 275-6666

This centre offers support, information and assistance to single parent families and their children. There is a weekly support group that runs from September to June as well as a drop-in support group. They provide counseling and find the right resources to help single parents. They also run a Single Parent Mentorship program called Along the Way, which matches clients with single parents who have "been there".

The Twins, Triplets and More association provides support and mentoring to single parents of multiples. For more information, see TTMAC listed above.

MEETUP.COM

www.singleparents.meetup.com

There is a Calgary Single Parents Meet-up Group that connects through the meet-up website. Membership is free and you can chat with other members through the message board as well as find out about group events. The group's goal is to provide support to members, create a social network of single parents and provide playmates for the children. Their meet-ups occur a few times a month, typically on Fridays or weekends.

Websites of interest:

- www.parentsworld.com This Calgary-based website for single parents was set up by a Calgary mom!

Suggested reading:

- Andrea Engber, *The Complete Single Mother: Reassuring Answers to Your Most Challenging Concerns* (Adams Media, 2006)
- Armin Brott, *The Single Father: A Dad's Guide to Parenting Without a Partner* (Abbeville Press, 1999)

PARENTING COURSES

There is no shortage of parenting courses and advice offered in Calgary for parents with young children. Below is a list of companies that provide courses, one-on-one coaching and even telephone counselling.

Annie the Nanny
Provider: Annie
Location: Varies
Phone: 836-5437 (KIDS)
Website: www.anniethenanny.ca
Age group: Any

This is Calgary's version of the Super Nanny. Annie provides consultation in Calgary and the surrounding areas. She offers in-home assessments as well as parenting courses. She also answers questions by e-mail.

Brilliant Beginnings Educational Centre
Provider: Melanie Gushnowski (founder)
Address: 207A 19 Street N.W.
Phone: 283-5437
Website: www.brilliantbeginnings.ca
Age group: Newborn to four years old

Brilliant Beginnings runs the following evening parenting workshops:
*   Sleepy Time for Infants
*   Taming the tiger! – Positive Approaches to Toddler behaviour
*   Picky eating No More!
*   Positive Discipline for Positive Kids
*   Peas in a Pod (deals with the stress and impact of having a baby on your relationship with your spouse)

These workshops start at $43 and run for two hours. Brilliant Beginnings also offers infant massage and baby signing classes. Individual developmental consultation is provided by a child development specialist for developmental issues such as sleep, tantrums and picky eating starting at $70 for one hour. The company also offers a variety of services for children with special needs. Check the website for details and up-to-date fees.

Calgary Health Region's Parenting Courses
Provider: Calgary Health Region (Perinatal Education Office)
Location: Varies
Phone: 781-1450
Website: www.birthandbabies.com
Age group: Birth and up

The Perinatal Education at the Calgary Health Region (CHR) offers a variety of courses for new parents.

- Baby & You for Moms - This FREE course provides a comprehensive overview of looking after your baby in the first year. It also covers family transition issues and a baby's effect on the relationship between parents. This course fills up quickly, so book as soon as possible. It is suitable for children eight weeks to nine months.
- Daddies & Babies - This FREE course is strictly for dads and their babies and mirrors the content of the Baby & You for Mom's course. There is a long waiting list for this one, so register early. It is suitable for children eight weeks to nine months.
- Helping Your Child Adjust to a New Baby ($25) - This course provides strategies for helping your child adjust to an addition to the family. It is suitable for children of any age.
- Playtime with Dad ($25) - This course teaches dads games for interacting with their newborns. Dads and babies must come without moms. Good luck, dads! It is suitable for children, birth to three months.
- New Baby, Old Pet? Introducing Baby to Rover ($25) The title says it all.

Paula says...

"The Baby & You for Moms course is an absolute must for all new moms. The course is free, you learn all about your new baby and meet many moms who are in the same stage of life and probably live very close to you. I am still in contact with most of the moms from my Baby & You class."

Families Matter

Provider:	Families Matter
Location:	Varies
Phone:	205-5178
Website:	www.familiesmatter.ca
Age group:	All ages

Families Matter has a number of parenting courses that cover the ages from newborn to twenty-four months as well as older children. Here are a few courses that you may be interested in. Check out the website for prices and locations of courses near you.

- Be a Great Dad
- Terrific Toddlers
- Parenting Tip Time Series
- Creating Family Balance
- Parent Effectiveness Training
- Promoting Nurturing Relationships
- Positive Discipline

In-Sync

Provider:	Calgary Family Services
Location:	Varies
Phone:	269-9888
Age group:	Birth to six years

This program is for parents and their children who want to strengthen and enhance their parent-child attachment. Parents can participate in the program at home, at Calgary Family Services or attend a parent-child group in the community. Please call Calgary Family Services to find out more.

Nobody's Perfect Parenting

Provider:	West Central Community and Family Resource Centre
Location:	3507A 17 Avenue S.W.
Phone:	543-0555
Website:	http://members.shaw.ca/westcentralcrc/who.html
Age group:	Birth to six years

This is an eight-week course specifically for young, single, low-income or socially/geographically isolated parents. The course provides information on infant/child health, safety, development and behaviour.

Paula says...

"I asked a few local parenting experts which books they would recommend for new parents. Their suggestions are listed below alphabetically by author.

- *Judy Arnall, Discipline Without Distress: 135 Tools for Raising Caring, Responsible Children without Time-Out, Spanking, Punishment or Bribery (Professional Parenting Canada, 2007)[1]*
- *Berry Brazelton, Touchpoints: 0 to 3 (Da Capo Press, 2006)[2]*
- *Calgary Health Region, Growing Miracles (Calgary Health Region, 2005)[3] [Note: This book is complimentary and available through your Public Health Unit.]*
- *Annabel Karmel, First Meals (Macmillan Canada, 1999)[4]*
- *Linda Kavelin Popov, The Family Virtues Guide (Penguin Group, 1997)[5]*
- *Robert MacKenzie, Setting Limits, Revised and Expanded (Prima Lifestyles, 1998)[6]*
- *William Sears M.D., The Baby Book (Little Brown and Company, 2003)[7]"*

---

[1] Recommended by Brilliant Beginnings.
[2] Recommended by Kitty Raymond from Raymond Parenting.
[3] Recommended by Judy Arnall of Professional Parenting.
[4] Recommended by Parenting Power™.
[5] Recommended by Parenting Power™.
[6] Recommended by Kitty Raymond from Raymond Parenting
[7] Recommended by Judy Arnall of Professional Parenting

Parenting Power™

Provider:	Julie Freedman Smith and Gail Bell
Address:	748 130 Avenue S.W.
Phone:	281-2524
Website:	www.parentingpower.ca
Age group:	Newborn to five years

Parenting Power™ provides parenting workshops and family coaching on a number of topics relevant to baby's first year. These include:

- Sleep – Remember When? - This course reviews various methods to train your child to sleep.
- Books and Babes - This course focuses on strategies for expanding your child's vocabulary and choosing age-appropriate, quality literature for your child at each developmental stage.
- Fun with Math - This course teaches how to use everyday activities to increase your child's conceptual skills.
- Positive Parenting - This five-week course on discipline helps parents unite their parenting styles.
- Family Coaching - Parenting Power™ will work with you to develop strategies for when you are struggling with the day-to-day process of raising a little one.

Parents and Children Together (PACT)

Provider:	Further Education Society
Location:	Varies
Phone:	241-8544
Website:	www.pact.9f.com
Age group:	Birth to five years
Cost:	$10 per session
	(subsidies available for low-income families)

This program consists of ten weekly morning sessions held in various locations around Calgary. Parents are divided into two groups. While one group supervises the children in the playroom, the other group has a discussion with a parent educator. The philosophy of the playroom is unstructured play in a safe environment. Lots of toys and activities are provided. Parents help with playroom setup and bring in snacks for children and parents.

Parents as Teachers (PAT)

Provider:	Families Matter
Location:	Varies
Phone:	205-5178
Website:	www.familiesmatter.ca (click on "Register Now")
Age group:	Pre-birth to three years
Cost:	Free

The PAT program is open to anyone, but families in crisis are a priority. Participating families receive monthly in-home visits from a parent educator. The program provides parents with research-based child development and parenting information and activities that help parents shape their children's early learning experiences. The parents receive:
- Age-based learning tools and play activities for their children;
- Skills in observing children and setting realistic expectations;
- Parenting information;
- Screenings that assess children's overall development;
- Meetings with other PAT parents to share parenting and child development information.

Professional Parenting
Provider: Judy Arnall
Location: Varies
Phone: 252-6513
Website: www.professionalparenting.ca

Professional Parenting offers classes and workshops on parenting topics. It also provides e-mail, telephone and in-home coaching. Applicable courses are listed below:
- Attachment Parenting for Everyone
- Ages and Stages – What to Expect When
- Sleep Easy – Solving Your Family Sleep Problems
- And Baby Makes Four – Smoothing the Way for the Second Child's Birth
- Your Terrific Toddler
- Parent Effectiveness Training

Raymond Parenting Centre
Provider: Kitty Raymond
Location: Varies
Phone: 242-3533
Website: www.raymondparenting.com
Age group: Newborn and up

Kitty Raymond offers parenting seminars to help new parents with children up to age five. These courses include:
- Sleep from the Start (prenatal/postnatal),
- Sleep from Now On (12lbs – 4 years)
- Setting Healthy Limits Age 1 – 5 Years
- Toilet Learning the Easy Way

Kitty also offers a membership-based website called Raymond ParentsNet™ which provides the latest in parenting research and answers your questions.

Women's Health Resources

Provider:	Women's Health Centre
Address:	Room 185, 1441 29 Street N.W.
Phone:	944-2270
Website:	www.calgaryhealthregion.ca (then follow these links: "Programs and Services", "Women's Health Centre", "Newsletter and Workshops")
Age group:	Various
Cost:	About $25 per workshop

This centre is partnered with the Salvation Army. It offers evening parenting workshops taught by experts for approximately $25 each. The centre also has a Women's Health Resources Library.

CHAPTER FOUR
HEALTH OF BABY AND MOM

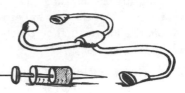

The first year of your little one's life will be filled with doctor's appointments, immunizations, measurements and developmental checks. You're not on your own; there are many sources of information and help available in Calgary and the surrounding area.

Paula says...

"I use 943-5465 (Health Link) as the first place I call since they are open 24 hours a day, 7 days a week and will let you know whether you need to go to Emergency or see a doctor in a short time frame, or whether you can wait longer. The staff is fully trained, extremely friendly and very helpful."

HEALTH HELPLINES AND WEBSITES

Health Link Line
Provider: Calgary Health Region (CHR)
Phone: 943-LINK (5465)
Website: www.calgaryhealthregion.ca
               (Click on "Health Link")
Hours: 24 hours, 7 days a week
Age Group: 2 months and up

This CHR information line is for everyone, including parents whose babies are over two months old. Calgary Health Link is a convenient and reliable way to access health information and advice around the clock.

Registered nurses answer the calls and provide health information on more than five hundred topics including nutrition and active living. The nurses can also give you information on which drugs and household products are safe for breastfeeding mothers.

CHR also operates the Early Start Parent Information Line specifically for parents of babies under two months of age (see "Chapter Two: Surviving the First Six Weeks"– "Early Start Parent Information Line").

Ask Dr. Sears
Website: www.askdrsears.com

This American website was created and is maintained by the renowned paediatrician and author, Dr. William Sears, and his family. It focuses on the health of children and especially babies. This is a very helpful website offering information on childhood ailments and more.

Caring for Kids
Website: www.caringforkids.cps.ca or www.cps.ca
                 (look under Children's Health Topics)

This website is developed by the Canadian Paediatric Society. Go to the "When your child is sick" section to find information on common illnesses.

Canadian Health Network (CHN)
Website: www.canadian-health-network.ca

This site is an affiliate of the Canadian Child Care Federation. It has thousands of links to bilingual health promotion information.

Canadian Institute of Child Health
Website: www.cich.ca

This website from the Canadian Institute of Child Health is dedicated to promoting and protecting the health, well-being and rights of all children.

GROWTH CHARTS

The National Center for Health Statistics
Website: www.cdc.gov/growthcharts

You've probably seen the public health nurse or your doctor mark your child on a length-for-age and weight-for-age chart. If you are interested in having one for yourself, you can have a look at the above website and print off your own clinical growth chart. The charts differ for boys and girls.

ALBERTA CHILDREN'S HOSPITAL

Address: 2888 Shaganappi Trail N.W.
Website: www.calgaryhealthregion.ca/ACH

Hopefully, you will never need to go to the Alberta Children's Hospital on an emergency basis. If you do need to go, here are a few tips about the hospital emergency room:

Before You Go

Here are a few things to bring:

- Alberta Health Care card for your child.
- Any prescription medication that you child is on.
- Sippy cups or bottles for your child since they are not available at emergency. Also note that the vending machines do not have milk, although they do have water.
- Diaper bag with a few easy changes for your little one.
- Healthy snacks for you and your child. *Check with the nurse to see if it is okay for your child to eat or drink while waiting.*
- Something to occupy your little one, e.g. blocks, toys or books.

Parking

Parking is available just outside the emergency entrance and is $1.25 an hour to a maximum of $10 for the day. If you are on your own, you can ask the security guard to help you purchase a ticket.

Upon Arrival

The emergency has a triage desk where they determine in what order to see you. When you arrive, ensure you check in with the triage desk. You may be given a number so that you don't have to stand in line until they can talk to you. *If your child's condition changes, notify a nurse immediately.* Be prepared to wait if your child does not need immediate attention.

The Main Hospital

The main hospital is accessible from the emergency room. Ask a nurse to let you through the doors and be sure to let them know that you are stepping out for a bit. They can page you in the main hospital. There are coffee shops and a cafeteria in the main hospital.

Baby Notes

There is a baby change-table in the handicapped stall of the emergency room. Unfortunately, there is no private area for nursing.

Paula says...

"While waiting to see a triage nurse, I put a chair in one of the small toy alcoves to get a bit of privacy for nursing. My daughter Ailish was too distracted by the toys on the walls to nurse. In hindsight, a blanket tented over us would have minimized the distractions as well as provided some privacy."

PELVIC FLOOR ISSUES

If you had a difficult birth and are experiencing pelvic floor issues, you may need to visit the Pelvic Floor Clinic at the Foothills Medical Centre:

Pelvic Floor Clinic

Address: Women's Health Centre, North Tower,
             1441 29 Street N.W.
Phone: 944-4000
Website: www.calgaryhealthregion.ca (follow these links:
             "Programs and Services", "Women's Health Centre",
             "Our Services", and finally "Pelvic Floor Clinic")
Hours: Monday to Friday: 8 a.m. – 4 p.m.

The clinic provides assessment and management of pelvic disorders in women. A referral from your family physician is required. There are long waits to be seen at this clinic.

There is also a physiotherapist based out of Springhill who provides pelvic floor physiotherapy.

Springhill Sport Physiotherapy

Address: 185 Scenic Acres Drive N.W.
Phone: 288-8877
Hours: Monday to Friday: 7 a.m. – 7 p.m.
Saturday: 8 a.m. – noon
Website: www.crowchildtwinarena.net/Physio.htm

IMMUNIZATIONS

Your baby's first immunizations are scheduled at two, four, and six months, one year of age and eighteen months. Many public health units provide immunization services. Your public health nurse will let you know during your first visit which unit you will need to report to. Waiting times can be longer than six weeks, so be sure to book your next appointment well in advance. Also, remember to bring the immunization card given to you during your first appointment and your baby's Alberta Health Care number. If your child has a minor illness, they can still be immunized unless they have a fever.

During the appointment, your baby will be weighed and her length and head circumference will be measured. The nurse will discuss your baby's health and the value of vaccinations with you. She or he will instruct you on how to care for your baby after the vaccination. After the injection, you will need to stay in the office for at least fifteen minutes to ensure that there is no allergic reaction. For a couple of days after the vaccination your baby may not be feeling well and be quite grumpy so try not to plan any major events or trips for this time.

If you are squeamish about needles, you may want to come with your spouse or partner. Nurses usually keep a little bell handy to ring right after the injections to distract the child from the pain. It works for some, but has no effect on others. Ask the nurse to try it and see if it works for your child.

Remember to pick up a copy of CHR's publication "Growing Miracles, The First Six Years with Your Child".

Flu shots are provided without charge for children between six months and two years old and their caregivers. The shots are offered every year starting at the beginning of the flu season in October. Call the Health Link line at 943-LINK (943-5465) to make an appointment or find out about the times and locations of drop-in flu shot clinics.

More information about immunizations in Calgary is available from the Calgary Health Region website at www.calgaryhealthregion.ca. Click on "Programs & Services", followed by "Vaccinations."

Jill says...

"I know a mom of triplets who took a playpen with toys into the clinic with her nanny. They managed the 'immunization rotation' much more easily this way."

Current locations of public health units and phone numbers are listed below or for listings, maps or details such as parking information, visit www.calgaryhealthregion.ca and look under "Hospitals and Community health care".

Northwest Locations:

North Hill Community Health Centre
Address: 1527 19 Street N.W.
Phone: 944-7400 (Appointments need to be booked through the Shaganappi office at 944-7373)

Northwest Community Health Centre
Address: 109, 1829 Ranchlands Boulevard N.W.
Phone: 943-9700

Thornhill Community Health Centre
Address: 6617 Centre Street N.W.
Phone: 944-7500

Northeast Location:

Village Square Community Health Centre
Address: 2623 56 Street N.E.
Phone: 944-7000

Southwest Locations:

Shaganappi Community Health Centre
Address: 3415 8 Avenue S.W.
Phone: 944-7373

8th & 8th Health Centre
Address: 912 8 Avenue S.W.
Phone: 781-1200

Southeast Locations:

Acadia Community Health Centre
Address: 132, 151 86 Avenue S.E.
Phone: 944-7200

East Community Health Centre
Address: 110, 112 28 Street S.E.
Phone: 943-9830

Forest Lawn Community Health Centre
Address: 3810 17 Avenue S.E., second floor
Phone: 944-7300

South Calgary Health Centre
Address: 31 Sunpark Plaza S.E.
Phone: 943-9300

Airdrie Location:

Airdrie Regional Health Centre
Address: 604 Main Street S., Airdrie
Phone: 912-8400

Cochrane Location:

Cochrane Community Health
Address: 213 1 Street W., Cochrane
Phone: 932-8700

Okotoks Location:

Okotoks Health and Wellness Centre
Address: 11 Cimarron Common, Okotoks
Phone: 995-2600

CHILD AND INFANT LEARNING AND DEVELOPMENT RESEARCH GROUP (Ch.I.L.D.)

Address: 2500 University Drive N.W.
Phone: 220-4955
Website: www.psychology.ucalgary.ca/CCD/child

The department of Psychology at the University of Calgary is always looking for children to participate in fun, game-like research projects. They invite children aged two months and older to participate in the study. Participation usually involves a one-time visit to the University of Calgary and the entire session lasts no longer than one hour. Appointments are available weekdays, weekends and evenings. They have free parking and they will accompany you and your child to the lab. They have four labs: Language and Cognitive Development, Speech Development, Cognitive Development and Language Processing.

CARING FOR YOUR NEW BABY'S TEETH

By Dr. Wendy Street-Wadey DDS

Many people ask, "Why worry about baby teeth when they are just going to fall out anyway?" Baby teeth are very important because they contribute to the proper development of speech and proper chewing, and because they guide permanent teeth into their proper positions. Inadequate care can lead to pain and infection. Caring for your child's oral health involves three essential components: regular brushing and flossing, proper nutrition, and regular visits to the dentist.

Brushing and Flossing

Begin daily cleaning of your infant's mouth at around two to four weeks of age. Using a damp piece of gauze or a baby washcloth, gently wipe on top of the upper and lower gums at the front of the mouth. As you become proficient in the front, you can begin to move towards the back of the mouth, but not too far, and always stay to the sides of the mouth. Avoid touching the delicate tissues near the throat.

Between birth and twelve months, usually at six months, teeth in the lower front of the mouth will begin to erupt. To clean these teeth use a damp piece of gauze, a baby washcloth, or a soft bristled infant toothbrush, and scrub gently using either short back-and-forth strokes or small circular strokes. Make sure that you clean from the gum line to the tops of the teeth on both the front and back surfaces. For a young infant, clean the teeth once a day. Ideally, in the older infant and toddler, the teeth should be cleaned after every meal. At a minimum, clean the teeth after the last meal of the day because food and bacteria left on the teeth overnight can cause rapid tooth decay. Also pick a time during the day when your child is most co-operative and do a very thorough job each day at this time. Cradle your child's head in the crux of your arm, or lay him between your legs facing either direction to hold him still.

Fluoridated toothpaste is essential for prevention of decay, but should not be used until your child is able to spit out after brushing, usually between two to three years of age. When you do start using toothpaste, swipe the tube across the bristles to obtain a small amount (less than the size of a pea). When your child takes an interest in brushing, let him brush his own teeth, but until he is able to use a knife and fork proficiently, he still needs you to brush for him to ensure a thorough cleaning. Always use an age-appropriate toothbrush.

Flossing should be started if your child has two adjacent teeth tight together, or once the molars have erupted. Keeping the floss pressed against the side of one tooth to form a "C" shape, gently glide the floss between the teeth using a sawing motion, and allow the floss to clean slightly below the gum line. Be very careful to use only light pressure. Look for children's flossing picks in the drug store to make flossing easier.

Nutrition

Foods that contain sugar are the most harmful to teeth. Feed your child nutritious foods that are low in refined sugar, and be aware that even healthy, natural foods can contain sugar. As the stickiness and sugar content of a food increases, so does the potential for tooth decay. Also, the longer that sugar is in the mouth and in contact with the teeth, the more likely that decay will occur. It is best to give your child highly nutritious foods that are as close to nature as possible. For example, give a piece of whole fruit, unsweetened canned fruit, or frozen fruit rather than dried fruits or fruit juices. Avoid raisins, fruit roll-ups, and fruit leathers. Limit juice intake to 1/4 – 1/2 cup per day. Choose unsweetened foods such as plain oatmeal and plain yoghurt, and add fresh fruit. Read labels and compare the amount of carbohydrates in similar foods. Avoid foods that have added sugars, such as those labeled "sweetened with fruit juice", or those in which the ingredient list contains syrups, dextrose, fructose, glucose, honey, sucrose or molasses.

At snack time choose calcium-rich snacks such as cheese and yoghurt. Calcium-rich, low-sugar foods help to neutralize the acids in the mouth that cause tooth decay, so give your child a piece of cheese following a sugary snack if you are unable to brush after the snack.

The frequency of eating can also affect the teeth. Grazing throughout the day, as opposed to three meals and two snacks, is very harmful to the teeth. Avoid giving your child a sippy cup or bottle to carry around all day, and if you must, make sure it contains water. Comfort nursing should be minimized.

Limit non-nutritious sugary treats to special occasions. Treats should be given with a meal rather than alone. If you must give your child a special treat, choose non-sticky treats over sticky candy such as jujubes or gummy bears. Ice cream contains calcium, so it is a better choice than candy for a treat. Be sure to brush your child's teeth after a treat.

Nighttime feedings can be very detrimental to the teeth, and long-term use of bottles and pacifiers can interfere with the proper development of the jaws. If your doctor is satisfied with your child's weight gain and has advised you that nighttime feedings are no longer necessary, stop feeding your child during the night in order to prevent "baby bottle decay". Never put juice into a nighttime bottle. Milk is also harmful to the teeth if a child falls asleep with the bottle in his mouth. If your child is dependent on a bottle at night, or likes to always have a bottle available during the day, gradually dilute the contents so that eventually you are giving your child water.

Visits to the Dentist

As a new mom, you should make certain that you adhere to your own six-month checkup schedule and that you are not neglecting your own dental health. Many new moms have problems with their teeth due to changes in dietary patterns and due to the lack of a daily brushing and flossing routine. An undiagnosed dental problem can affect both your health and your energy levels. Before you go for your checkup, ask the dental receptionist what the policy of the office is in regard to bringing children. Some dentists will ask you to bring your child with you to your checkup so that your child's mouth can be observed and to discuss your family's general dental habits. Other dentists might prefer that you leave your child at home, so that your appointment is uninterrupted. Also, some dental offices may not have an appropriate place for your child to wait nor appropriate supervision for your child.

The Canadian Dental Association recommends that a dentist examine your child within six months of the eruption of the first tooth, or by age one. Lift up the lip to view the teeth, and if you notice any darkening, or any dull white, black, or brown spots developing on your child's teeth, your child should see a dentist as soon as possible. If you have a family dentist, ask at what age he or she would like to see your child. If your dentist does not treat children, ask to be referred to a pediatric dentist. If you do not have a dentist, then it would be wise to have your child seen at six months by a pediatric dentist, especially if you have had problems with your own teeth. To find a paediatric dentist, look under "Dentists – Pediatrics" in the Yellow Pages.

What can you expect at your child's first visit? First, you will be asked a series of medical and dental questions to help the dentist establish your child's overall health and your level of dental care at home. Generally, your child will be given a ride in the chair and told that the dentist is going to count her teeth. The dentist will observe the facial structures and jaws of your child to assess for developmental and chewing problems. Next the dentist will look at your child's oral tissues and teeth to see if there are any obvious problems or concerns. Often the first dental appointment is short, but a quick examination of the mouth, and time spent with you and your child, may reveal developing problems and will give the dentist an early understanding of your child's dental health. If your child is co-operative, a detailed examination will be done, and, if necessary, radiographs will be taken. Very receptive children might have their teeth polished and fluoride applied. Instructions on caring for your child's teeth should be provided. Depending on the extent of the examination and the time taken, expect to pay a minimum of $75 for the examination, plus separate fees for radiographs, polishing, and fluoride, if applicable.

With the early establishment of routine brushing, healthy eating and regular dental visits, your child will likely have a healthy and happy smile that lasts a lifetime.

Other Dental Concerns

PACIFIERS AND THUMB-SUCKING

Infants will suck on their thumbs and fingers as a normal part of oral development. Thumb-sucking and pacifier use will usually diminish and stop by age two. Pacifiers should be used judiciously. Do not put sugar, honey, or any other substance on the pacifier.

TEETHING

Although teeth can begin to erupt at any time during the first year, the first tooth will usually appear at six months. You may notice redness, slight bleeding and swelling around the tooth as it erupts, and your child may experience discomfort. To ease the pain, apply light pressure to the gums using your finger, a teething ring, or the back of a cold spoon. Avoid medicated teething gels because they can numb the mouth and throat. Avoid teething biscuits because they can cause tooth decay. Contact your physician if your child has a fever, severe pain or other signs of illness, as teething does not cause these symptoms.

FLUORIDE

Fluoride is incorporated into the teeth as they form and makes the surfaces of the teeth harder and more resistant to decay. The City of Calgary adds fluoride to the water to help reduce the incidence of tooth decay in the city's population. If you live outside of Calgary, if you drink bottled or filtrated water, or if you are using bottled water to cook, then you should contact your local health authority to discuss fluoride supplements for your child.

INJURIES

If your child has an accident limited to the mouth and you notice any changes in the position of a tooth, any fractures to the teeth, or any bleeding or lacerations in the mouth, contact your dentist or the Alberta Children's Hospital immediately. If you are uncertain as to whether your child should be seen by a dentist, err on the side of caution and call your dentist. If anything, a quick visit to your dentist will give you comfort. If your child has also injured other areas of her body, immediately contact your physician or the Alberta Children's Hospital, and then contact your dentist.

FURTHER INFORMATION

To obtain further information about your family's oral health and to view illustrations on brushing and flossing, visit the website of the Canadian Dental Association at www.cda-adc.ca and click on "Your Oral Health".

DENTAL CARE FOR FAMILIES IN FINANCIAL NEED

The Alberta Child Health Benefit offers free children's dental care to low-income families. Find out if your family is eligible and if so, you can make appointments for your children to see a private dentist at no fee. You can also contact 22TEETH at 228-3384 to find other dental services that are available or look at the website at www.calgaryhealthregion.ca/dental.

Calgary Urban Project Society (CUPS) is a not-for-profit community health centre in Calgary's downtown core that offers health services to people in need. Contact CUPS at 221-8797, or look at the website at www.cupshealthcentre.com.

SPEECH THERAPY AND LANGUAGE DEVELOPMENT

The Calgary Health Region has a two-page document online to help you determine if your child is on track for speech and language development. They stress that it is important to seek early intervention if your child is behind. You can find this document on www.calgaryhealthregion.ca. Click on "Programs and Services", followed by "Speech-Language Therapy", followed by "Preschool Programs" and finally "Listening and Talking". The provincial government has another document on www.health.gov.ab.ca entitled "Will I outgrow it? Milestones and warning signs for speech and language development". Look under "Health information", then "Publications", then "Pregnancy/Childbirth/Post-Natal".

If your child needs speech therapy, you do not need a referral to see a speech language therapist. There are three routes that you can follow for help: private, public or both. Unfortunately, there are long waits (three to six months) for Alberta Health Care-funded speech therapists. You can register your child for an assessment in the public system by calling the Speech-Language Pathology department:

Speech-Language Pathology Department
Main Location: East Health Centre 112 28 Street S.W.
Phone: 943-9830
Website: www.calgaryhealthregion.ca and then click on "Programs and Services" followed by "Speech-Language Therapy" followed by "Preschool Programs".
Hours: Monday to Friday, 8 a.m. – 4:30 p.m.

After your child is assessed, he will be registered for speech therapy at a clinic relatively close to you. There are waiting lists for both stages: assessment and therapy. Even if your child has had an assessment completed by a private speech therapist, you cannot be moved to the therapy waiting list until your child has had an assessment by a Calgary Health Region speech therapist.

The Calgary Health Region Speech-Language Pathology Department has a Preschool program for children from birth to kindergarten age. This program works with parents and children to address each child's specific issue. They also provide a free seminar "Talk by 2" which provides an overview on the typical language development from birth to two years old. Call the Speech-Language Pathology Department to find out the details of the next seminar. Their website also has suggestions on how parents can encourage their children to talk. These suggestions are found on the pages "Building your baby's language skills (Birth to 12 months)" and "Building your toddler's language skills (1-2 years)".

Private speech therapists are more quickly available; however, they typically cost $115 per hour. There are often additional charges for report writing. Some work benefit plans cover this cost and it is considered a tax-deductible medical expense. The speech therapist can complete an assessment in one visit. The Speech-Language Therapy Department will provide you with a list of private speech therapists but are not able to give any recommendations. There is an association of private speech language practitioners. Their details are listed below:

Alberta Speech-Language Association of Private Practitioners (ASAPP)
Phone: (780) 988-2217
Website: www.asapp.ca

Here you can find a listing of speech language pathologists in Calgary and throughout Alberta, click on "SLP Listing". They have information on each speech-language practitioner's area of interest.

Alternatively, you can find private speech therapists listed in the Yellow Pages under "Speech Therapists". Be sure to ask whether they have experience working specifically with your child's particular difficulty.

You can always start with a private speech therapist and move to the public system once they have space available. Be sure to register your child in the public system as soon as possible.

Tip! *Families Matter often has speech pathologists come to their centre for the day. You can join them to discuss any issues that your child might be having. Call 205-5175 to find out when the speech pathologist will be at the centres.*

EYE CHECKUPS FOR YOUR BABY

According to the Calgary Health Region, your child's eyes should be checked by a family doctor, paediatrician or an eye care specialist (optometrist or ophthalmologist) at the following times:

- at birth in the hospital, or at the first doctor's visit if born outside a hospital
- at about six months old
- at three to four years old (before entering school)

Family doctors and pediatricians do an eye exam on almost every visit in the first few years. These checks are for basic eye health; if there are any issues, your child will be referred to an ophthalmologist.

Optometrists and ophthalmologists review your child's vision; these eye exams are covered by Alberta Health Care, so be sure to bring their card to the appointment. All optometrists by training have expertise in checking babies' and toddlers' eyes.

A great deal of information is available through the following websites.

The Alberta College of Optometrists
Phone: 1-800-668-2694 (Alberta only)
Website: www.collegeofoptometrists.ab.ca (click on "Vision Care Information" and then "Parents")

This website has information about things to look out for with your children's eye health.

The Alberta Association of Optometrists
Phone: (780) 451-6824
Website: www.optometrists.ab.ca

This association also has a database that provides a list of optometrists in the city. The list is a bit daunting since it lists the optometrists alphabetically, as opposed to by location.

The Canadian Association of Optometry
Website: www.opto.ca

Follow links to "Eye Info" followed by "Children's Vision". They have great information on children's vision. They also have a database of optometrists. You can enter your postal code and obtain a list of the optometrists near you.

GROSS MOTOR DEVELOPMENT RESOURCES IN CALGARY

By Nicola Sadorra, Paediatric Physiotherapist

A child's first year of life is filled with learning. Motor, cognitive, social, and language development are all taking place concurrently. Motor development (a child's ability to move) is the most obvious development and, as a result, is typically the first concern for many parents. While we parents try not to compare our child to endless lists of motor milestones, our concern for our new child often leads us to check the lists, ask our friends and quiz other new moms to see how our child is doing. Keep in mind that all children develop at their own individual rate and progress differently through common stages of development. Some may even skip a stage entirely.

Information about typical child gross motor development can be found on the Calgary Health Region website. You can find lists of general development by going to the www.calgaryhealthregion.ca website, clicking on "Programs and Services" and going to the "3 Cheers for the Early Years" section. Enter the site, and then under the "3 Cheers for Parent's" tab, you will find information on development under "Everyday Miracles" and information on appropriate toys under the "Play" link at the top of the page. The CHR also hands out the "All About Me" Growth and Development pamphlets developed by Alberta Health and Wellness. Parents are usually given the appropriate-age pamphlet at each Immunization visit or during the Parent Drop-in clinics held at each local health unit. Information on the Parent Drop-In clinics can be accessed on the above webpage or by calling 943-LINK.

If you have concerns about your child's motor development, there are a number of resources in Calgary to provide help. The four main resources are:
1) the Early Intervention Program;
2) your physician or paediatrician;
3) publicly funded Physical Therapy; and
4) privately funded Physical Therapy.

1) The Early Intervention Program

The Early Intervention Program (EIP) is a Calgary Health Region initiative that works with families to provide suggestions to encourage their child's development. The goals of the program are to enhance a child's development, strengthen a family's ability to parent, and encourage effective use of community supports and services. The EIP can be accessed through self-referral by calling 943-9840, or by having a professional, such as a doctor, nurse or therapist, make a referral. After a referral is made, the Intake Coordinator will schedule a visit within two weeks to review your family's needs. If your child is appropriate for the EIP, a child development specialist will schedule a home visit to meet you and your child. Together, you and the specialist will discuss your family's needs and concerns to develop a program that is compatible with your individual family situation. Wait-lists can be up to two months long but vary with the season.

2) Your physician or paediatrician

Your physician is another primary resource for assistance and reassurance. If you have concerns regarding your child's development, do not hesitate to ask your family doctor. A physician's referral is necessary to access any further public resources, namely a paediatrician or services at the Alberta Children's Hospital. Waiting lists for paediatricians can be up to two to four months depending on the urgency of the motor delay.

3) Publicly-funded physical therapy

Gross motor delays are often assessed and treated by a Developmental or Paediatric Physical Therapist (Physiotherapist). Most public physiotherapy resources are geared toward children over three years (preschool- and school-aged children receive public funding through the school system to pay for therapy to address developmental delays). Here are two clinics that are geared to children under three years old:

Alberta Children's Hospital
Rehabilitation Department
Phone: 955-7912

A family physician or paediatrician referral is necessary to access the clinics at the Alberta Children's Hospital. The referral is triaged by the Intake Department of the hospital and sent to the most appropriate clinic depending on the concerns your doctor has indicated in the referral. Waiting lists are common and length varies between clinics. Most lists are long, so do not hesitate to ask your doctor for an early referral. Early intervention and assistance can be key in diagnosing and treating a child's motor delay. Furthermore, with early treatment a motor delay can often be modified and the child may be left without any noticeable reminder of early concerns.

Calgary Youth Physiotherapy
Address: #230, 7720 Elbow Drive S.W.
Phone: 259-8534
Website: www.calgaryyouthphysio.com

You can access a physiotherapist directly through Calgary Youth Physiotherapy. This physical therapy clinic is both privately and publicly funded and has licensed physical therapists specializing in the motor development of children from birth to eighteen years of age. This is an excellent facility that can provide both assessment and treatment services and assist you in evaluating your child's gross motor skill level. You do not need a physician's referral to access this clinic. Alberta Health Care will pay for up to ten sessions of therapy each year if your child qualifies for funding. If you do not qualify, and you still want therapy, you will have to pay privately. Note that not all private clinics qualify for public funding. There is currently a three-month waiting list for funding, but you can access a therapist immediately if you are paying privately.

4) Privately-funded physical therapy

Private therapy for children under three is limited or often difficult to track down. Most physiotherapists have limited training in child development. Be cautious about going directly to a general physiotherapist listed in the Yellow Pages. A paediatric physiotherapist has extra training in child development, and understands the physical needs of a child's growing body. Ask about their qualifications and experiences in child development, and seek references before you engage their services. Calgary Youth Physiotherapy has private paediatric physiotherapists available. There are also two other private paediatric physiotherapists available. Typical rates for private therapy are $65-100/hour. These costs may be reimbursable by your work benefit plan.

Some private paediatric physiotherapists include **Betsy Mustard,** (Phone 282-6598) and my own company **Tiny Talk and Walk** (Phone 479-TINY [8469]) for in-home therapy.

If you do not have immediate concerns about your child's development but would still like to enhance their ability to move, play and interact with their environment, playgroups are a great resource. Some good options in the city are:
*   Gymboree (www.gymboreeclasses.com) - offers movement, art and music classes in a play based format for various age groups.
*   Brilliant Beginnings (www.brilliantbeginnigs.ca, 283-5437) - offers playgroups for infants and toddlers that include motor skill development. They are located at 207A-19 St N.W.
*   Many community associations and local churches offer playgroups that include a gross motor component in their play-based program that will help your child develop their ability to move and explore their environment.

There are other options listed in this book under "Chapter Twelve: Activities" – "Playgroups".

There are many books that list developmental milestones and suggest activities to enhance development. See "Chapter Thirteen: Toys, Books and Games" – "Games to Play with your Little One."
Additional information on the practice of physical therapy can be found on the following websites:
- www.physiotherapy.ca
- www.albertaphysio.org
- www.cpta.ab.ca

Although all the sites listed above have a "Find a Physio" directory, none of the sites have a comprehensive listing of physical therapists in the province.

CHAPTER FIVE
HEALTHY EATING FOR BABY AND TODDLER

This chapter provides you with a summary of courses available, how to find a dietitian, books and useful websites on how to maintain healthy eating for your baby and you.

CALGARY HEALTH REGION

Introducing Baby to Solid Food

Once your baby reaches about six months of age, the Calgary Health Region suggests that you start to introduce solid food. The CHR provides a free course called "Feeding Your Baby". A registered dietitian teaches the course. The dietitian will answer all of your questions about breastfeeding, formula feeding, introducing solids, preventing allergies and other topics related to feeding your baby in the first twelve months. It is a good idea to attend the class when your baby is between four and six months of age. The class is scheduled every few months. Feel free to bring your baby to the class. In the class, you will be provided with handouts, suggestions on feeding your baby and a list of useful books.

To register for this course, contact Calgary Health Region Perinatal Education at:

Address: 214, 906 8 Avenue S.W.
Phone: 781-1450
Fax: 234-9089
Website: www.calgaryhealthregion.ca/prenataled
Hours: Monday to Friday: 8 a.m. – 4 p.m.,
             Saturday: 8:30 a.m. – 2:30 p.m.

Among the handouts distributed at the course is a booklet entitled "Feeding Baby Solid Foods" published by Alberta Health and Wellness. It is also available from your public health nurse at your baby's six-month vaccination or you can download a copy from the Alberta Health and Wellness website at www.health.gov.ab.ca (select "Health Information", "Publications", and then look under "Nutrition"). The booklet provides excellent information on introducing solids to your baby, including instructions on how to make baby food, so be sure to get a copy.

Feeding Your Toddler

The Calgary Health Region also offers a course called "Picky Eaters" regarding toddlers aged one to three years old. The course covers developmental stages of feeding, parent challenges, physical activities as well as the quantity of food eaten at this stage. This is a free, two-hour course that is taught by dietitians. For more information about upcoming classes call 943-8121 or see www.calgaryhealthregion.ca/nutrition.

Brilliant Beginnings Educational Centre offers a parenting workshop on Picky Eating NO More that costs $43. See "Chapter Three: Parenting Help" – "Parenting Courses" – "Brilliant Beginnings Educational Centre".

The Alberta Health and Wellness website mentioned above also has the handout entitled "Healthy Eating and Active Living for Your 1 to 5 Year Old". Another handout entitled "Food Serving Sizes for Children 1 to 3 years old" can be found on the same website or obtained from a public health nurse.

DIETITIANS

If you need to speak to a dietitian, you can call the CHR's Health Link line at 943-LINK and ask to speak to a dietitian. They will call you back directly. It is also possible to ask your physician to refer you to a dietitian. You will usually be referred to the Alberta Children's Hospital to speak to a dietitian on staff.

If you work outside the home and your employer provides an employee assistance program, you may be able to consult a dietitian through such a program. Call your employee assistance program provider to find out.

REFERENCE BOOKS ON MAKING BABY FOOD

There are many books on making baby food. Here are a few that I have enjoyed:
- Brenda Bradshaw and Lauren Donaldson Bramley, *The Baby's Table* (Random House of Canada, 2004)
- Louise Lambert-Lagace, *Feeding Your Baby the Healthiest Foods* (Fitzhenry & Whiteside, 2004)
- Diana Kalnins and Joanne Saab, *Hospital for Sick Children, Better Baby Food: Your Essential Guide to Nutrition, Feeding and Cooking for All Babies and Toddlers* (Robert Rose, 2001)

In addition, the CHR's "Feeding Baby Solid Foods" booklet mentioned above provides information on making your own baby food and simple recipes.

USEFUL WEBSITES

Here are a few useful websites:

- www.calgaryhealthregion.ca/nutrition - See "Alberta Health and Wellness Infant Feeding Handouts" for handouts on breastfeeding, infant formula and solid foods.
- www.todaysparent.com - Look under "Food and Nutrition", "Baby" to read articles on feeding your baby.
- www.healthlinkalberta.ca - Select "Your Health", then "Health and Wellness", then "Healthy Eating and Nutrition". This website provides information on infant nutrition and covers a wide range of topics from breastfeeding to solid foods.
- www.cspinet.org - If you are interested in finding out about food additives, check out this website of the U.S.-based non-profit organization Centre for Science in the Public Interest. Click on "Food Safety", then "Food Additives" to find an extensive glossary of food additives and information on their safety.
- www.dietitians.ca/eatwell - See "Let's make a meal" or "Virtual Kitchen" to plan a meal and learn nutrition facts.
- www.healthcanada.ca/nutrition - Select "Food and Nutrition" then "Canada's food guide to healthy eating". Unfortunately, there is no specific information on feeding babies.
- www.canadianparents.com
- www.tinytummies.com
- www.nutritionforkids.com
- www.cfc-efc.ca/startup/about.htm - Select language preference and search for "Nutrition".

BUYING BABY FOOD

There are many options available for baby food that is not mass produced. A number of new businesses are now providing baby food using wholesome foods for your baby:

Baby Gourmet
Address: Lakeview Plaza, 11, 6449 Crowchild Trail S.W.
            Calgary Farmers' Market S.W.
Phone: 614-9821
Website: www.babygourmetfoods.com
Hours: Monday to Saturday at Crowchild Trail location, closed Sunday,
            Thursday to Sunday at Calgary Farmers' Market.

Baby Gourmet provides healthy baby food for infants aged six months, eight months and twelve months and up. There are two locations in the city. Baby Gourmet delivers within the city limits when you order online. The delivery charge is $20 for orders over $50.

Bobobaby.com

Website: www.bobobaby.com

This company was started by a mom in British Columbia who was searching for convenient organic food. They carry twelve different age-appropriate frozen baby meals (for infants six, seven, eight months and older). Their products are distributed in Calgary by the following stores:

Amaranth Whole Foods Market
Website: www.amaranthfoods.ca
North Location:
Address: #7 Arbour Lake Drive N.W.
Phone: 547-6333
South Location:
Address: Chinook Centre S.W., Upper level, north side by Sears
Phone: 253-2711

Planet Organic
Website: www.planetorganic.ca
North Location:
Address: 4625 Varsity Drive N.W. (at Shaganappi Trail)
Phone: 288-6700
South Location:
Address: 10233 Elbow Drive S.W. (corner of Southland)
Phone: 252-2404

Sweet Pea Baby Food
Phone: 1-877-650-BABY (2229)
Website: www.sweetpeababyfood.com

Sweet Pea Baby Food is a company founded by a mom and her friend. They provide flash frozen baby food in ice cube size portions (to minimize waste) from organic ingredients without preservatives. There are eight flavours to choose from, and the food is appropriate for infants six to eight months and older. Three stores distribute their products in Calgary: Amaranth Whole Foods Market, Planet Organic and Community Natural Foods.

Community Natural Foods
Website: www.communitynaturalfoods.com
Tenth Avenue Market & Cafe:
Address: 1304 10 Avenue S.W.
Phone: 229-2383
Chinook Station Market:
Address: 202 61 Avenue S.W.
Phone: 541-0606

CopperPot Creations

Phone: 585-4717
Website: www.copperpotcreations.com

This company uses 100% organic ingredients and makes age-appropriate single-size servings. They are packaged in re-sealable bags, so it is easy to take out just what you need. Purées are available for babies about six months old, combination foods are available for babies about eight months old and toddler fare is available for infants over twelve months old. Delivery is $5 for orders over $50.

Calgary Farmers' Markets

If you are buying fruits and vegetables in bulk for homemade baby food, check out Calgary's farmers' markets. You can find great prices on seasonal produce. Below is a list of Calgary markets. For up-to-date information, see the Agriculture, Food and Rural Development website at www.agric.gov.ab.ca (follow the links to "Directories", "Food", "Alberta Farmers' Markets", then select "Town listing"). Alternatively, visit www.calgaryarea.com/community/eventspsa/farmers/farmermarket.htm.

Calgary Farmers' Market

Address: Currie Barracks Hanger #6,
4421 Quesnay Wood Drive S.W.
Phone: 244-4548
Website: www.calgaryfarmersmarket.ca
Hours: Thursday to Saturday: 9 a.m. – 5 p.m.,
Sunday: 9 a.m. – 4 p.m., year-round

Crossroads Flea Market

Address: 1235 26 Avenue S.E. (Blackfoot Trail and Ogden Road)
Phone: 291-5208
Hours: Indoor Farmers' Market (all year):
Friday, Saturday and Sunday: 9 a.m. – 5 p.m.;
Outdoor Farmers' Market (summer months only):
Friday, Saturday and Sunday: 8 a.m. – 5 p.m.

Crossroads Flea Market includes a flea market, antique market, indoor farmers' market, international food fair and seasonal outdoor farmers' market.

Hillhurst-Sunnyside Farmers' Market

Address: Hillhurst Sunnyside Community Centre,
1320 5 Avenue N.W.
Phone: 283-0554 (Ext. 223)
Hours: Wednesday: 3:30 p.m. – 8 p.m., early June to Labour Day;
3:30 p.m. – 7:30 p.m., Labour Day to early October

South Fish Creek Farmers' Market

Address:	333 Shawville Boulevard S.E.
Phone:	201-8652
Hours:	Friday: 3 p.m. – 7 p.m., early June to late September

Blackfoot Farmers' Market

Address:	5600 11 Street S.E. (Access off Blackfoot Trail and 58 Avenue S.E.)
Phone:	243-0065
Website:	www.blackfoodfarmersmarket.com
Hours:	Saturday: 8 a.m. – 5 p.m., Sunday: 10 a.m. – 4 p.m., end of May to end of October

This market includes an arts and crafts village, a petting zoo and a playground. No dogs or other pets allowed.

Calgary Grassroots Northland Farmers' Market

Address:	Northland Village Mall parking lot, 5111 Northland Drive N.W.
Phone:	239-8231
Hours:	Tuesday: 3:30 p.m. – 7:30 p.m., middle of June to late September

Calgary Bearspaw Farmers' Market

Address:	Bearspaw Lions Clubhouse, 25240 Nagway Road
Phone:	239-0201
Hours:	Sunday: 11 a.m. – 3 p.m., early June to late September

CHAPTER SIX
BABY SAFETY

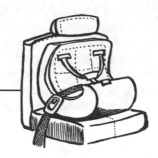

BABYPROOFING
When to Do It?

Typically, babies begin to crawl between six to nine months, however some start earlier and some later. Some even skip crawling and go straight to walking, even at nine months old! To really be prepared for the "mobile" stage, think about childproofing your home when your baby is about four to five months old. Wait! Having said that, babies don't tend to suddenly start walking, so you may not have to do everything at once. You can babyproof in stages as your child expands his exploring skill set.

Sources of Information

There are a lot of sources of information about how to babyproof your house. Ask friends or family members who have recently babyproofed for advice or help. Even inexperienced helpers can be very useful if they have the time to do some research and crawl around your house. Don't underestimate the value of a fresh pair of eyes to spot trouble areas or to come up with creative ideas on how to handle difficult spots.

Paula says...

"When we brought our daughter Ailish home, she was the source of a lot of curiosity for our son, Declan, who was two at the time. We quickly learned that we could not put her down for a second if Declan was awake! We devised a place in each room where Ailish was safe from Declan's poking fingers. The playpen and the high chair with the seat reclined and the tray in place provided safe respites for her."

Here are some other sources of information:

CHR'S SAFETY FIRST COURSE

This one-day course covers babyproofing as one of the topics. The babyproofing portion is mostly a brainstorming session among the attending parents with additions by the instructor. Take notes during the discussion and you will end up with a pretty good list. (Note: the course covers a lot more than babyproofing; see "Chapter Fourteen: Courses" – "Courses on Safety, First Aid and CPR".)

The course costs $60 per person or $100 per couple. To register, contact Calgary Health Region Perinatal Education:
Address: 214, 906 8 Avenue S.W.
Phone: 781-1450
Fax: 234-9089
Website: www.calgaryhealthregion.ca/prenataled
Hours: Monday to Friday: 8 a.m. – 4 p.m.,
              Saturday: 9 a.m. – 3 p.m.

BABYPROOFING CONSULTANTS

There are two companies in Calgary that specialize in babyproofing.

Safe and Sound Babyproofing Ltd.
Phone: 201-1609
Website: www.safeandsoundbabyproofing.com

Two local moms with young children own this company. They perform in-house inspections for $99 for the main and upper level of a 2,000 sq. ft. house. There is an additional charge for a larger area. The inspection takes two to three hours. The client is provided with a checklist after the inspection. Generally, inspections should be booked a week in advance but they try to accommodate immediate concerns. They recommend calling for an inspection when your baby is about six months of age (a month or so before crawling for most babies). In addition, they can come out to look at a specific area of concern for $45 (about a half-hour visit). The company also sells safety products and installs these products at the rate of $55 per hour. Their catalogue focuses on high-end, high-quality products that are otherwise difficult to find in Calgary.

Little Tigers Childproofing Services
(Formerly Safe Beginnings Childproofing Experts)
Phone: 289-5975
Website: www.littletigerschildproofing.com

This company has been around for eight years. The in-house inspection takes half an hour to an hour and costs approximately $55. The client is provided with a written report by e-mail after the inspection, which includes a product recommendation and exact quotes for installation costs (these run at $55 per hour). The client is also provided with a catalogue of the company's products, which are mostly imported from the U.S. and are not otherwise available in Calgary. If a client has a specific area of concern, a picture of the area can be e-mailed to the manager, who will reply with a recommendation and a quote for installation. If you require larger gates than those available through local stores, Little Tigers can order gates to fit.

WEBSITES

Just search for "babyproofing" or "baby proofing" and many websites will come up! Here are some of the better ones that I have found:

- www.childsafetyexperts.com - Go to the "Home" section.
- www.about.com - Follow the links to "Parenting and family", then search for "baby proofing". This site has articles on safety and relevant products and safety quizzes.
- www.safebeginnings.com - Online shopping catalogue for safety products. You can ask a question, read answers to Frequently Asked Questions (FAQs) or check out a self-help library containing articles on product selection and childproofing.
- www.safety-council.org - Find the link for "Child Safety".
- www.ConsumerReports.org - This website published by the U.S.-based non-profit organization Consumers Union provides ratings of child safety products and general children's safety information.
- www.safetymatters.com - Lists of safe house and garden plants, harmful household products and walk-through tips.
- www.babyzone.com/parenting/safety/proof.asp - This site provides tips on babyproofing.

> **Tip!** Don't forget to keep your two year old out of infant equipment such as bouncy chairs and baby swings as they are not designed for older children!

BABY CARE BOOKS

Check out all of those baby care books that your friends and family passed on to you! Most of them have advice on babyproofing and discussions on general safety issues.

Alberta Health and Wellness provides a free booklet entitled "Safe and Secure: A Guide to Prevention of Injuries to Preschoolers", which was reprinted in July 2004. It is a great source of information on keeping your baby safe through various age ranges, from newborn to four years. You can get this booklet from a public health nursing station near you or go online to www.health.gov.ab.ca.

Where to Buy Babyproofing Products

Most stores that carry baby products will have some safety products as well. The two babyproofing companies listed above also have catalogues of products that they will happily sell to you and help you install. These catalogues offer some interesting products that are not available through regular baby stores.

Note: The babyproofing tips included in this chapter are not intended to replace your own common sense, professionally manufactured products or guidelines to safeguard your babies.

Top Safety Products and Tips from our Parents' Club

I polled our Parent's Club for their recommendations on babyproofing. Here's what they recommended:

Top recommended products:
Baby Gates
- First Years Hands-Free Gate – pressure gate with foot pedal, very convenient;
- Kidco Safeway gate – steel for the top of stairs, high safety ratings;
- Whole-panel sliding plug covers – Safe-Plate by Elfe at Wal-Mart and Superstore;
- Magnetic cabinet locks – Totloc brand, at Rona;
- Foam floor mats for creating a comfortable play area on a hard floor – four interlocking foam mats by Sof-Styles, at Home Depot;
- Play yard fencing for creating a baby containment area or protecting baby from dangerous items. These are available at Toys "R" Us.

Top babyproofing tips:
- Duct tape! Use it to cover sharp corners along with bubble wrap, foam piping insulation or swimming pool noodles.
- Bungee cords for securing cabinet doors. They are also great for babyproofing when travelling.
- Turn buttons or butterfly knobs for locking doors are sold very cheaply at all hardware stores.

QUICK AND CHEAP TRICKS FOR BABYPROOFING

Coffee table edges and corners: duct tape quilt batting, foam insulation or bubble wrap along the edge and cover the results with a decorative cloth, which could be duct taped to the underside of the table to keep it in place. You can also use pipe insulation for the sharp edges of coffee tables and duct tape (various colours are available at Canadian Tire) to make sure that your furniture and your little one are safe. Cover the insulation as it comes apart easily if your baby chews on it.

Finger guard for doors: drape something thick, such as a towel, over the top of the door. You may want to secure it with duct tape.

Gates for wide spaces: if you have an opening wider than 42" (the maximum width for most standard gates), build a support frame from the wall at one side. Use the frame to mount a standard gate, which are quite a bit cheaper than the special extra-wide gates. Extra-wide gates can be ordered through babyproofing companies but they are rather expensive.

Cabinet door latches: simple plastic door safety latches work well and can be easier to install than magnetic locks. You may think that opening doors with these latches will be a lot of trouble, but it's likely that after a couple of weeks you won't even notice them anymore.

Ultimately, the cheapest and easiest method of babyproofing is to identify the area that your baby will be in during the day and move just about everything out of this area (except age-appropriate toys!). You can also create a baby playroom with none of the natural household hazards.

BABYPROOFING

GENERAL INFORMATION ON KEEPING BABY SAFE

Safety Organizations

Safe Kids Canada
Phone: 1-888-723-3847
Website: www.safekidscanada.ca

Safe Kids Canada provides information one-on-one and through a website. They produce fact sheets and brochures on a wide range of safety topics. The materials are written for parents and caregivers, and provide information needed to keep children safe. Materials are free and can be ordered by calling or obtained directly from the website.

One-on-one information is provided through the 1-888-723-3847 line, as parents sometimes have questions that aren't covered in the fact sheets and brochures. Safe Kids Canada staff provides answers to these questions by phone or refers callers to another organization that can help.

Children's Safety Association of Canada
Phone: (416) 620-1584 or 1-888-499-4444 toll-free
Website: www.safekid.org

This organization publishes a Child Safety Reference Manual with information on car seats, water safety, childproofing, poisons, toy safety and home safety. To get your free copy of the manual, check out their website or give them a call.

Shriners Hospitals for Children
Website: www.shrinershq.org

The Shriners Hospital provides a very informative booklet entitled "Burn Prevention Tips". Most of this information is also published online. Go to the Shriners website and click on "Hospitals" followed by "Prevention and Safety". Select "Burns and Scalds". They have a great section on kitchen safety.

Child Find Organizations

Across Canada, over 60,000 children are reported missing every year. Most of these children are in their teens. Thousands more require immediate medical attention. Losing a child is any parent's worst nightmare. There are three services in Canada that help parents prepare information to have available in the event that their child goes missing: Kidz Printz, Child Find Alberta and Child Save.

Kidz Printz, The Identification Kit Company

Address: 259 King Street West Suite 201, Kitchener, Ontario
                N2G 1B1
Phone: (519) 585-0050
Website: www.kidzprintz.com

This company produces two types of identification kits: Kidz Printz Child Fingerprint Identification kits (for children eighteen months to twelve years of age) and Kidz Printz Baby Footprint Identification Kits (for babies from birth to eighteen months). In the event a child goes missing, the completed Kidz Printz Identification Kit is "a vital investigative tool" for law enforcement when trying to locate a child within a critical time frame. Police services worldwide recommend that families hold on to these kits and keep the information up-to-date as their children grow.

The identification kits, designed by law enforcement for law enforcement, provide an area for a child's profile information to be entered, as well as an area to attach a recent photograph and DNA sample. Most importantly, a disposable forensic ink strip is included together with a designated area for the child's fingerprints/footprints to be recorded.

In Canada, millions of Kidz Printz Identification Kits are being printed for the RCMP with the financial assistance of corporate sponsors. These identification kits are available, free of charge, at over seven hundred RCMP detachments across Canada.

You can order a free kit from the company's website or call them directly. There is a minimal shipping and handing fee required ($1.50 for a kit, $0.50 for an additional kit).

Child Find Alberta

Address: 3751 21 Street N.E.
Phone: 270-3463, 1-800-561-1733 (Hotline)
Website: www.childfind.ab.ca

Child Find Alberta is a non-profit charitable organization. Their goals are to locate missing children and to increase public awareness of the issue of missing children in Canada. They provide a booklet called "All About Me I.D." which is a fingerprinting program for children. The passport-type booklet includes space for basic identifying information, medical data and a current photograph. The program was started to impress upon parents the need to keep an up-to-date record of their children. Child Find Alberta holds public clinics for fingerprinting, or you can simply drop by their offices to pick up a booklet and have your children fingerprinted. This is a free service.

Child Save Canada
Phone: 1-800-409-4600
Website: www.childsave.com

Child Save Canada is a North American-based organization that focuses on electronic identification for children. Should a child go missing, you can call and provide them with your child's tracking number. Within minutes, they are able to retrieve your child's pertinent medical and emergency information, including a recent colour photo, and provide it to the police to anywhere in North America. The service is $62 per year and covers all of your children.

Emergency Phone Numbers

Post a list of emergency phone numbers by the telephone (see the Reference Sheet for Babysitter in Appendix 1: Reference Sheets and Checklists). Keep the number for the local poison control centre near the phone:

Poison and Drug Information Centre - Alberta Poison Control Centre (24 hours)
Phone: 944-1414 (emergency line in Calgary)
              Toll-free: 1-800-332-1414

When calling a Poison Control Centre, have the name of the product available, the amount taken, and the time of the incident.

TOXIC PLANTS

According to the "Toxic Plant Guide" booklet available at most greenhouses in the city and at your public health unit, eating plants accounts for many accidental poisonings in children and animals. Each year, the Alberta Poison Control Centre receives over 2,000 calls about plant ingestion in children under five years old.

Below is a very brief list of toxic indoor plants from the "Toxic Plant Guide". This list is not exhaustive, but covers the most common indoor plants:

- Cactus
- Dieffenbachia*
- Philodendron*
- Rubber Plant
- Schefflera*

* If your child eats any of these plants, phone the Alberta Poison Control Centre immediately.

These websites also list poisonous items and plants:

- www.safekid.org
- www.greengate.ca (click on "Poisonous Plants")

You can also call the Alberta Poison Control Centre to ask if certain plants are poisonous. Many common annuals are not recommended if you have young children (e.g. sweet peas or violas).

CHAPTER SEVEN
CLOTHING, ACCESSORIES AND OTHER SUNDRY

It's remarkable how much clothing and equipment you will go through in the first year of your baby's life. Sometimes babies can outgrow items in just a few weeks. It can be helpful to pull together a list of items required for each season. Combined with an estimate of your child's size for each season, this list will help you plan your purchases for the months to come. This way, you won't end up with five sweaters that only fit during the summer months.

BABY PRODUCT ADVICE

So, you're looking for the inside scoop on baby products. You head to the store and eleven types of car seats, fourteen strollers and six types of cribs are on display. How do you choose from the plethora available? Here are two sites that can help you out:

babyScoop™
There is an interesting new website called babyScoop™ that can be found at www.thebabyscoop.com. This company was started by two moms who found that they could not find good advice on products for babies. They found that the best advice came from other parents, but that information was patchy. On this website they have established a forum for parents to provide and receive advice on products for infants and toddlers. Reviews are available for all sorts of products, from baby slings to baby monitors. You cannot buy any of these items through their website, you just get the scoop!

Consumer Reports
Another great site for product reviews is Consumers Reports at www.consumerreports.org. This website is maintained by the independent non-profit U.S. organization, Consumers Union (look under "Babies & kids"). Car seat ratings and buying advice on baby equipment and products are available.

BABY RETAIL STORES

Below is an alphabetical listing of some of Calgary's main sources of new baby clothes and accessories. I have included comments about each store that may be helpful to you. I am not able to mention all stores here, so I have listed the stores where my friends or I have shopped. If you are looking for a particular item, it is a good idea to inquire if a store will price match. Please refer to the phone book for addresses and phone numbers. Check the Yellow Pages under "Baby Accessories", "Baby Furniture" and "Children's and Infants' Wear – Retail" for other stores.

The Bay

You will find baby clothing, accessories and equipment at the Bay. The selection tends to vary considerably from store to store. You can find very good deals during sales events such as Bay Days.

bo bébé Fine Baby Products

Website: www.bobebe.com

This store carries most baby accessories: breast and bottle-feeding supplies, toys, some safety products, car seats, strollers, high chairs and furniture. There are three locations: Shawnessy Village, Market Mall and Crowfoot Village (the largest). bo bébé is also launching an online store. Check their website for details. This company also publishes a free magazine called "Birth of a Mother", which is available for pick-up at the stores (see "Appendix 2: Even More Organizations and Publications").

The Children's Place

Website: www.childrensplace.com

This children's clothing store has four locations in Calgary's major malls. They carry good-quality and attractive clothing in all price ranges.

E-Children

Website: www.e-childrenonline.com

This store mainly sells furniture for nurseries and children's rooms. It also carries some baby accessories. The store is located in Calgary's south end.

Gap Kids

Website: www.gapkids.com

There are four Gap Kids locations in Calgary: Chinook Centre, Market Mall, Southcentre Mall and TD Square. Gap Kids sells good-quality stylish clothing and clothing-related accessories (hats, shoes, etc.).

Great Outdoors Junior Outfitters

Website: www.members.shaw.ca/thegreatoutdoors

As the name implies, this store specializes in outerwear for kids. Products for children under one year of age include swimming clothes (UV suits, hats and shoes), bunting bags, jackets, hats and much more. It is located on Memorial Drive just north of downtown.

Gymboree

Website: www.gymboree.com

The Gymboree Corporation started thirty years ago with Gymboree Play & Music (see "Chapter Twelve: Activities" – "Playgroups" – "Gymboree"). Its retail stores specialize in high-end children's clothing and coordinates. Gymboree tends to have end-of-season sales with large markdowns. Usually there are a couple of permanent sale racks at the back of each store.

Kacz' Kids

Website: www.kaczkids.com

Kacz' Kids has two stores in Calgary. They have a great selection on all sorts of baby accessories, equipment and clothing. The stores are located in Deerfoot Meadows S.E. and Deerfoot Outlet Mall N.E. They carry one of the best selections of babyproofing items; these items tend to be higher-end. Twice a year there is a huge sale. Call the store to find out when the sale will be held.

The Mom Store

Website: www.themomstore.ca

This store has recently opened in Chinook Mall. They have a wide range of products for babies, toddlers and moms. Check out their equipment and clothing, strollers and diapers as well as their organic baby food!

Mountain Equipment Co-op (MEC)

Website: www.mec.ca

Mountain Equipment Co-op sells infants' and toddler's outdoor wear including rain suits, bunting bags, one-piece fleece suits, hats, gloves, slippers and full-coverage sun suits. The infant and toddler wear section is located on the second floor of the store. MEC also sells infant back carriers and sleds for taking babies cross-country skiing.

Old Navy

Website: www.oldnavy.com

Besides adult clothing, all Old Navy stores in Calgary sell good-quality clothing for children and infants. Old Navy is actually owned by Gap. There are three locations: Chinook Centre, Market Mall and the newest one in Sunridge Mall.

Please Mum

Website: www.pleasemum.com

Please Mum is a Vancouver-based Canadian company with almost 80 stores across Canada, four of them in Calgary. It designs, manufactures and sells attractive good-quality clothing for babies and children.

Real Canadian Superstore

Website: www.therealcanadiansuperstore.ca

The Superstore carries some baby accessories (bibs, rattles, bottles, feeding supplies) and a pretty good selection of baby clothes at budget prices. Often there is a sale rack of children's clothing with prices further reduced. It stocks a good selection of cereals and baby food. Organic baby food is sold here at good prices. The Superstore also sells some of the lowest-priced brand name disposable diapers in town. There is a small selection of baby safety products, some of which are sold at low prices.

Sears

Website: www.sears.ca

Sears carries a large selection of infant and toddler clothing – look for sales here. It also sells baby accessories and equipment. You can check the product catalogue, complete with pictures and current prices, at www.sears.ca (look under "Baby Needs" or "Baby & Kids").

Sears Advantage Family Outlook: This program costs $25 annually and provides you with a Sears Advantage membership card, a $5 Sears' gift card as well as coupons and offers. Annually, you will receive coupons and offers totaling $1,000, a members-only magazine subscription, members-only website and an e-newsletter.

Sproutz Metro

Website: www.sproutzkidzmetro.com

This location is owned by the same people that own Sproutz Kidz but caters to a considerably different clientele. If you are looking for high-end designer clothing for babies through tweens, this may be the store you have been looking for. Prices for jeans range from $20 to $165. You can get brand names like "True Religion" and "Echo" for your kids so that you and your baby can both be stylish. The store is located on Country Hills Boulevard in the north of Calgary. They have a quiet nursing area at the back of the store and a washroom with a change table.

Toys "R" Us/Babies "R" Us
Website: www.toysrus.ca

The Babies "R" Us department at Toys "R" Us carries a large selection of baby accessories including feeding, diapering, bathing supplies, safety products, car seats, toys (of course!) and clothes. Stores with a Babies "R" Us department have a great private nursing room and change tables. Keep on the lookout for sales. Ask the staff about the Toys "R" Us "Resource Guide", which includes two pages of coupons for in-store items.

Twice Upon a Time
Address: 5, 49 Elizabeth Street, Okotoks
Phone: 995-3488
Website: www.twiceuponatime.ca

This new Okotoks store sells maternity, infant and children's clothing. Drop by to check out the store.

Wal-Mart
Website: www.walmart.ca

There are many Wal-Mart outlets in the city. One corner of the store is usually dedicated to newborns and infants. The toddler section is typically beside the infant section. Wal-Mart carries a good selection of clothing, equipment, diapers, and formula. Selection tends to vary by store. Some outlets are open until quite late, which can be useful if you are in a bind.

Zellers
Website: www.hbc.com/zellers

Zellers carries a large selection of clothing for infants and toddlers. There is also a good selection of accessories. A limited selection of car seats and high chairs is available.

Online Stores

Online stores are handy if you don't need the items immediately. This way, you can sit at home and peruse the product listings and take your time choosing. You don't need to pack up baby, time baby's feeding just right and try to get your shopping done within baby's nap time. Makes life a little more relaxed! This is by no means a comprehensive list, but it features mostly Alberta, if not Calgary based, companies.

Baby Love Products / Kidalog (Online Store)
Phone: (780) 672-1763
Website: www.kidalog.net

This Camrose-based online company sells baby products and specializes in unique and hard-to-find parenting and children's products. Please note that delivery cost is in addition to the catalogue prices.

bo bébé Online (Online Store)
Website: www.bobebe.com

The popular bo bébé store is launching an online version of their store. Check their website for details.

The Baby Marketplace (Online Store)
Phone: (780) 416-0110
Website: www.thebabymarketplace.com

This online store based in Sherwood Park was started by a mom several years ago. It has a tremendous catalogue of diapers, accessories and a phenomenal listing of toy products. Shipping is $8 or free with orders over $75.

Claudia's Choices: Envirosponsible Products for a Modern World (Online Store)
Address: 311 17 Avenue S.W. (Jane Doe Marketplace & Café)
Phone: 613-2274
Website: www.claudiaschoices.ca

This is a Calgary-based online store that focuses on hard-to-find, environmentally friendly products for families who want to protect their families while minimizing their household's impact on the environment. Free Canada-wide shipping is available with orders over $250.

Cocoon Baby (Online Store)
Phone: 689.0678
Website: www.cocoonbaby.ca

This Calgary-based store was founded by two moms who were looking for stylish yet functional baby items. They design the items themselves and their products are all manufactured in Calgary.

eBay (Online Store)
Website: www.e-bay.com

eBay has a tremendous amount of items for baby, from toys to strollers and baby gear. You can even purchase diapers through eBay. The baby clothing is very reasonably priced. eBay has items that are new and used.

Golly Geez Baby (Online Store)
Phone: 390-6315
Website: www.gollygeezbaby.com

This is a website with some functional items for both dad and mom. They even have diaper bags and clothing for dads!

Growing Up Organic (Online Store)
Phone: 618-1780
Website: www.growinguporganic.ca

This store is part of a growing trend of using organic clothing and articles for infants and toddlers. This is a Calgary-based store.

Little Beanstalks Clothing (Online Store)
Phone: 968-5221
Website: www.littlebeanstalks.com

Little Beanstalks Clothing is a children's used clothing company that is located in Calgary. They specialize in high-end, brand name clothing for children. Select your items online and they will mail you the items. Postage cost is additional to the prices. They will ship items anywhere! Anything that you buy has a buy-back guarantee of 30% of the sale price provided as in-store credit. You need to mail in your consignment items. They will inventory them and send you a confirmation. You will receive 50% of the final selling price, which can be collected as cash or as a store credit. Anything unsold will be donated to the Foster Parents Association.

MegaMood Baby Boutique (Online Store)
Phone: 708-5043
Website: www.megamood.com

This is an Okotoks-based online store that sells newborn, infant and toddler clothing and accessories.

Mountain Baby (Online Store)
Phone: 1-888-990-2292
Website: www.mountainbaby.com

This store is based out of Nelson, British Columbia, and has an online catalogue. It has been around for over thirteen years. The owner is a mom and an avid outdoors-woman. Her company is dedicated to providing the very best outdoor gear for families. They have everything from children's backpacks, baby carriers, lifejackets, and wool long underwear to sunscreen.

Sproutz Kidz Metro (Online Store)
Website: www.sproutzkidzmetro.com

Sproutz Kidz Metro is going online in addition to having a location in Country Hills. Have a look online for designer clothing for babies through tweens.

Tiny Gem Baby Solutions (Online store)
Phone: 837-8117
Website: www.tinygem.ca

This is a Calgary-based online store that focuses on solutions and innovative products for all your baby needs, including feeding, nursing and diapering. Choose your items from the list and simply enter the address where you would like them delivered. They have discount coupons for members of MommyClub and Calgary Moms. Delivery is free within the City of Calgary.

SECOND-HAND STORES

Second-hand stores in Calgary are a great source of gently-used clothing, equipment and toys. Prices are typically significantly less than retail stores. Some second-hand stores also sell new equipment at lower prices than other children's stores.

One other benefit with second-hand stores is that you can sell your own gently-used clothing, equipment and toys. Some stores will purchase your gently-used items on the spot, while others will price them and provide you with funds only when the items sell. Typically, it is possible to receive either cash or in-store credits for items.

Whenever you are considering purchasing a "safety" item from a second-hand store, make sure that the product is completely intact. Purchasing car seats from second-hand stores is not recommended unless they have been officially screened and tested. It is a good idea to contact the manufacturer of any equipment you are considering purchasing to determine whether there have been any retrofits or recalls. Manufacturers are typically more than happy to ensure that you receive the correct parts or retrofits.

Here is a list of most secondhand stores in Calgary and area as well as one online consignment store. There are more listed in the Yellow Pages under "Clothing – Second-hand" and "Children's & Infants' Wear – Retail".

Cater Tot Consignment

Address: #101R, 2002 Luxstone Boulevard, Airdrie
Phone: 912-2700
Website: www.catertot.ca

Cater Tot Consignment is located on the south side of Airdrie and carries gently-used children's clothing to size six, maternity clothing, equipment and more than 100 new products. Cater Tot Consignment only carries name brand items. They sell furniture, equipment and brand name toys, with the exception of cribs, car seats, breast pumps and plush toys. You can drop off consignment clothing Thursdays through Saturdays, and your items will be displayed for up to sixty days. You will receive 40% of the final selling price, which can be collected as cash or as a store credit. You can pick up unsold items in the last week of display, or Cater Tot will donate the clothing to charities that give directly to needy families.

Craig's List

Website: www.calgary.craigslist.com

This site provides a free forum in which to post items and services for sale or purchase. Prices look tremendous.

Great Things in Store

Address: #5, 104 Railway Street, Cochrane
Phone: 851-5211
Website: www.greatthingsinstore.com

Great Things in Store Consignment is located in Cochrane and carries gently-used children's clothing for newborns to teens, maternity clothing, ladies' clothing, baby equipment and a number of new products. They have great amenities for shopping with kids including a stocked baby-change room and a play area with TV and VCR. They also have a rocking chair in a semi-private area for nursing. You can drop off consignment clothing on Tuesdays, Thursdays and Saturdays without appointment, and your items will be displayed for up to sixty days. You will receive 40% of the final selling price, which can be collected as cash or as a store credit. Anything unsold will be donated to the Canadian Diabetes Association.

Huckleberry Kids
Address: 15566 McIvor Boulevard S.E. (Copperfield)
Phone: 257-7373
Website: www.huckleberrykids.com

Huckleberry Kids consignment store has over 3,000 sq. ft. of retail space in Calgary. They specialize in high-end, brand name, children's clothing, furniture, books, toys and maternity wear. They pay for items on the spot when you bring them in. Appointments are not required and items from all seasons are taken.

Little Beanstalks Clothing (Online Store)
Phone: 968-5221
Website: www.littlebeanstalks.com

See "Online Stores" in this chapter for a description of Little Beanstalks.

Lollipop Children's Fashions
Address: 763 Northmount Drive N.W.
Phone: 220-0154

Lollipop is a consignment store that focuses on newborn to tween ages. They have clothing, toys, furnishings, books, toys and maternity wear. You can drop off your items at any time, however, they do need to be relevant to the current season or the next season. If you wish to have unsold items returned to you, you will receive 20% of the sold price. If you allow unsold items to be donated to charity, you will receive 40% of the sold price. All clothing needs to be laundered and in good condition.

Lullaby Lane Children's Consignment
Address: 1314 9 Avenue S.E. (Inglewood)
Phone: 264-2625
Website: www.lullabylane.org

Lullaby Lane is an intimate consignment store located in Inglewood that offers clothing and equipment for preemies to eight year olds. They carry both second-hand and new items. They sell clothing, toys, furnishings, strollers, books, games accessories and maternity wear. If you are consigning, all items need to be clean, of good-quality and suitable for the current or the next season. Unsold items are donated to a number of local charities.

Once Upon a Child

Website: www.ouac.com
Northwest Location
Address: 4625 Varsity Drive N.W.
Phone: 543-1068
Southeast Location
Address: 9250 Macleod Trail S.E.
Phone: 543-1066

Once Upon a Child stores buy and sell quality used children's clothing, toys, videos, safety equipment, books, maternity wear, furniture and shoes. Discounts are usually about 50% of retail. The stores also carry new equipment such as cribs.

No appointment is necessary if you wish to bring in used items. They will review your items carefully and select those items that meet current style, safety and condition standards. Payment is offered on the spot for all items accepted but if you choose to accept a store credit you may receive an additional 15%.

Sproutz Kidz Inc.

Website: www.sproutzkidz.com
Glendale Shopping Centre
Address: 3803 26 Avenue S.W.
Phone: 242-9877
Canyon Meadows Centre
Address: 13226 Macleod Trail S.E.
Phone: 225-8877

Sproutz Kidz has two consignment locations in Calgary. They carry clothing ranging in size from newborn to size sixteen, furniture, equipment, toys, and maternity wear. The Canyon Meadows store boasts 5,000 sq. ft. of floor space. You can drop off your consignment items during regular store hours except on Saturdays. All items must be delivered freshly laundered and free of any odours. You receive between 40% and 60% of the sale price. Check out the website for more details on consignment.

UsedCalgary.com

Website: www.usedcalgary.com

This is a website where you can post your own used items, or buy other peoples' items. There is typically a great selection of clothing and equipment for sale.

Value Village

Website:	www.valuevillage.com
Hours:	Monday to Saturday, 9 a.m. – 9 p.m., Sundays 10 a.m. – 6 p.m.

South location

Address:	104 58 Avenue S.E.
Phone:	255-5501

Northeast location

Address:	3405 34 Street N.E.
Phone:	291-3323

Southeast location

Address:	Unit #1, 240 Midpark Way S.E.
Phone:	201-5350

The Northeast and Midnapore stores tend to have the biggest selection of children's clothing. Clothing is priced between $0.50 and typically no more than $5. Some equipment and toys are also sold at Value Village. Please note that clothing is not washed prior to being sold.

COMMUNITY SALES

During the spring and fall, many community associations hold sales. These are a fabulous source of second-hand clothes and toys.

Cost of entry is usually free but can be up to $2 per person. Be sure to arrive at the sale at least thirty minutes before opening, as there are typically long lines, particularly at the larger community sales. Bring a laundry basket or big box for carrying items. Dress warmly for the wait and bring a cup of coffee! Leave your little one at home if you can.

The Twins, Triplets and More Association of Calgary hosts the largest and most organized sales at the Bowness Sportsplex. They even have security on site during the sale, I suppose just in case something gets out of hand. This sale is specifically geared for multiples and features items that are harder to find for twins and multiples. All items are labeled and sorted based on gender and age. If you are there in the afternoon, specially marked items are sold at half price. Yes, that is half of an already low price! I found many items that had never been worn and that still had the original tags on them.

If you are a vendor at a community sale, you typically get to shop prior to public access. There are usually some fantastic deals to be had on large play items. You will usually be required to volunteer your time during the sale. For your efforts you will receive about 70% of the sale price.

To find out when these sales are on you can check community associations' newsletters and websites or contact them directly. You can find contact information for your community association by searching the Federation of Calgary Communities website at www.calgarycommunities.com. Look under

"Communities", then "Organized Communities" and search for your community association's name. Alternatively, my website at www.babyguidetocalgary.com lists any community sales that I know about. Click the "Community Sales" button on the main page.

DIAPERS
Available Options

Many arguments can be made about which type of diaper is most convenient, environmentally friendly and better for your baby. I am not about to take sides; my goal is simply to tell you about what options are available to you in Calgary. One thing I do know and that everyone can agree on, is that you are going to use a lot of diapers in your baby's first year. Your choices are disposable diapers, a diaper service or cloth diapers that you purchase and wash yourself.

DISPOSABLE DIAPERS

Obviously, you can buy disposable diapers anywhere: drug stores, grocery stores, baby stores. Below I offer ways to reduce your diaper costs since in the first year you will probably use about 2,700 diapers. At about $0.30 per diaper on average, you will spend about $800 in the first year on disposable diapers ALONE! So, even a 10% cost reduction is a significant saving.

Paula says...

"Determine which brand of diapers fits your baby best, based on leakages and blowouts. My son required 'supreme' diapers and I ended up paying a higher price as a result."

Here are some of my suggestions for lowering the cost of diapers in the first year:
- Buy as large a box as possible and compare brands on a cost-per-diaper basis.
- Look for sales and stock up. (Be sure to you consider how long your baby will be in a given size.)
- Try generic brands as these offer considerable savings.
- Look for sales that are a result of re-branding. Sometimes the exact same diapers are sold for considerably less only because the packaging has changed.
- Buy on a customer appreciation day at your grocery store.

Elena says...

"I found that Safeway's or Superstore's generic diapers worked very well for my kids during the day and cost less. Once they started sleeping longer at night, I used fancier diapers for the nighttime since they were in these diapers for longer periods of time."

CLOTH DIAPERS

Cloth diapers can be purchased at a variety of stores in Calgary and area. There is one wholesaler of diapers called Diaper Depot:

Diaper Depot

Address:	417 38 Avenue N.E.
Phone:	277-8855
Website:	www.gabbys.net

Diaper Depot is a wholesale manufacturer of cloth diapers that has been around for two years. They also manufacture Gabby's swimwear, bibs and accessories. The store offers a selection of flat, fitted and all-in-one diapers (which have waterproof polyester outer layers). Waterproof polyester covers and wraps are also available. Sizes range from newborn through to toddler and prices range from $25 to $85 per dozen. You will need about two dozen. When your child has outgrown them, take them to your local second-hand shop (clean, of course!). All diapers have Velcro closures. Since Diaper Depot is a wholesaler, its prices are typically about 20% less than retailers. You will also find 20%-off coupons in the "From Here to Maternity" book. Their products are sold online through www.claudiaschoices.com and www.babymarketplace.com.

CLOTH DIAPER SERVICE

There are only two companies that provide weekly diaper service to Calgary. Both are based out of the Edmonton area:

Happy Nappy Diaper Service

Phone:	(780) 980-4040
Website:	www.happynappy.ca

Rates are quoted on a weekly basis and include drop-off, pick-up service and laundering. Give them a call before your baby arrives and they will provide you with a free pre-birth delivery package. They will also review available options with you and answer any of your questions. Once your baby arrives home, call them to activate your service. Diapers for infants under twelve months of age are $22 per week. That translates to about $0.18 – $0.55 per diaper depending on the number of diapers used.

Diapers for babies older than twelve months cost $15 per week. This translates to $0.12 – $0.37 per diaper. You will also need to purchase diaper covers: three for $16 each or rent them for $0.20 each per week. Finally, you will need to buy a diaper container, which is a one-time purchase of about $30. You do not need to rinse or soak the diapers. Delivery day and time are dependent on your geographic location.

Rockadry Baby
Phone: 1-888-232-4666 or (780) 469-5100
Website: www.rockadrybaby.com

Three styles of diapers are available:
* Form-fitted snaps (these have gathered legs and waist with 5 adjustable snaps).
* Mid-snap flat (a looser-style diaper in the shape of an hour glass).
* Rectangular flat (like the old-fashioned diapers).

All styles come in small (<10 lbs), medium (<15 lbs), large (<22 lbs) and extra large (<35 lbs).

Rates are quoted on a weekly basis and include drop-off, pick-up service and laundering. Seventy diapers per week cost between $21 and $25 depending on the style and size. That translates to about $0.30 – $0.33 per diaper. Ordering fewer than seventy (e.g. forty) is more expensive on a per-diaper basis, costing between $19 and $22 per week or $0.46 – $0.55 per diaper.

You will also need to purchase diaper covers: either the pull-up variety at three for $16 or wraps at $10 each. They recommend that you purchase at least three covers. Finally, you will need to buy a self-sealing hamper, which is a one-time purchase of about $27.

CAR SEATS
General Information

Regulations demand that you bring your baby home from the hospital in a car seat. Infants from birth to 22 lb (10kg) are required to be in rear-facing child safety seats. By law, all child car seats must meet Canadian Motor Vehicle Safety Standard 213 (they will have a CMVSS label on them to indicate compliance with the standard) and all children must be restrained in a car seat until they weigh 40 lbs (18 kg).

The Calgary Health Region provides a free car seat or booster seat education class that is held twice a month (once a month in the summer). Call 943-5465 (LINK) for dates, times and to pre-register for the two-hour program. Courses are held in the evenings from 7 p.m. – 9 p.m. at the Children's Hospital. The course reviews the proper use of car seats, installation, and positioning a baby in a car seat.

There is a new service in Calgary called Keepin' Baby Safe Inc. This company has two Certified Child Restraint System Technicians. They provide clinics and information on how to ensure the car seat is installed appropriately. For more information, check their website at www.keepinbabysafe.ca or contact them at 969-1054.

The Canada Safety Council has excellent tips to help you make sure your child is properly protected in the car. You can find them on the Canada Safety Council's website at www.safety-council.org. Follow the links for "Information", "Child Safety" and then "Child Car Seats". Alternatively, you can ask for the Canada Safety Council's brochures on car seats using the following contact information:

Address: 1020 Thomas Spratt Place, Ottawa, Ontario, K1G 5L5
Phone: (613) 739-1535

You can also go to the Alberta Government's Service Alberta website at www.servicealberta.gov.ab.ca and follow the links for "Becoming a Parent", "Healthy Baby" and then "Child Safety Seats". This website has a comprehensive list of all aspects of child safety seats.

In the past, Calgary fire stations would install or check car seats. Please note that fire stations are no longer doing these safety checks.

The Calgary Police Service holds regular check stops across the city and tickets drivers who are using car seats incorrectly. Drivers are subject to a fine for each improperly secured child. At the time of printing, you can be fined $115 for driving with a child who weighs less than 40 lbs (18 kilograms) if:

• Your motor vehicle is not equipped with a child seating assembly; or
• The child seating assembly is not properly installed; or
• The child is not properly secured in the child seating assembly.

Current information regarding tickets and fines can be found on the Government of Alberta's Infrastructure and Transportation website at www.trans.gov.ab.ca (click on "Drivers Info/Traffic Safety" menu and select "Traffic Safety Act"; under "Road Traffic and Transportation", select "Offences and Penalties under the Traffic Safety Act and Regulations").

Car Seat Recalls

For information on public notices about recalls of car seats, visit Transport Canada's website at www.tc.gc.ca and look under "Child Safety". You will also find recall information on www.consumerreports.org, a website maintained by the independent non-profit U.S. organization, Consumers Union (look under "Babies & kids"). In addition, this website provides ratings of car seats and buying advice.

Recycling Car Seats

Unfortunately, there is no location within Calgary or the surrounding area where you can recycle your car seat. Historically, the Interfaith Thrift Store had them inspected and provided them to needy families.

The Next Car Seat

You may have a petite child who can safely use his or her first seat for a long time, or your child may outgrow the first seat in a few months. In either case, if you buy a "bucket seat" (as opposed to a convertible car seat) for your child's first seat, you will eventually need to buy another.

For more information see www.calgaryhealthregion.ca/carseats

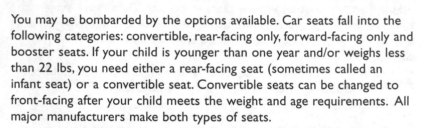

Paula says...

"Declan outgrew his first car seat at three-and-a-half months, not in height or weight but in width. Broad shoulders meant that we needed a new car seat, and fast. We had to wait four weeks for the new car seat to get delivered to the store."

You may be bombarded by the options available. Car seats fall into the following categories: convertible, rear-facing only, forward-facing only and booster seats. If your child is younger than one year and/or weighs less than 22 lbs, you need either a rear-facing seat (sometimes called an infant seat) or a convertible seat. Convertible seats can be changed to front-facing after your child meets the weight and age requirements. All major manufacturers make both types of seats.

Your car seat choice may depend on budget, ease of installation and fit in your car. There is a lot of variation on all of these points. Most common car accident injuries are due to improperly installed car seats, so many reviews and ratings consider ease of installation a key factor. The Insurance Corporation of British Columbia (ICBC) has an excellent website that rates car seats for use in Canada. You can find it at www.icbc.com. Click "Road Safety", then "Child seats", then "Buying a child seat" and finally "Child Seat Ease of Use Ratings".

Seats rated in the U.S. may not be available in Canada. Keep that in mind if you are doing your research on the Internet. Even with the same manufacturer, some seats rate well and others poorly, so focus on the specific model (even the model ID number) and not the brand. Make sure you try out the seat with your baby and your car for fit and ease of installation.

Considering a New Car?

If you are considering buying a new car to make room for your new addition to the family, make sure that your car seat (or future car seat and baby stroller) will fit in it. Another consideration in choosing a new car (besides fuel efficiency) is crash test rating. These can be found at the Crashtest.com website at www.crashtest.com. Look under "Introduction to Safety" and "New Car Assessment Program for North America".

> **TIP!** *If you have twins or multiples you may want to put three car seats across the back seat. Options are limited but do include the Honda Odyssey. If you have four or more child or baby seats, you may want to consider a Suburban vehicle. A number of dealers in the city provide discounts on new car purchases with a membership in the Twins, Triplets and More Association.*

BABY'S FIRST SHOES

Your baby will likely need some shoes in her first year. The Canadian Paediatric Society has reaffirmed its position that shoes are for protection and not correction. It goes on to say, "[u]ntil toddlers have been walking a few months, the only purpose of footwear is to protect the child's feet and to offer some grip on a smooth surface. For pre-walkers, shoes are not necessary."[8]

As for determining fit, the Canadian Paediatric Society has the following suggestions:
- You should never buy shoes unless the child is present to try them on.
- Shoes must fit the foot properly at the heel and allow enough room for the toes, leaving about 1.25 cm between the longest toe and the tip of the shoe, measured when the baby is standing up. This allows for sufficient movement of the toes and reasonable room for growth.

In terms of types of shoes, the Canadian Paediatric Society indicates that:
- Soft-soled footwear for protection and warmth is appropriate.
- For early walkers, shoes provide better fit, stability and safety than sneakers.
- Used shoes that have lost their shape should be avoided.

For more information, visit the society's website at www.cps.ca and search under "Footwear".

There are two stores in Calgary that specialize in baby and toddler shoes. These stores have trained staff who will measure your baby's feet and recommend appropriate brands and types:

Happyland Children's Shoes
Address: 3867 17 Avenue S.W.
Phone: 249-6500

High Steppers for Children
Address: 11G, 3265 Shaganappi Trail N.W. (Market Mall)
Phone: 247-2660

Elena says...

"I have found that Wal-Mart and Payless Shoes are good places for very reasonably-priced shoes."

A number of places in Calgary carry Robeez, which are soft-soled shoes for infants. Check out Robeez' website at www.robeez.ca, click on the store locator tab and enter your postal code. The website will provide you with a list of all the stores that carry Robeez within a 10 km radius. It is unbelievable how many stores sell these shoes!

Pedipeds is another soft-soled shoe designed for infants and toddlers. Check them out at www.pedipeds.com and find the many stores in the Calgary region that carry them.

If you like online shopping you can buy brand name shoes at a discount from Softmoc at www.softmoc.com/ca (follow the link for "Baby Shoes").

In Calgary, The Shoe Company offers brand name shoes at a discount. Once you know your baby's shoe size and the appropriate brand and type, you may be able to find those shoes there. The Shoe Company has four stores in town, one in each quadrant. See the White Pages for the closest location.

BABY'S FIRST HAIRCUT

Around your baby's first birthday you will probably start to wonder about giving or getting your baby a haircut.

Paula says...

"When I cut Declan's hair, I leave the top at 'three fingers width', the sides at 'two fingers width' and the back as 'one fingers width' in length. It takes a long time and usually dad entertains Declan during the process. Sometimes it takes about two days to get the full cut."

There are a few options for this first momentous occasion:
- Cut your child's hair yourself. Use extreme caution.
- Talk to the baby's grandparents. They may be comfortable cutting children's hair.
- Bring your baby along to your own hairdresser. They often won't charge for a few snips here and there.
- Try hairdressing salons that specialize in kids' haircuts, such as Beaner's Fun Cuts for Kids (see below). Beaner's feature fun chairs that look like cars and horses and charge $12 for a young child's haircut. For first hair cuts they will provide you with a certificate and a lock of hair in a tiny envelope as a keepsake. Ahhhhh! Appointments are recommended.

Beaner's Fun Cuts for Kids

Locations: 3408 Bow Trail S.W., Phone 217-1444
19, 4307 130 Avenue S.E., Phone 257-8228
4820 Northland Drive N.W., Phone 220-1444
Shawville Boulevard S.E., Phone 873-1225

Website: www.beanersfuncuts.com

Paula says...

"Declan loved it at Beaner's and the cut only took about fifteen minutes. The hairdresser was very patient even though Declan tried three different chairs."

Elena says...

"Daniel's hair only needed a cut at the back by the time he was a year old and it didn't seem worth my while taking him to a haircutter's for that. Instead, I quickly trimmed his mullet while he was asleep and his dad held him upright."

CHAPTER EIGHT
SHOPPING WITH YOUR BABY

GROCERY SHOPPING

Grocery shopping may become a complex logistical operation once you have a little one. Here are a few useful things that you may not have known or thought about:

Both Safeway and Calgary Co-op have shopping carts with permanently attached infant seats (usually a few at each store). Look for them among the shopping carts at store entrances or ask at customer service. These seats are only good up to about 18 lbs, so make sure you read the maximum size on the infant seat.

Buckle your toddler in while they are sitting in the shopping cart seat. Be sure to fasten the buckle securely. Stay with your child at all times and do not allow any children to ride in the basket. It is recommended that the child be at least six months of age and up to no more than 35 lbs or four years of age. In 2005, over 24,000 children were injured in the U.S. while riding in shopping carts and most of those injured were under the age of two. You can always bring your own strap to ensure that your child is always buckled in. Some people use a luggage strap since they are two to three inches wide. You can also purchase a portable cloth high chair that ties your child safely into any chair. Many of these are available for sale on eBay.

Having a stroller to which you can attach your car seat and that has a large built-in shopping basket underneath is very convenient. Another good option is using a front baby carrier while you push a regular shopping cart. This works well up to the point when your baby becomes too heavy or when he starts trying to grab at everything within reach (both usually at around nine months).

Do ask for help at the checkout! Store employees can load your groceries into the car while you do the same for your baby. Parcel pick-up can be a useful option as well.

Washrooms at both Safeway and Calgary Co-op have either change tables or wide counters for changing babies.

TIP! *If you have two or three children in the "stroller stage", you can try pushing the stroller and pulling the cart behind you. (Watch out while maneuvering around corners!) The other options include: limiting your grocery shopping to what you can fit in your stroller basket; shopping when you have a sitter; or just ordering in groceries.*

Elena says...

"I often used a stroller with a basket underneath while grocery shopping and then asked the checkout clerk for help carrying the packed bags to my car. Once the groceries are packed in bags, they often don't fit back in the stroller basket!"

MALLS AND BABY FRIENDLY STORES AROUND CALGARY

The table on the next four pages summarizes the baby-friendly features of most Calgary malls and some baby friendly stores:

Jill says...

"We have gone to IKEA just for lunch because the children love the ambiance and the meatballs. We often check out the kids' section and call it a day."

MALL CONTACT INFO	BABY-CHANGE AREA	FAMILY WASHROOM	FAMILY PARKING	STROLLER AVAILABILITY	NURSING ROOM	NOTES
Calgary Eaton Centre & TD Square 206-6490 www.coreshopping.ca	TD Square: 3rd floor, by the Gap. Eaton Center: 4th floor by the food court.	Same location as the baby-change areas.	None	Stroller rentals – customer service kiosk on 2nd level.	Same location as the baby-change areas.	Devonian Gardens located on the 4th floor of the TD Square (see "Chapter Nine: Activities" – "Calgary Sites").
Chinook Centre 255-0613 www.chinookcentre.com	2nd floor in the food court.	2nd floor in the food court.	A few spots by Zellers.	Wagon rentals at customer service (no strollers).	2nd floor in the food court.	
Eau Claire Market 264-6450 www.eauclairemarket.com	In the food court.	None	None	Complimentary strollers are at customer service on main floor by the escalators.	None	
Westbrook Mall 249-0052 www.westbrookmall.com	In all washrooms.	None	At Wal-Mart entrance.	None	None	
South Centre 271-7670 www.southcentremall.com	In the family washroom on the second floor in the food court.	Located on the second floor in the food court. Includes a small play area.	Located at south and north doors.	Strollers are free at customer service on main floor, northeast doors. Strollers are available for one child or two children.	Private nursing area in the family washroom.	

MALL CONTACT INFO	BABY-CHANGE AREA	FAMILY WASHROOM	FAMILY PARKING	STROLLER AVAILABILITY	NURSING ROOM	NOTES
Market Mall 288-5466 www.marketmall.ca	In all men's and ladies' washrooms and in the private nursing rooms. Complimentary diapers and wipes are available at the customer service kiosk.	None	At north and south entrances and in the underground garage.	Complimentary strollers are available at customer service. A piece of photo ID is required.	Private nursing rooms are located down the hallway next to HMV. Keys to the nursing rooms are available for sign-out at customer service. There is also a Mothers' Room in the ladies' washroom in the food court, where you can find several nursing chairs and a microwave.	Kids at Play indoor playground (see "Chapter Nine: Activities" – "Drop-in Playhouses").
Marlborough Mall 272-9233 www.marlboroughmall.com	In the family washroom and the ladies' washroom (both near the food court). Diaper packs (1 large diaper, wipe, cream and change pad) are available in vending machines for $1.00 in all washroom facilities.	Near the food court.	At entrance #2 (west side, near Smitty's) and entrance #6 (east side, near Sears).	Free strollers available at customer service (need to leave a government-issued photo ID as deposit).	Nursing station in the family washroom near the food court. You can lock the door of the family washroom for privacy.	

MALLS AND BABY FRIENDLY STORES

MALL CONTACT INFO	BABY-CHANGE AREA	FAMILY WASHROOM	FAMILY PARKING	STROLLER AVAILABILITY	NURSING ROOM
Sunridge Mall 280-2525 www.sunridgemall.com	In the family washroom near the food court.	Located just off the food court. Includes a play area.	None	Free strollers are available at the customer service (upper level by the escalators). Photo identification is required as deposit.	Private nursing area in the family washroom.
Northland Village 247-1393 www.northlandvillagemall.ca	In the family washroom near the food court.	Near the food court.	None	Free strollers available at the Information/Lottery booth at the south end on the mall. Picture ID required as deposit.	None
Deerfoot Outlet Mall 274-7024 http://deerfootmall.shopping.ca	In the family washroom and the ladies' washroom (both near the food court). There is a diaper vending machine in the family washroom.	By the food court and is equipped with a toddler-size rest area, private nursing and attached play area.	Near Wal-Mart.	Free single strollers are available at the Info Booth. Government issued identification is required for deposit.	Private nursing area in the family washroom. Bottle warmer is available in the family washroom.

STORE CONTACT INFO	BABY-CHANGE AREA	FAMILY WASHROOM	FAMILY PARKING	STROLLER AVAILABILITY	NURSING ROOM	NOTES
IKEA 8000 11 Street S.E. (Deerfoot Meadows) 273-4338 www.ikea.ca (Go to "IKEA near you", then "IKEA Calgary")	In the family washroom.	On the second floor, near the restaurant. Washroom has a change table and free diapers.	Designated family parking near the entrance.	The store does not provide strollers, but there is a space for a child to sit in the shopping carts. They also have "baby" shopping carts for toddlers!	Comfy nursing chair in the family washroom.	In the restaurant you will find a couple of microwaves for public use and high chairs.
Wal-Mart www.walmart.ca ("Store Finder" in the top right corner)	Located in all washrooms.	In the older stores there are family washrooms with chairs for nursing.	Indicated by a red sign with a stroller on it and is usually located next to the handicapped parking spots.	None	In the newer stores, there is a larger stall in the washroom where you can bring your stroller and have a comfortable chair for nursing.	
Zellers 1-866-746-7422 www.hbc.com/zellers (look for "Store Locator")	Located in most washrooms.	None	Available at all locations as well as pregnancy parking identified by a yellow sign.	None	No specific room, but you are welcome to use the fitting room.	

MALLS AND BABY FRIENDLY STORES

CHAPTER NINE
JUST FOR YOU!

"It was the best of times, the worst of times. It was the age of wisdom, it was the age of foolishness."

Charles Dickens

You're a parent now! Congratulations. But don't forget about yourself during this time. It is easy to do when you and everyone else is so focused on the little addition to your family. Even the first edition of this book was focused largely on what to do with your little one. However, in this edition I thought I would include something to recognize parents and the tough, but rewarding, job that parenting is.

DEALING WITH ADVICE

Undoubtedly, as a new parent, you will have much advice bestowed upon you. Think of it as a gift, but just as you did with that pair of orange socks you got for your birthday, feel free to say "thank you" and then not wear the socks!

Grandparents, great-grandparents, aunts and other mothers have a huge need to pass along their tried-and-true methods. Some advice falls into the useful category, but some is completely ridiculous.

In the useful category:
- "Use a frozen face cloth for a teething baby."
- "Use a safety pin on your bra strap to mark which side you last breastfed from."

In the completely ridiculous category:
- "Why don't you give up the breastfeeding and start your baby on solids, then he will sleep through the night." (In respect of a two-month-old baby)
- "You don't need a car seat to travel with a baby."

Here are a couple of tactics for dealing with the utterly ridiculous advice:
- Ignore it by changing the subject.
- Thank the person for the advice and suggest that the most recent information is slightly different.

Always check any advice you receive because standards and information on children's health have indeed changed in the twenty to thirty years (or longer) since many of the advice-givers were new parents.

Jill says...

"Accept the 'You must be busy!' comments with a smile and a nod."

SIMPLIFYING YOUR LIFE

It is not physically possible to do everything that you used to do now that you have a baby in your life. There are not enough hours in the day or days in the week. So, you will need to simplify your life. You probably swore that this baby was not going to change your life significantly. Who's kidding whom? It is amazing how much change a little one who weighs less than twelve pounds can bring.

Here are a few suggestions to help;

1) Make a meal plan

Meal plans not only make life a little easier, but they minimize wasted food and reduce the cost of your groceries. Meal plans only take fifteen to thirty minutes to do and can easily save you that much when you don't have to head back to the grocery store. I find that quick trips to the grocery store to pick up milk or bread end up as $100 grocery runs. You can make your own meal plan or get Wovenfare to help you with it:

Wovenfare.com
Website: www.wovenfare.com
Phone: 809-1678

This is a Calgary-based business that will provide you with meal plans customized to your tastes and cooking ability. Costs for meal plans vary between $3 to $5 per week (seven dinners), depending on how many weeks you subscribe for. The service provides you with a weekly calendar of meals and a grocery list. You can even enter your own recipes and they will be incorporated into the grocery list. Their Wovenfare Recipe™ comes from some of the best Canadian cookbook authors and their Inspired Recipe™ is typically quick and easy to make. The website also has some great tips on food handling, cuts of meat and more. You can sign up for a free two-week trial of the service.

2) Make your meals in bulk

Every time you make a meal, make enough for at least two dinners and freeze the leftovers. Make sure you date and label the meal; otherwise it will get lost in the freezer and emerge unrecognizable months from now. On days when you get home late, you can just grab the meal out of the freezer and have supper ready in as long as it takes to thaw and heat the meal in the microwave.

There are some interesting services in Calgary that will help you make dinners in a commercial kitchen to take home and stash in the freezer. They do the shopping, prepare all the ingredients, provide take-home containers and clean up afterwards. The meals are typically for four people; however, you can usually make half-size meals. They can also arrange a party, where you bring a bunch of friends and get a whole lot of cooking done with a lot of fun.

Entrees Express
Phone: 252-3801
Website: www.entreesexpress.ca

You can choose six to twelve entrees from their list of recipes. Book a session online for either one or two hours. Prices per entree are about $6 to $7 per person plus GST. Alternatively, you can have them assemble the entrees.

The Liberated Cook
Phone: 233-2665
Website: www.theliberatedcook.com

Self-assembly meals cost about $7 to $9 per meal plus GST. Choose to make either five or ten entrees. Simply register between Thursday and Saturday and choose your meals online. Entrees are portioned for four people; however you can also choose half-sized meals for two people. You can also have them assemble the meals as well as deliver!

Make or Take Meals
Phone: 277-6325
Website: www.makeortakemeals.ca

Self-assembly meals cost about $5 to $6 per meal. Choose to make either five or ten entrees. You can book one- or two-hour sessions depending on the number of meals you are making.

3) Outsource

LAWN MOWING AND SNOW SHOVELING

When Canada Post refuses to deliver your mail because trudging through the snow on your walkway is too great of a risk, it is time to call for help. (Yes, this happened to us.) Mowing the lawn at night with a headlamp is also an indication that your lifestyle is a bit hectic. (Yes, this was the only solution I could think of at the time.) Try to find a local teenager who is interested in making a few extra dollars either mowing the lawn or shoveling the walks in the winter.

RECYCLING

We were at the point of perfecting the following technique: *1.* quickly open the recycling closet, *2.* stash another milk bottle, *3.* quick as a flash, close the doors so that the load of recycling does not come crashing down. Then we discovered that there are companies that provide residential recycling pick-up. If you are in the same boat, give them a dingle. At the time of writing, the City of Calgary was considering a home recycling service.

Curbside Recycling Association of Southern Alberta
Phone: 276-7555
E-mail: crasa@shawbiz.ca

You can contact Curbside Recycling Association to find out who provides recycling services in your area.

Residential Recycling
Phone: 245-4451
Website: www.residentialrecycling.com

This company services most communities in the Southwest and Southeast of Calgary and Valley Ridge in the Northwest. They take plastic, newsprints, mixed paper, metal and glass. Weekly pick-ups are offered with a maximum of two blue recycling bins worth of material each time. You can choose packages from three months, to one year. Cost is between $3 and $6 per weekly pick-up.

Greenway Recycling Inc.
Phone: 263-9025

This is another Calgary-based company that provides curbside recycling in Calgary.

THE HOLY GRAIL...ACHIEVING BALANCE

Have you ever tried to balance a seesaw or a teeter-totter? It is pretty difficult: the weight on both ends needs to be exactly the same. There is a constant need for adjustment. Even a touch one way or another and the entire seesaw becomes lopsided. If balancing a seesaw is tricky, can we really achieve balance in our own lives? Well, the answer really depends on your timeframe. Maybe not every day, but over a week or a month, it may be doable!

Recommended readings:
* Lisa Belkin, *Life's Work* (Simon & Schuster, 2002)
* Caitlin Flanagan, *To Hell with All That* (Little Brown and Company, 2006)
* Kathryn Sansone, *Woman First Family Always* (Georgetown Publications, 2006)

Paula says...

"Balance? Of course I have balance! Their names are Carol, Angela and Dora. Without them I would not be able to keep the house clean or have time for errands or to write this book!"

KEEPING YOUR MIND ACTIVE DURING YOUR PARENTAL LEAVE

While being a new parent has its joys, it can also leave you yearning for some mental stimulation. Here are a few ideas:
* If you plan on returning to work, keep up with what is going on in your industry through industry websites or journals.
* Take up or continue a hobby through one of Calgary's many continuing education classes. This will get you out of the house at least one night a week and will provide you with an outlet for creative expression.
* Try the crossword puzzle or Sudoku in your daily or weekly newspaper.
* Head down to the library and pick out a book or two for reading.
* Try some of the videos that are available at the library.
* Get a paper delivered once a week; this will keep you up to speed with what is going on in the world and in your own community.
* Try some books on tape or CD that you can listen to in the car while driving to various appointments.
* Log on to www.calgaryherald.com or www.theglobeandmail.com to keep up with the headlines.
* Write the book you have always wanted to!

- Listen to daytime CBC 1010AM talk shows and learn about interesting national and local topics, or attend one of CBC's Learn at Lunch talks (see below).
- Keep in contact with your friends and family by phone, e-mail or the Web.
- Pick up a copy of Bill Corbett, *Best of Alberta: Day Trips from Calgary* (Whitecap Books, 2006) and take one trip each month.
- Start a Parents' Club.

Paula says...

"I took a course through the Southern Alberta Institute of Technology (SAIT) on photography and did my assignments with baby in tow. It was great to rekindle my love of photography during my parental leave."

CBC's Learn at Lunch

If your baby is still easily transportable (usually under five months old) you can attend one of CBC's Learn at Lunch discussions. The series is intended to stimulate debate about current issues and give Calgarians a forum in which to voice their thoughts. Every month CBC's Learn at Lunch presents a new topic for discussion in the lobby of the Jack Singer Concert Hall in the EPCOR Centre for the Performing Arts, 205 8 Avenue S.E. in downtown Calgary. The discussions are hosted by a local CBC personality and provide an opportunity to hear an expert on the chosen topic, ask him or her questions or simply express your opinion. For more information, check out www.cbc.ca/calgary and search for "Learn at Lunch".

Salsa Baby!

This is a course that is focused on Mom, but your baby will enjoy it as well.
Salsa Babies
Location: Varies
Phone: 451-7198
Website: www.babybusy.ca
More info: www.salsababies.com

Salsa Babies is brand new program to Calgary. Put your baby in an upright front-facing carrier and learn a few Latin numbers: salsa, meringue and the cha-cha. As long as your doctor gives you the okay, and your baby can hold his head up, you are good to go. Sessions are eight weeks long and are offered in three locations, two in the south and one in the north. Contact Salsa Babies to find out the locations. The courses are about $12 each session. You can drop in for a free class before you register in the program. The course is taught by a dance instructor who is also a mom. Salsa Tots is a program for you and your children who are too heavy to put in a carrier.

DEVELOPING YOUR OWN PARENTING STYLE

As you journey into parenthood you may find yourself trying to determine your own parenting style. You may look around to see how others are parenting and naturally, you will reflect on your own upbringing and sift through those experiences to determine what parts you would like to keep and what parts you would like to leave behind. Developing your own style will take some time. Try attending some of the parenting courses listed in "Chapter Three: Parenting Help"-"Parenting Courses". The books listed below can also help you gain a sense of what is a parenting style and what style you might be interested in:

*   Jean Clarke, *Growing Up Again Second Edition* (Hazelden, 1998)
*   Alyson Schafer, *Breaking the Good Mom Myth* (John Wiley & Sons, 2006)
*   Paula Spencer, *Momfidence* (Three Rivers Press, 2006)

Paula says...

"Here is a packing list that I keep around to help me out...
*   *A little patience (need to order more),*
*   *Backup plan for all plans,*
*   *One lullaby,*
*   *Sense of humour (large container),*
*   *Maps for each child's tickle spot (find more),*
*   *Four nursery songs that can be repeated for hours,*
*   *Appreciation for any food made by someone else,*
*   *Five minutes for a cup of tea and a quick read of a magazine,*
*   *Knowledge of all types of trucks, cranes and diggers in Calgary."*

Jill says...

"When you are out with babies or toddlers, things usually don't go according to plan. If you are going to laugh about it later, you might as well laugh about it now."

ORGANIZING YOUR PARENTS' CLUB

You may be lucky and already have lots of friends who are at the same stage in life (i.e. new parents). Or perhaps you have supportive relatives in town. But chances are, you are like many Calgarians who do not have either. So, what do you do? Well, you could organize your own Parents' Club (or find another new parent who's done it already).

It sounds intimidating, but it is easier than you think. For example, you can meet other people at exactly the same stage in life in a prenatal class or at the free CHR's Baby and You class. Take the time to chat and exchange e-mail addresses with the parents you seem to get along with. Invite them over for a baby-friendly gathering. Pick a set time every week to get together after that. You can go for walks in the park (presumably to try and lose some of that pregnancy weight) or just get together for a lunch and a chat. Encourage parents to invite a friend of a friend who has just had (or is expecting) a baby. Before you know it, you've got yourselves a Parents' Club!

In our club, we find that the easiest way to keep in touch is by e-mail. We host lunches and walks from our houses on a rotating basis. As babies grow into toddlers, the walks tend to become trips to local playgrounds. Parents volunteer to host a few weeks in advance and one of us circulates the roster by e-mail. The key is to get a large enough group so that at least a few can make it every week. Some Parents' Clubs arrange day hikes during the summer months.

Alternatively, you can meet new parents at Playcentres, at baby-friendly movie screenings, playgrounds or your paediatrician's office. All it takes is a bit of effort and in return you obtain a wonderful support network, regular outings and other parents to compare notes with and to learn a lot from.

Paula says...

"My co-workers have commented that it must be really lonely and isolating to be a new mom at home. Thanks to my Parent's Club I have a busy week, exercise and a new social network of parents with children all around my son's age."

DING DONG, A MASSEUSE AT YOUR DOOR

Here is an idea that you might enjoy. Get a group of friends together and hire a masseuse for a morning. Take turns looking after the kids and head for your wonderful massage. There are three services in Calgary that exclusively provide massage service in your own home. They arrive with massage table and oil in hand. You could even have your in-home massage after your baby has gone to sleep for the evening, no babysitter required. Check with your health care benefit provider to see if the cost of your massage is covered. A number of private masseuses do mobile massages, so check with your regular masseuse to see if you can arrange an in-home massage. There is even a business that brings the spa to your home!

Massage Medics

Phone: 512-9842
Website: www.massagemedics.ca

A registered massage therapist will come to your home. Massages are charged at $1/minute.

Spagoes

Phone: 521-2282
Website: www.spagoes.ca

This is a Calgary business that started in 2003. This is a mobile spa, offering more than massages. You can book online. Their therapeutic one-hour massage costs $99 and they offer a couple's massage for $175. Facials, pedicures, manicures and exfoliating scrubs are available. They even have specials for dads!

Synergy in Motion

Phone: 681-5080
Website: www.synergymassage.ca

This masseuse specializes in sports massage but can also do relaxation massage. This is a chair massage with prices starting at $65 for a one-hour session.

Urban Therapeutics

Website: www.urbantherapeutic.com
Cost for a one-hour deep relaxation massage is $80. You can book your appointment online.

HAVE BABY, WILL TRAVEL (TO SPA)!

I have always wished for a spa that had a daycare attached. Finally, there is one spa and salon in Calgary that provides this service on the first Friday of every month:

Chic Mama

Address: 100, 850 16 Avenue S.W.
Phone: 606-2441
Website: www.chicstudios.ca

Chic Mama provides pampering for moms with babies in tow. The first Friday of every month is reserved exclusively for moms and babies or toddlers. Don't forget to book ahead to reserve your spot. Their rates are reasonable and they offer manicures, pedicures, facials and hot stone back treatments. They also have visiting experts in fashion, food and jewelry.

In addition, they sell makeup tips for busy moms who are interested in a five-minute morning makeover. Come and mingle with other moms and enjoy the child care, beverages, food, snacks and appetizers, all for just $5 more than if you went without your baby. Their babysitters are certified and are typically moms themselves. Bring your baby to the studio and you can either spend your treatment with your little one or opt for a more quiet setting with your baby being looked after by a child care attendant. The children's area is for kids between four weeks and two years old. Check out their website for more information.

OUTGROWN CLOTHING AND EQUIPMENT

It is amazing how much clothing and equipment is collected from pregnancy through to baby's first and second years. Babies' shoes and clothing are probably worn for about eight to ten weeks before they no longer fit. By month six, you will no longer be wearing your maternity clothes and will be fitting into some, if not all, of your regular clothing. It's time to pack things into storage for your next baby, loan them to friends or start figuring out what you are going to do with them. Here are a few ideas.

Hand-me-down trades: It is a great idea if you can find a mom with children just nine to twelve months younger. Send your clothing and equipment over as a loaner, but recognize they are not going to be coming back in the same shape.

Donation

There are a number of charities that are interested in precisely the types of things that you are finished with. Here is a list of some of them:

BABY ITEMS AND MATERNITY WEAR
Calgary Pregnancy Care Centre
Address: 925 7 Avenue S.W.
Phone: 269-3110 (24-hour hotline to make appointments)
Website: www.pregcare.com
Hours: Monday, Wednesday: 9 a.m. – 5 p.m.
              Tuesday, Thursday: 9 a.m. – 8 p.m.
              Friday: 9 a.m. – 3 p.m.

Calgary Pregnancy Care Centre offers material support to single or low-income parents. Gently-used maternity clothing and baby clothing up to size twenty-four months are accepted. They do not accept toys and equipment. Donations need to be dropped off during office hours.

HOUSEHOLD GOODS AND CLOTHING
Women in Need Society (WINS)
Website: www.womeninneed.net

This society operates five thrift stores that accept donations of household goods and clothing. Please drop off donations Monday to Saturday between 9:30 a.m. to 4 p.m. as they cannot use any donations that are dropped off after hours. Contact the stores directly to determine if they have capacity for your donations.
- Fisher Park, 134 71 Avenue S.E. Phone: 255-7514
- Killarney, 2907 Richmond Road S.W. Phone: 242-4969
- Bowness, 6432 Bowness Road N.W. Phone: 288-4825
- Connaught, 1403 14 Street S.W. Phone: 245-1556
- Dover Sort Facility, 3525 26 Avenue S.E. Phone: 235-6448 (furniture available only at this store)

USED TOY DONATIONS

You can donate your used toys to the Bowness Montgomery Family Resource Centre where they will be used in the toy bank.

Bowness Montgomery Family Resource Centre, 4615 85 Street N.W. Phone: 288-1446

COMMUNITY SALES

Community sales are typically run in the spring and the fall. For a list of upcoming community sales go to www.babyguidetocalgary.com and click on "Community Events". You can receive about 70% of the sold price. The nice thing is that it only takes a day or two of your time and you typically get access to the sale ahead of the public in order to get some great deals.

CONSIGNMENT STORES

Consignment stores specialize in exactly this kind of problem. Bring in your unwanted gently-used clothing and you can receive about 40% of the sold price. They may take several months to sell, but at least you have cleared your closet and made a bit more room in your house. For more information, see "Chapter Seven" – "Second-Hand Stores".

MATERNITY CLOTHING

Most consignment stores that offer children's clothing also have a maternity section, such as Lullaby Lane, Once Upon a Child and Sproutz Kidz. There is also a consignment store that specializes in maternity clothes:

Maternity Cupboard
Address: 245, 9737 Macleod Trail S.W.
Phone: 253-2766
Website: www.maternitycupboard.com

They accept clothing anytime during business hours. Clothing must be clean, pressed and on hangers. Maternity Cupboard will get back to you within two business days and make you an offer on your clothing. Maternity Cupboard will pay you cash for your gently-used maternity clothes.

DECIDING TO GO BACK TO WORK OR NOT

The decision to return to work after your parental leave is for you and your family to make. No one else can make that decision, nor judge you for it. The good news is that returning or not returning are really only two ends of the spectrum. There is a myriad of options, particularly in the Calgary labour market. Here are a few alternatives:

- Start working only forty hours a week, instead of the long hours you put in before.
- Return to work full-time.
- Return to work part-time.
- Job share.
- Work part-time from home.
- Start your own consulting business so you can determine your own hours (mostly).
- Let your friends and neighbours know that you are available for work and the kind of work you would like to do.
- Sign up with temp agencies for occasional work.
- Turn a hobby into a business.
- Start a dayhome.
- Don't work outside the home.

Recognize that you, your partner or, in some cases, both of you can opt for any of the choices listed above. Good luck! Remember, you can try something for a year and then re-evaluate the situation.

Some recommended readings:
- Leslie Morgan Steiner, *Mommy Wars* (Random House, 2007)
- Susan Douglas, *The Mommy Myth* (Simon & Schuster, 2005)
- Wendy Sachs, *How She Really Does It* (Da Capo Lifelong, 2006)
- Allison Pearson, *I Don't Know How She Does It* (Anchor Canada, 2003)
- Valora Douglas, *From Colic to Career* (Momenta Publishing, 2007) – This is a local Calgary author.

JUST FOR MOMS

Parenthood is probably one of the largest transitions in your life and in your relationship with your spouse. Marriage and graduation seem like nothing in comparison. The transition to motherhood in Hallmark cards is one filled with butterflies, flowers and rhyming triplets. Let's talk reality. The transition is huge- physically, spiritually, emotionally, and psychologically. For the rest of your life you will always be a mother. There is little time to reflect on the transition since life is now filled with laundry, diapers, belly laughs, meals to prepare, tables to clear, lullabies and pointing out every excavator every time you pass by a Calgary construction site (which is often). Find yourself a few minutes to enjoy a cuppa and a quick read of a magazine!

Here's some suggested reading material that you might be interested in:
- Rachel Cusk, *A Life's Work* (Picador, 2003)
- Jack Canfield, *Life lessons for Busy Moms* (Health Communications, 2007)
- Cori Howard, *Between Interruptions: 30 Women Tell The Truth About Motherhood* (Key Porter Books, 2007)

Paula says...

"I once said to another mother that I felt that I had lost part of myself. She replied, "That is because you have, but you have also gained so much!" I think both need to be recognized: the loss of your non-mother self and the gain of this amazing little one who you have been blessed with."

Tough Job

Get ready! The sleep-deprivation in the first few months can be unbelievable. Decide whether you should be driving with your level of sleep deficit. Watch your hair fall out in the shower and clog the drain. Notice your morphing body take on different shapes, even after all your baby fat leaves (well, mostly). Your clothing will drape and cinch in areas it never did before. You'll reach a new level in the multi-tasking Olympics of everyday life. You will become a master of prioritizing, knowing what needs to be done now and what can definitely wait till later.

Paula says....

"Some mornings it appears that my children did not receive the memo that we are in a hurry."

Jill says...

"Schedules are often the lifeline for parents of multiples. My children's nap schedules didn't coincide, which meant that at any time at least one child was taking a nap, with the exception of meal times. Sometimes you have to throw the schedule out. Outings as a family sometimes mean that someone has to delay or cut short a nap."

Support for Moms (and Dads too)

Here are ten things that you can do for yourself to give yourself a boost.

1. The five hundred foot zone – Take some time for yourself every day. Get a sitter, or get your spouse to look after the little one, and take thirty minutes every day at least five hundred feet away from the cry of your baby. Get a cup of tea/coffee, a trashy novel, a magazine, go for a short walk or just sit and process everything, or not! You need this. It is important for you and all your relationships.

2. Throw away your to-do list – You are kidding yourself if you think that you can get a lot accomplished in the day. Focus on the basics, get your baby and yourself fed and everything else is a bonus.

3. Accept help – When someone offers to help, take them at their word and graciously accept any help you get. This may be different than what you are used to, but life is different now.

4. Walk and walk and walk – Getting back into shape through walking is good for the body and mind. Put the kids in the stroller and head out. There are a number of walks in this book for you to try. The kids typically fall asleep in the stroller, so just keep on walking. Bring your iPOD (or, in my case, my old cassette tape Walkman with the album Footloose!) with you.

5. Babysitter – Get at least three people on your babysitter list. Bring the sitters over often to make sure the kids are comfortable with them. Having multiple babysitters means that you can go out on your own schedule.

6. Uncle! Uncle! – Have someone that you can call on to cry uncle! When you are ready to wave the white flag, make sure that someone sees it and can trade off with you relatively quickly. Even if it is someone with whom you can chat on the phone as you go about your daily routine in the house, having another adult to converse with can be a lifesaver.

7. Keep a journal – One of the best things you can do during this time is to keep a journal. It will capture this time in writing, provide stress reduction, help problem-solve, and strengthen your sense of self. It's easy and private.

8. Find a buddy in the same stage of life – It is great to be able to share your experiences with someone who is in the same stage of life. You can share stories of your child's development and your own journey with someone who understands because they see it first-hand. Take the free Baby & You course from the Calgary Health Region to find other mothers in similar situations.

9. Create a sanity list – Determine the absolute minimum that you need to do every evening to ensure that the next day will be a little saner than the previous... this is what I call the sanity list. Here are a few things on my sanity list: at least five diapers available at the change table, at least two changes of clothes for my baby, a change of clothes for me, milk in the fridge, fruit for my toddler, a replenished diaper bag and a snack on hand for myself. With that list done, I am ready for anything.

10. Keep the music on – Turn off the television and turn on the radio. Turn to a channel that you enjoy with upbeat music and local, national and international news. You'll feel more connected with what is going on in the world, and the upbeat music will seep into your mood.

Elena says...

"I always have the radio on when I am at home. A light music station alternating with CBC gives me the right balance. A bunch of CD's for the car that both kids and parents like are indispensable!"

Jill says...

"When we play music and dance with the kids, they always smile and laugh and so do we!"

Mommy Forums
MOMMY MODE
Website: www.mommymode.ca
Phone: 998-9897

Mommy Mode is a group of women that focuses on moms helping moms. It provides an evening out once every month or so and there is always an interesting speaker on a relevant topic. "Mommy Mode is a community to bring ideas, perspectives and solutions to one central place. A place that doesn't exist anywhere else." The cost to attend is $25 per event and the funds collected are donated to a charity called Generations of Hope, which provides support for those who are not able to afford in vitro fertilization. Mommy Mode is currently on hiatus but will resume in 2008.

ONLINE FORUMS

Online forums are the new sororities of motherhood. Mommy websites and blogs have blossomed over the past two years. They vary in terms of how much advertising they host, whether they charge fees, and whether they provide a newsletter. Some, not all, of these websites receive advertising from the manufacturers of products they review. Keep this in mind when reviewing articles on products. The following is a summary of a number of websites that you might be interested in visiting:

Site	Fees	Social Events	Online Forum	Newsletter	Chat Room
Airdrie Mommas http://airdriemommas.proboards84.com/index.cgi	Free	•		•	•
www.babyhood.smfforfree2.com	Free	•	•		
www.babyvibe.ca	Free	•	•		•
www.CafeMom.com	Free		•		•
www.calgarybabies.com	Free	•	•		
www.calgarymoms.com	$20/yr				
www.hipmama.meetup.com	Free			•	•
www.mommychats.com	Free	•	•	•	
www.mommyclub.ca	Free				
www.momsandtots.ca	Free			•	•
www.moxie-moms.com	$58/yr				•
www.savvymom.ca	Free				•
www.savvymom.com	Free	•		•	•
www.swankymoms.com	$40/yr			•	
www.urbanmoms.ca	Free			•	•
www.yummymummysite.com	Free	•	•		•

The following is a summary of the websites tabled:

www.ProBoard.com
This website claims to be the Internet's premier forum provider, hosting over seventeen million members at two million forums! You can create your own forum for free, or if you need help with your existing forum head on over to the support forum. There are many different groups and boards for moms. One example is Airdrie Momma's: http://airdriemommas.proboards84.com/index.cgi

www.babyhood.smfforfree2.com
This website has a forum and a posting site. You can post your thoughts, questions and start threads.

www.babyvibe.ca
Babyvibe informs new and expecting parents in Alberta and B.C. through a free e-newsletter sent right to your inbox three times a week. Their newsletter focuses on products and services on Mondays, helpful tips on Wednesdays and fun, family-friendly event listings on Thursdays.

www.CafeMom.com
Café Mom is an online community created especially for moms. Moms can swap stories and advice on a huge range of topics, share photos, and connect with friends. Café Mom users each get their own homepage which they can customize. They can start public or private groups with other moms about common interests.

www.calgarybabies.com
Calgary Babies website is advertising-based reference website for products, services and resources for your baby in Calgary.

www.calgarymoms.com
This local website was started in 2005 and has a large mom membership. Its goal is to provide a supportive environment for moms to connect and develop friendship. There is a lot of information available for free on the website; access to the chat room requires membership, which costs $20 per year. Events, playgroups, parenting classes, scrapbooking, slumber parties, weight loss challenges, retreats and other clubs are a summary of what is available through Calgary Moms.

www.hipmama.meetup.com
This site hosts almost every type of meeting one could possibly imagine, need or want. Membership is free. Most of the moms are first time moms. They have a tremendous number of events and get-togethers. You will not be bored if you join these meet-up groups.

More from Meet-Up
- http://mommymilk.meetup.com/cities/ca/ab/calgary/
- http://newparents.meetup.com
- http://moms.meetup.com/1824

www.mommychats.com
Mommy Chats is a live chat community that focuses on developing mom-to-mom friendship and support. This website does not include any forums, only chats. It also has a mom-business directory to enable moms to shop from moms and for mommy-business owners to get more exposure.

www.mommyclub.ca
This is a membership-based Canadian site that offers services that support balance, connection with other mothers, adventure, and knowledge.

www.MomsAndTots.ca
This is a non-profit organization committed to bringing moms together in their own communities. Forums are divided into Airdrie, Cochrane, and Calgary quadrants. The forums also list playgroups based on childrens' ages. Members can meet others, join playgroups, enjoy a night out, access childcare, as well as buy and sell children's clothing and gear.

www.moxie-moms.com
Moxie Moms is dedicated to help new and experienced moms find a community of moms for friends, fun and fitness. Moxie Moms provides information on fitness-oriented events as well as deals on "mommy tools". MommyBuzz is a partner website with Moxie Moms that provides a chat room. www.mommybuzz.com is a site within the network of Moxie Moms. This chat site is free.

www.savvymom.com
Savvy Mom has a posted forum for moms. Topics focus on moms and babies. They have a significant question and answer forum.

www.savvymom.ca
Savvymom.ca is a free e-mail newsletter delivered to your inbox. "We are mom's secret weapon: the trusted voice for mothers who are looking for tried and tested solutions to their everyday dilemmas." You will find tips on home and family life, places to go, shortcuts, and tips.

www.swankymoms.com
Swanky Moms has message boards, chat rooms, product giveaways and a blog spot.

www.urbanmoms.ca
This is an online community of Canadian women whose members help create the message. You can comment on posts, contribute content or join in the online forum. Members have access to benefits designed with busy moms in mind. These benefits include a regular member e-mail and a research and testing panel. Members are selected at random to participate in everything including book reviews, participation in events and large-scale product reviews.

www.yummymummysite.com
This site has a significant number of articles available about motherhood and achieving balance. It also has a chat room.

JUST FOR DADS

"If I were to give you three pieces of advice to you as a father it would be to: Be there! Be there! Be there!"

Mark McGarrigle (Paula's brother)

Stay-at-Home Dads

More and more families are opting to have Dad stay at home rather than Mom for a variety of reasons. Full-time dads who are used to being traditional breadwinners can sometimes feel isolated. Playgroups with other stay-at-home dads and their children can offer a great socialization opportunity for both Dad and children. See "Chapter Twelve: Activities" – "Playgroups".

Courses for Dads

Although the majority of courses in Calgary are aimed at moms, a growing number of activities and courses focus on dads as well. If you are your baby's primary caregiver, there is no reason why you can't attend most of the classes listed elsewhere in this book, unless noted otherwise.
Courses for dads are typically available on evenings and Saturdays. Here are some courses specifically aimed at dads:

COURSE/ACTIVITY	CONTENT	PROVIDER	COST	AGE RANGE
Playtime with Dad	Focuses on games and activities that help your baby's development and are fun.	Calgary Health Region (CHR)	$25	0 to 3 months.
Daddies & Babies	You learn about your baby's development and the challenges of being a new father. There are long waiting lists for this course, so register as soon as possible.	CHR	Free	8 weeks to 9 months.
Especially for Fathers	This is a short course where discussions center on fatherhood and entering your new role.	CHR	$30	Any age.
Coffee & S'cream	Sunday mornings at Coffee & S'cream are dominated by dads and their kids. Head down for a coffee and chat with other dads while you watch your kids play.	Coffee & S'cream	$5	6 months to 5 years.
Be a Great Dad!!	This course is two and a half hours each week for five weeks.	Family Matters	$100 Subsidies are available	Any age.
Papa Bears Mother-Goose Program	This is a free program offered by Family Matters.	Family Matters	Free	6 months to 5 years.
Daddy & Me days	Saturdays cost only $5 for the day if your child is with a male care-giver!	Gymaniacs	$5 per entry	6 months to 5 years.

COURSES FOR DADS

Organizations and Websites for Dads

Family of Men Support Society
Phone: 242-4077
Website: No website

This society is based in Calgary and offers peer support on a number of issues including parenting.

Dads Can
Phone: 1-888-DADS-CAN (1-888-323-7226)
Website: www.dadscan.org
E-mail: info@dadscan.org

This is an Ontario-based organization that promotes responsible and involved fathering by supporting men's personal development into fatherhood and healthy fathering patterns. They offer fathering tools, a chat room and a fathering information network directory.

Men's Educational Support Association
Phone: 228-6366
Website: www.mesacanada.com
E-mail: info@mesacanada.com

This Calgary-based organization provides support and education to fathers who are experiencing a family breakdown.

Relevant Websites
* www.babycenter.com/dads
* www.calgarydads.com
* www.daddyshome.com
* www.fathersforum.com
* www.fathersonline.com
* www.newdads.com

Recommended readings:
* Armin Brott, *The New Father: A Dad's Guide to the First Year* (Abbeville, 2004)
* Gary Greenberg and Jeannie Hayden, *Be Prepared: A Practical Handbook for New Dads* (Simon & Schuster, 2004)
* Robert W. Sears, *Father's First Steps: 25 Things Every New Dad Should Know* (Harvard Common Press, 2006)

CHAPTER TEN
TRAVELLING WITH BABY OR TODDLER

Before you had children, the thought of a holiday away from home was relaxing and reinvigorating. Now your plans have to incorporate meals, warming bottles, heating up puréed food, diaper changes in teeny-weeny airplane washrooms and babyproofing. Oh my, will this be relaxing? With some careful preparation, travelling with your baby can be relatively enjoyable. Here are a few tips to make your life a little easier when you travel with your infant.

BEFORE YOU GO

* Determine whether your proposed destination is appropriate for a baby. There may be environmental risks, such as pollution and disease, which will cause you to think twice. If you still want to go, then make sure that you and your baby have been properly vaccinated for your destination. You can find out what vaccinations are recommended by contacting any one of the Calgary travel clinics (see below).
* If you are travelling internationally, apply for your baby's passport and allow sufficient time for processing. See "Chapter One: Administrative Issues" – "Passport for Baby".
* If the baby is travelling without both parents, you may need a letter of consent from the absent parent. See "Chapter One: Administrative Issues" – "Passport for Baby" for details.
* Keep it simple when planning your itinerary and route. Try to find direct flights that are at a good time for your baby. Travelling during nap time may be best, unless your children don't like to sleep on airplanes...

Paula says...

"When we travelled, we brought our car seat so that we would have a chair for Declan on the plane. Also, we were not confident that the rental company's infant car seats would fit our son, who has broad shoulders."

Elena says...

"A colleague told me how she once thought she could do without a diaper bag on a relatively short flight with her baby. Turns out, babies are familiar with Murphy's Law and she ended up having to ask other mothers on the plane for spare diapers."

- Try to stay in each destination for a minimum of three nights since packing and unpacking may take considerable time and is unsettling for the children.
- Plan only one or two activities a day. Travelling is tough on little ones and at times they may become over stimulated. This isn't good for anyone!
- Respect children's nap times. It will make the trip more enjoyable if you work around their schedule.
- Decide whether you will bring a car seat or rent one. Most car rental companies have infant seats available, but they can cost up to $75. I recommend that you reserve an infant seat ahead of time and get them to confirm specifically that the rental location has car seats. Make sure you let the company know what approximate weight your baby will be during the rental period. Also ask what brands they carry so that you can confirm that it will be suitable for your baby. If you are uncertain at all about the safety of the seats you may be renting, simply bring your own.
- Ask for cribs or high chairs ahead of time. Having all of this equipment at your destination is easier than hauling it all the way there. Keep in mind that not all countries have the same safety standards as North America. Consider bringing your own playpen if this is the situation.
- Try renting baby equipment at your destination. A number of baby equipment rental businesses have sprung up in major cities, and many will deliver to your location. These businesses rent everything from snowsuits and baby gates to car seats and strollers. Some of the rental businesses in Calgary have affiliations with similar businesses in other cities. Check out the following websites:
  - **www.littletraveller.ca**
  - **www.onetinysuitcase.com**
  - **www.toylend.ca**
- If you're visiting with relatives or friends, they may also be able to borrow equipment on your behalf from their friends.
- Try to find accommodation with a kitchenette. Alternatively, ask for a microwave and fridge in the room in order to keep baby food refrigerated and to heat it up for meals.

- Plan ahead for packing. Make a list (See "Appendix 1: Reference Sheets and Checklists" – "Packing List for Travelling" for a sample packing list) and start packing at least three days in advance.
- Try to stick to your baby's routine. If you have shifted time zones, consider staying on your home time.
- Keep a well-stocked diaper bag with you, including extra clothes, toys, books, diapers, wipes and a plastic bag for soiled clothing and old diapers.
- Bring a "babyproofing kit" of bungee cords, duct tape and bubble wrap.
- Call your accommodation to find out if they have babyproofing items available on site.
- Take a first-aid kit and ensure that you have appropriate medication for your baby (e.g. acetaminophen, electrolyte solution, etc.).

Jill says...

"Our paediatrician encouraged us to travel when our first child was about six months old. At this age babies are: easily portable, probably not crawling, easy to contain, sleep a lot and are just starting solid food. We traveled to England and also went on a road trip to Vancouver Island. We used the Baby Bjorn backpack carrier and our lighter stroller for the trips."

Calgary Travel Clinics

Travel clinics can provide you with information about immunizations recommended for your target destination. There is one public travel clinic in Calgary operated by the CHR:

International Travel Clinic
Address: 323 7 Avenue S.E.
Phone: 944-7100
Hours: Monday to Friday: 8 a.m. – 4:15 p.m.,
             Every other Saturday: 8:15 a.m. – 4 p.m.

Most appointments take one hour. You need to bring any vaccination records that you have to the appointment. There is a service fee for each person receiving a vaccine: $30 for adults and $10 for children under eighteen. There are additional charges for the vaccines themselves.

There are many private travel clinics in Calgary:

Calgary Travel Clinic/Bowmont Travel Clinic
Address: 6535 Bowness Road N.W.
Phone: 247-9797
Website: www.bowmonttravel.ca

Odyssey Travel & Tropical Medicine Clinic
Address: Suite 208, 2004 14 Street N.W.
Phone: 210-4770

Starpoint Health Corp. – Foothills Industrial Park
Address: 202, 3716 61 Avenue S.E.
Phone: 236-8400

The ECM Group
Address: Suite 1020, 101 6 Avenue S.W.
Phone: 216-6120

MEDISYS Health Group
Address: 960, 321 6 Avenue S.W.
Phone: 232-6244

Jill's husband says...

"Before children, we were into adventure travel. Now having three children under three years old, it is an adventure getting out the door!"

TRAVELLING BY CAR

The first rule of travelling by car is that it takes about twice as long to get there as it did before children. Try to plan for this. Feeding, changing or getting a baby out for a stretch takes up considerable time. There is an interesting website called www.momsminivan.com that has suggestions of what to do on long car rides for babies and toddlers.

Try to keep the following easily accessible in the car:
- Bottle with breast milk or formula
- Cooler with ice packs (to keep milk fresh)
- If breastfeeding, portable breast pump with sterile bottle and nipple (to pump the next bottle)
- Thermos with hot water and container for warming milk or formula, or other warming device
- Snack for baby if she is eating solids
- Extra wipes for cleaning up spills, spit-up etc.
- Toys and books for entertaining the baby
- Receiving blankets (for spit-up and anything else)
- Diaper bag with a minimum of four diapers
- Two sleepers for the baby
- Pillow (for feeding or for taking a nap)
- Baby blanket

TRAVELLING BY AIR

Here are some hints to help you enjoy travel by air with your baby:

- If your baby is a newborn, check with your airline before departure. For example, Air Canada prefers not to have infants younger than seven days old travel by air.
- You are typically allowed extra baggage when travelling with an infant; many airlines allow you to bring a car seat, a bassinette and a stroller. Check with your airline.
- Consider taking a car seat onboard since your child is more familiar with this seat and it is more comfortable to sleep in.
- On some airplanes, you can request a bassinette if your baby is under 25 lbs and unable to sit up. Check with your airline to check their requirements. Not all planes have bassinettes, and those that do make them subject to availability, so make your request ahead of time.
- Infant meals are usually available on the plane (strained vegetables and fruit), but request these ahead of time.
- Let your kids have a good run and play at the airport before or between flights.
- On many airlines, infants under the age of two travel for free within Canada and the United States. However, the airlines do not provide a seat for the child. When travelling overseas, some airlines charge 10% of the regular fare for children under two years of age; at this rate, they will not provide you a seat but you will receive an additional baggage allowance for the baby. If you absolutely need a seat, you will need to pay an adult fare.
- On long flights or overnight flights, it may be worth it to buy an extra seat for your child even if they are under two. You and the children will have more space, which makes for a better start and end to the trip.
- Find out about your airline's limitation of liability. Most airlines limit their liability to $150 per item, so if your stroller gets mangled, you will likely be out-of-pocket.

- Remember that you cannot take a luggage cart past security. You can, however, take your stroller right up to the airplane door. If you are not bringing your stroller, you will need to carry all your on-board baby items past security yourself.
- Psychologically prepare yourself to change your baby in the cramped quarters of an airline washroom. There is usually a table that pulls down over the toilet. There are straps available; however, there is not much room to move once you have the table down. Prepare before you pull the table down by getting your diapers, wipes and anything else you need ready.

Air Canada has a section on its website that provides tips on travelling with a baby. Go to www.aircanada.com and look under "Information and Services", then "Infant – Children – Unaccompanied Minors", then "Travelling with an Infant or Child".

Vacation Time for Single Parents

Travelling alone with young children can raise a little anxiety for any parent. There are some companies that specialize in single parent travel tours. Your kids will also have friends to play with.

Single Parent Tours
Website: www.singleparenttravel.net

This is a U.S.-based agency that offers a wide range of vacations for single parents. Historically, they have arranged tours to places such as Patagonia, Alaska and even Nova Scotia!

Small Families
Website: www.smallfamilies.co.uk

This UK company offers trips that support travelling as a single parent family. Their travel tends to focus on Europe and the Mediterranean.

Paula says...

"We brought a portable DVD player with a lot of DVDs along on our last trip to Europe. It was a great distraction on the long drives and long airplane rides for the children."

Jill says...

Calgary International Airport

We recommend that you contact the Airport Information Line at 735-1372 when inquiring about airport facilities.

There is a baby-changing room with a nursing chair on each level of the airport. Look for the signs for baby-changing facilities or ask at the information desk. Beyond security on the departures level, all washrooms are either equipped with change tables or have a large enough counter to use as a changing area. There's also a nursing room beyond security marked with a sign. Each boarding gate has a play area for children.

There is a Space Port in the main food court. This is a children's play area with space-related exhibits. It is mostly for older children. There is a small play area, however, to the right of the movie room that you may find suitable for walking babies.

There is a big playground on the Departures level by the West Jet check-in. It has foam floor structures for bigger kids to climb and some of those wall panel toys for younger kids. There is another smaller playground on the Arrivals level that is suitable for babies.

There are high chairs located in the centre of the main food court. If you can't find them, ask one of the cleaning staff. Montana's restaurant (221-1792), on the Departures level, has a few high chairs and so does Cheers Restaurant (503-2210 extension #3) in the main food court.

If you find yourself in dire need of diapers, Bloomsbury's (221-1913), on the Departures level, sells them. They also carry baby wipes and a few other baby items. The pharmacy carries a few baby supplies but at the time of writing did not carry diapers.

Paula says...

"After checking our bags for an overseas trip we realized that we didn't have enough clothes in the diaper bag for the flight. Declan had already gone through two sets of clothes since we left the house. We quickly scoured the Calgary airport for a children's clothing store and found undershirts and sleepers at Fan Attic, all with Calgary Flames logos. A little more expensive than we had hoped for, but they turned out to be very handy on the flight!"

BABY-FRIENDLY GETAWAYS FROM CALGARY

If you are not considering long-distance travel, there are a lot of options for a getaway close to Calgary. All you need is to do a bit of research to ensure that the hotel or lodge of your choice will be suitable for a baby. In addition to the tips provided in the "Before You Go" section earlier in this Chapter, here are a few more things to think about before making a reservation:

• Avoid fireplaces if your child is mobile. You will not be able to use them much anyway with a crawling baby around and they can be difficult to babyproof.
• Look for a place with carpeted floor and avoid tiled floors, especially if your baby is starting to walk.
• Look for a place with a kitchenette complete with a microwave, especially if your baby is eating solid foods.
• Ask the staff how supportive they would be if you babyproofed a common lounge area and how easy it would be to babyproof (this could mean a lot to you if you are holidaying with other families with young children).
• If your baby is accustomed to sleeping in his own room at home, then a suite with a separate room for the baby can help all of you sleep better at night.

Here's one option for a getaway that I have tried:

Mount Engadine Lodge
Phone: (403) 678-4080
Website: www.mountengadine.com

This rustic lodge is located just off the Smith-Dorrien/Spray Lake Trail (Highway 742), about thirty-six kilometers past Canmore. The drive from Calgary's western limit takes about one-and-a-half hours. Accommodation options include lodge rooms with shared bathrooms, lodge suites with private bathrooms and three cabins with private bathrooms. There is a two night minimum stay. The daily rate ranges from $150 to $200 per person depending on the accommodation option and the season. Children under four are free. The price includes three meals a day and snacks.

Elena says...

"We visited the lodge for a Family Day weekend with a group of families with small children. We found the lodge rooms and the cabins relatively easy to babyproof. Please note that the lodge suites feature fireplaces and seemed harder to babyproof. Our group of families made up most of the guests that weekend, so we practically took over one of the lounge areas, babyproofing it to suit our needs. We found the staff supportive and friendly."

Banff Hotels
Websites: www.explorealberta.com (go to "Banff Hotels and Accommodations"),
www.discoverbanff.com/WheretoStay

Banff provides a wide range of options from fancy hotels, to chalets, to motel rooms. The one and a half hour drive is easy to accomplish during your baby's nap. The websites listed above provide listings of Banff accommodations and links to their websites. Use the tips listed above when looking for accommodation.

HELPFUL WEBSITES

Family Travel Files
Website: www.thefamilytravelfiles.com

This U.S.-based website is not solely dedicated to travelling with a baby, but it is interesting nonetheless. It offers some pertinent travel advice including tips on travelling with a baby to tropical destinations and on babyproofing your vacation space.

Foreign Affairs Canada
Website: www.voyage.gc.ca

Click on "Children and Travel" to find information on documents required for travelling with children, including passports. The website also provides general travel information such as travel updates and country profiles.

Health Link Alberta
Website: www.healthlinkalberta.ca

Click on "Health Information", then "Health Topics" and "Travel Health" to find information on travel-related health issues.

CHAPTER ELEVEN
FITNESS AND GETTING BACK INTO SHAPE

As a new mom, your body has undergone tremendous changes over the past year. Getting back into shape can be a lot of fun for both Mom and Dad through walks, hiking, running, cycling, and downhill and cross-country skiing. It may be trickier for moms with multiples, so take a bit of extra time to make sure you are ready to take on getting back into shape. Here is some research that may help you get back into your favourite sports and activities with baby in tow!

WALKS

A few weeks after your baby's birth, you may feel like heading out on some walks in order to get out of the house and get some exercise and fresh air. It's pretty easy to bring your baby along with the help of baby carriers. Just make sure that on a cold day your baby is warm enough and tucked in close to your body. In the summer, make sure he or she is not too hot and is sheltered from the sun. Babies will often sleep while you walk, as long as you keep moving.

There are many different baby carriers available, ranging in cost between $30 and $140. Two major brands are Baby Bjorn and Snugli, the former being the more expensive of the two. Carriers are sold in most stores listed under "Chapter Seven: Clothing, Accessories and Other Sundry" – "Baby Stores".

Once your baby weighs over twenty pounds, you will likely only be able to use a front carrier for short stints. Even before that, at about fifteen pounds, it is advisable to use a stroller rather than a carrier to save your back. Alternatively, you can consider a back carrier once your baby can sit up (see "Hiking" below). A stroller with a basket is also handy to carry all of your baby paraphernalia including entertainment for the little one. After you switch to a stroller, your choice of walks will be limited to stroller-friendly ones but you will be able to walk for longer periods.

Paula says...

"I don't recommend walking if it is below five degrees Celsius in Calgary since the weather can turn quickly and the winds can have a bite to them."

Here are some tips for your walks:

- Bring lots of water for yourself.
- Bring a snack for yourself and your baby.
- Bring a nursing blanket in case you need to nurse on a bench.
- Bring an umbrella.
- In summer, bring mosquito netting for the stroller.
- Bring extra layers of clothing for you and your baby and an extra blanket.
- Remember to restock and bring the diaper bag.
- Carry a cellphone (if possible).
- Hook up with a friend for the stroll.
- In winter, make sure that you have gloves, a toque and a coat for both you and baby.
- In summer, bring child-safe sunscreen (if your baby is over six months), a hat and an extra blanket to help keep your little one in the shade.
- Pack a plastic cover for the stroller to shield your baby from the wind and rain. They are inexpensive, usually less than $15, and a great idea for Calgary weather.

The walks on the following pages have been designed for the stroller-pushing mom or dad. They all offer free parking and are no longer than eight kilometers in length. They each have plenty of benches en route, are paved, do not have any stairs, have washrooms, and all except one have a place to get a cup of coffee.

There are many other walks that have not been included in this list. Pick up the Calgary Pathway and Bikeway Map and find out what is around your community. The map can be purchased for $2 at most bike stores. Alternatively, you can order it by calling the City of Calgary at 311 or visiting the city's online store at www.calgaryonlinestore.com. There is a shipping and handling charge of $1. The most recent edition at the time of printing was from 2006.

I find that walks with babies typically take one-and-a-half to two times longer than the same walks did before children. Stops for feeding, changing and picking up toys take quite a bit of time. Also, getting ready for the walk takes considerably more time than it did before. Leave plenty of time in your schedule! I hope you enjoy these walks as much as I have. One word of caution...watch out for bicycles that share the same paths as you.

WALKS

Legend

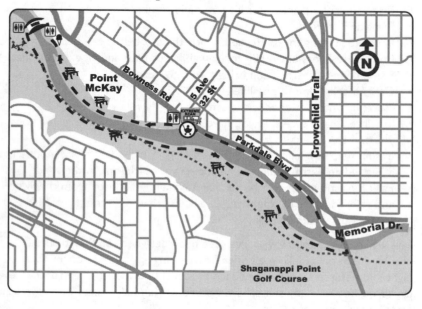	• Coffee shop		• Baby-change station
Ⓟ	• Parking		• Seating
	• Walk start		• Ice cream
	• Playground		• Washrooms

Bow River Valley Walk

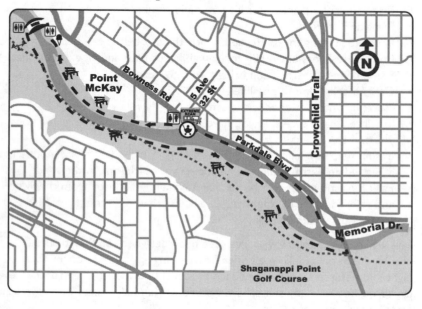

Length:	8 km
Time:	2 hours (without stops)
Hills:	Flat with one small hill.
Parking:	Extreme Bean, 3303 Bowness Road N.W. (Just off Memorial Drive at 33 Street N.W.)
Winter suitability:	Not good in winter since paths are not usually cleared.

There is free two-hour parking beside Extreme Bean or you can park in the Extreme Bean parking lot if you are going to stop there and grab a bite. Take the walking path along the Bow River valley heading north (right). There are two paths: the walking path is closest to the river and the bicyclists and rollerbladers take the path that is closest to the road. There are still a lot of joggers on the walking path, so be sure to keep to your right. There are many benches along the path as you travel north. To the right of the Harry Boothman Bridge there is a washroom with a water fountain (but without change facilities). There is also an outhouse located near the bridge. There is a lovely ice cream stand in the summer that sells coffee, iced cappuccino and ice cream of various kinds.

Take a left over the bridge. There is a great playground with infant swings on the other side, lots of benches and a building with washrooms. Follow the path across the railway tracks and take a left on the Bow River Pathway. (Note that there are not many benches along this side of the river). Continue along the path and cross the railway tracks again. At the fork in the path, take a left, which will give you a short reprieve from the joggers and bicyclists.

At the next path junction take a left; this will lead you towards the bridge under Crowchild Trail. Cross the pedestrian bridge and take a left when you reach the north bank. At the next fork in the road, take the left path, which is the pedestrian walking path. Be aware that this walk is very busy on summer weekends, and there are a lot of bicyclists who do not heed the signs to give you the right of way. I found that it is better to walk this route mid-week during the summer months.

Griffith Woods Walk

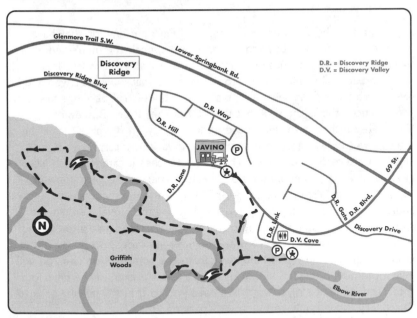

Length: 5 km
Time: 1 hour 15 minutes (without stops)
Hills: Flat
Parking: Beside Javino or parking lot at trail head
Winter suitability: Not good in winter since paths are not usually cleared.

Griffith Woods Regional Park is a special protection natural area located in the community of Discovery Ridge. You can get to Discovery Ridge by heading west on Highway 8 (south of Westhills) and turning left at 69 Street or Discovery Ridge Boulevard. The park is ninety-three hectares in size and provides an amazing setting. If you ignore the transmission line, it feels like you are in Banff National Park with fifty foot evergreen trees. The land was owned by a private family who ran a horse-riding business out of the area. It was donated to the city and is currently under a restoration program.

You can choose to start this walk from either Javino Coffee & Wine Bar or Discovery Ridge Link Parking lot.

Javino Coffee & Wine Bar (10 Discovery Ridge Hill S.W., 246-8466) has coffees to go, washrooms with baby-change tables, beautifully comfortable leather armchairs, a small play area for older children and breakfast, lunch and snack items. Unfortunately, they do not have a high chair; however breastfeeding is welcomed in the nice leather chairs or in the booth by the washroom. It is a great place to hang out and wait for your group to meet before starting the walk. If you start your walk from Javino you can walk east along Discovery Ridge Boulevard until you reach the path that connects you to Griffith Woods Regional Park.

If you start at the Griffith Woods Regional Park parking lot, they have great washrooms with baby-change facilities in both the men's and women's washrooms. These washrooms are available seasonally May through September. Head west along the main trail, which is paved and even has a yellow line separating traffic. Continue straight at the first trail intersection (this is the trail that joins Discovery Ridge Boulevard). Continue on the north side of the park and stay on the paved trail. The trail weaves its way around the stream and various interpretive signs highlight interesting vegetation. There are benches located at each inter-pretive sign. As you reach the northwest corner of the park you will reach the transmission line corridor. There is an intersection with a gravel multi-use trail. Take a left and head south along the gravel trail. At the first intersection, still under the transmission corridor, take a left and fol-low the transmission corridor. At your next intersection, take a right and head south into the woods and away from the transmission line. You will reach the next intersection quickly; take a left. At each of the next four intersections take a right, which will lead you to the trail leading back to Discovery Ridge Boulevard or to the parking lot.

Heritage Park to South Glenmore Park Walk

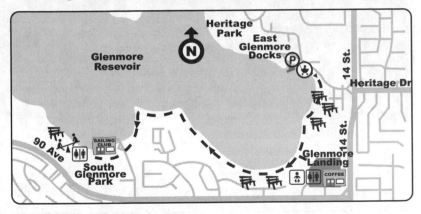

Length:	6 km
Time:	1 hour 15 minutes (without stops)
Hills:	Mostly flat with small hills.
Parking:	East Glenmore Docks beside Glenmore Reservoir at Heritage Drive.
Winter suitability:	Not good in winter since paths are not usually cleared.

There is a parking lot that faces the water just past the big "H" sign for Heritage Park. Parking is free and there is no time limit. Take note that it is quite windy along the path so if there is a cold wind at all, bundle up. Take the path heading left (east), away from Heritage Park and follow it along the shore. There are a number of benches along the way. If you are interested in a coffee or a washroom break, you can take the path that leads to Glenmore Landing. There is a Good Earth Café, Starbucks and a McDonald's at this shopping plaza. Good Earth Café has a high chair and a large washroom on the main floor but no change table. Starbucks has a washroom, but again no change table. McDonald's has a large change table in each of the men's and women's washrooms.

Head back on the same path that took you to Glenmore Landing and go up the hill to rejoin the main path. At the fork in the path, take a right. This part of the trail is by the water and has a lovely view of the reservoir and the mountains. If it is windy, however, take the left path through the trees for a bit of shelter. Cross the road in front of the sailing club building and continue on the path on the other side. Take a right and head to the playground ahead. There are lots of benches, picnic tables, infant swings and a building with washrooms that are open in the summer. The area has a rubber surface so it is good for mobile kids, even if they take a tumble. After you have enjoyed the playground, simply take the same path back to the parking lot near Heritage Park.

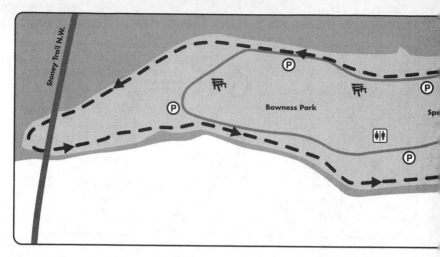

Bowness Park Walk

Length:	4 km
Time:	I hour (without stops)
Hills:	Flat
Parking:	Any of the parking lots within Bowness Park.
	8900 48 Avenue N.W.
Winter suitability:	Not good in winter since paths are not usually cleared.

Bowness Park is actually an island that is thirty hectares in size and is located in the Bow River. On the south side of the park, there is a lagoon where you can skate during the winter and even rent a boat during the summer. In summertime, the park is filled with facilities such as a spray pool, water fountains and picnic areas. A concession called Park Side Café (286-8668) has food and a large range of coffees. Washrooms are in a separate building. A ride on a miniature train (afternoons only) costs $3 per person and tickets can be bought at the concession. Parents can accompany children on the train. The ride is fifteen to twenty minutes long and goes around the lagoon. Mini golf is available just north of the concession.

Park your vehicle at any of the parking lots at Bowness Park and head to the concession. Start your walk from here. Travel east on the perimeter path located beside the lagoon. Pass the playground and picnic shelter and you will reach the paved cul-de-sac for cars. Take the west path along the river and continue to the westerly tip of the park/island before the path curves and brings you along the south edge back to the concession.

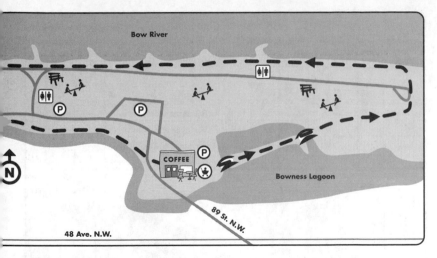

River Park Walk

Length:	5 km
Time:	1 hour and 30 minutes (without stops)
Hills:	One large hill at the end.
Parking:	Bell's Bookstore Café at 34 Avenue and 14 Street S.W.
Winter suitability:	Good for winter, paths are usually quite clear.

Start your trip at Bell's Bookstore. They have great coffee and snacks and it is a cozy place to meet your friends as you begin your trip. Head south on 14A Street until you cross 38 Avenue. Enter River Park and continue south. Cross one of the many bridges and meet up with the main gravel path. There are many benches along the edge of the ravine just east of the main path and overlooking the Elbow River. Watch out for dog poop if you cut across the field to use the benches. At the crest of the hill, look behind you: there's a beautiful view of downtown Calgary and the Elbow River.

At the end of the gravel path, turn left and head down an asphalt path on the Elbow River Pathway towards Sandy Beach Park. This is a two-way bike path, so keep to your right. At the fork, keep to your right, stay on the walking pathway and head towards the playground. Beside the playground there is a shelter with seats and washrooms. There are also lots of benches around the playground and by the river. The path turns left at the river. Cross the suspension bridge and follow the asphalt path that curves left. There are a couple of benches right before the path turns into Riverdale Avenue. You will have to walk on the road a short distance to reach the sidewalk. There are many interesting houses to look at and tall trees along this stretch.

Take the bridge (on your left) across the Elbow River. Note that there is a bench under the bridge on the south bank of the river. To access it, follow a small path to the left of the entry to the bridge. This is one of

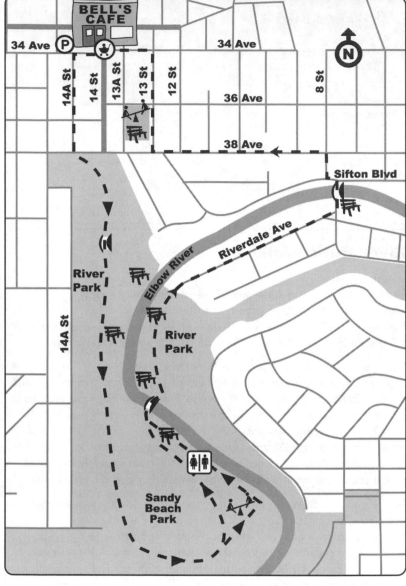

the last benches on the walk. Cross Sifton Boulevard at the crosswalk and turn left at the school. Take your next right on 8 Street and then turn left onto 38 Avenue S.W. Get ready for a steep hill. Turn right onto 13 Street and you will pass a park and playground on your left with benches. Turn left onto 34 Avenue. Be careful when crossing 14 Street as it is quite busy. It is worth the one block detour to get to the lights on Council Way/33 Avenue. Head east on 34 Avenue and you will return to Bell's Bookstore.

Paula says...

"On one of my walks with a friend, I had to breastfeed in River Park, a place popular with dog-walkers. I sat on a bench and my friend tried to provide me with as much privacy as possible by standing in front of me and using her stroller as a shield. Unfortunately, I attracted the attention of a large number of dogs... perhaps the smell of milk! All of the dogs came running over with their owners close on their heels. I quickly learned to be a lot more comfortable breastfeeding in public after that."

Marda Loop Walk

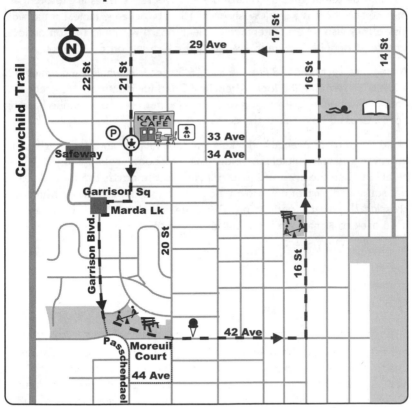

Length:	5 km
Time:	1 hour and 15 minutes (without stops)
Hills:	One hill at the end.
Parking:	Kaffa Café at 2138 33 Avenue S.W.
Winter suitability:	Good for winter, paths are usually quite clear.

WALKS

Start at Kaffa Café. There is a change table inside and some discreet corners if you need to breastfeed. The café has a wonderful deck, but it is tricky to get your stroller up the steps; try pulling your stroller up the steps backwards. To start the walk, cross 33 Avenue at the pedestrian crosswalk. Head south on 21 Street, cross 34 Avenue and continue south. Turn right at Marda Link (the courtyards) and head towards the monument.

Take a left at Garrison Square and head south on Garrison Boulevard. Cross St. Julien Drive and veer into the playground where there are lots of benches. There's also an interesting plaque about the battle of St. Julien. Take the path east through the park. In winter, this stretch can be quite icy, so instead you can head south on Paschendale, east on 44 Avenue and come north again on 20 Street.

Cross 20 Street and stop for a break at My Favorite Ice Cream Shoppe. You may be tempted to try one of the 72 flavours. Benches are located outside and there is a small washroom inside. No change table, I am afraid! Inside, they also have an interesting bulletin board with information on local services. Continue east on 42 Avenue and take a left onto 16 Street.

At the intersection of 38 Avenue and 16 Street is Kiwanis Park, which has a lovely playground and lots of benches. Continue north on 16 Street until 34 Avenue where you jog to your right in order to continue heading north. Cross 33 Avenue at the crosswalk.

Head north to 29 Avenue and take a left. You will pass another playground, however, it is only suitable for older children. Look around and you will be able to see the crest of Nose Hill Park to the north, the foothills to the south and part of downtown. Be sure to use the crosswalk when crossing 20 Street. Continue on 29 Avenue, take a left at 21 Street and head back to Kaffa Café for a well-deserved rest.

North Glenmore Park Walk

Length:	5 km
Time:	1 hour and 15 minutes (without stops)
Hills:	None
Parking:	Weaselhead Flats, 37 Street and 66 Avenue S.W.
Winter suitability:	Not good in winter since paths are not usually cleared.

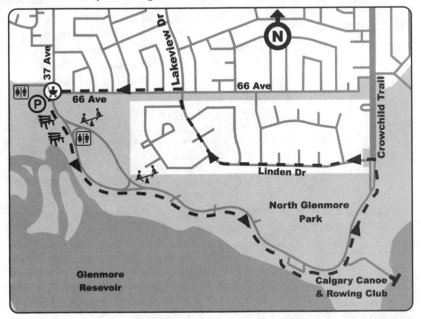

Park at the Weaselhead Flats and take the path towards the edge of North Glenmore Park. There is an outhouse on your right as you enter the park, but it does not have any change facilities (you may want to hold your breath while using it!). Take a left along the path that is closest to the edge of the ravine. There are two paths: a bike path (closest to the road) and a walking path (closest to the ravine); be sure to stay on the walking path. Benches dot this part of the walk. Washrooms (without change tables) are located across the road in a cream-coloured building. There is a lovely play area just north of the road that has infant swings.

Continue along the path and pass a blue building that houses the Canoe Club. Here the path heads north along a golf course. There are no benches or washrooms after the Canoe Club building. Continue past the golf course and cross the road to make a left on Linden Drive. Keep on the sidewalk and enjoy a look at the houses that back onto North Glenmore Park. Continue along Linden Drive until you meet 66 Avenue, where you will take a left. You can head along the north side of 66 Avenue where there is a sidewalk. Continue along until you arrive at 37 Street and Weaselhead Flats. This walk is particularly beautiful in mid-September when the leaves start to turn colour.

Stanley Park to Talisman Centre Walk

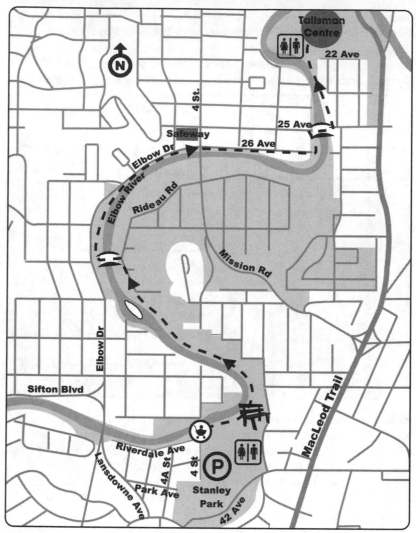

Length:	6 km
Time:	1 hour 45 minutes (without stops)
Hills:	Flat with minor hills.
Parking:	West side of Stanley Park
Winter suitability:	Not good in winter since paths are not usually cleared.

Park on the west side of Stanley Park. The park is a beautiful place to walk through, with large poplars right beside the river, barbeques, benches, picnic tables, washrooms, water fountains and a baseball diamond. Head north along the path and enjoy the views of the Elbow River. Continue on the path until it turns into Rideau Road. Take a left across the suspension bridge over the river. Continue north along the river between

Elbow Drive and the river. When you come to 4 Street, you can make a washroom stop at Safeway, which is located on the north side of the road. Alternatively, you may want to head up to 4 Street and 24 Avenue to stop at the Second Cup coffee shop. If you don't need a break, cross 4 Street and continue on the path beside 26 Avenue. At the end of the road, the path veers to the left. Take the bridge across the river at 25 Avenue and then continue north on the east side of the river past Erlton until you reach Talisman Centre. There you will find washrooms and refreshments. Enjoy a little rest before you head back the same way to Stanley Park.

Jill says...

"It often seems difficult to get out of the house with your children but if feels fabulous when you are out. Sometimes a walk outside didn't work for us – but a mall walk worked well. The malls are warm in winter and cool in summer, great when it is raining outside, bug-free and without the risk of sunburn. There is always a nursing room nearby and someplace to get a snack or a coffee. One of the perks is that you may receive compliments on your babies, and you can meet lots of other mothers. If you have multiples, I recommend that you lunch at off-peak times so that you can get all the high chairs that you need!"

Mall Walking

During the winter head to your local mall and enjoy your walk indoors. Do a little window shopping and enjoy a break after your walk. Market Mall is an excellent location for mall walking. There is a circular route, a play area for the children, family nursing rooms, a mother's room and also a Petland, which is a big hit with the children.

Jill says...

"One triplet mother I know would put two babies in a double stroller, the third in a Baby Bjorn carrier and happily hit the mall by herself. It is doable and even enjoyable."

The Forzani Group Foundation Mother's Day Run and Walk

Address: The walk usually starts in downtown Calgary but may change from year to year.

Website: www.mdrunandwalk.com

Cost: Approximately $30 to $40 per adult.

The Forzani Group Foundation Mother's Day Run and Walk is held every year on Mother's Day in Calgary, as well as in other Canadian cities. The walk raises funds for a different charity each year. You can choose to walk 5 km, run 5 km or run 10 km, and you can do any of these with or without your baby. The first few hundred women to pass through the finish line usually receive a rose and all participants get snacks and drinks. You can register online or at Forzani's Tech Shop.

HIKING

Hiking should be relatively easy while your baby is being exclusively breastfed or bottle-fed. If he is still rather light, you can just use a front baby carrier; however, stick to smooth and easy trails as it is difficult to see your feet while wearing it.

Back carriers can make hiking a lot easier. They place the bulk of your baby's weight on your hips and allow Junior to enjoy a new vantage point. The babies have great naps in the back carriers. My research has shown that most back carriers are similar in design, with variations in the hip belt and release of the stand. Be sure to test the carrier with your baby inside it before purchasing. Mountain Equipment Co-op sells its own brand of backpack and also carries Deuter. Kelty brand is sold at Coast Mountain Sports and Kacz' Kids, while Snugli is sold at Toys "R" Us and Sears.

Paula says...

"I was so nervous on our first hiking trip that I brought a large backpack of 'emergency' items. We weren't exactly travelling light on that 4 km hike but we were ready for anything!"

Here is some suggested reading material on getting out there with little ones:

- Goldie Silverman, *Backpacking with Babies and Small Children* (Wilderness Press, 1998)
- Nena Kelty and Steve Boga, *Backpacking the Kelty Way* (Berkley Pub. Group, 2000)
- Steve Boga, *Camping and Backpacking with Children* (Stackpole Books, 1995)
- Barbara J. Euser, *Take 'Em Along: Sharing the Wilderness with Your Children* (Johnson Press, 1987)

Some good short hikes within a short drive from Calgary include the following:

Gillian Daffern, *Kananaskis Country Trail Guide Volume 1* (Rocky Mountain Books, 1996)

- Ribbon Falls (Kananaskis)
- Upper Kananaskis Lake (Kananaskis)
- Elbow Lake (Kananaskis)

Graeme Pole, *Classic Hikes in the Canadian Rockies* (Altitude Publishing Canada Limited, 1999)

- C-level Cirque (Banff)
- Johnston Canyon / Ink Pots (Banff, Highway 1A)
- Plain of Six Glaciers (Lake Louise)

Brian Patton, *The Canadian Rockies Trail Guide, Sixth Edition – Revised* (Summerthought Ltd, 1994)

- Boom Lake (Banff)

> **Tip!** *Don't forget to bring lots of water, food and emergency supplies in case the weather turns. Finally, remember to pack out dirty diapers and any other garbage.*

RUNNING

If you are interested in jogging to keep in shape while on parental leave, you may be able to justify the investment in a jogging stroller. Decent jogging strollers cost between $200 and $800. Most models have three large bicycle-style wheels: one in the front and two in the back. Harness systems are used to keep your baby strapped in. A safety screen keeps out bugs, keeps your baby out of the wind and provides cover in case of inclement weather. Many jogging strollers have attachments for cycling or cross-country skiing. You will also need a safety strap that attaches the stroller to your wrist. In cold weather, I recommend using a very warm stroller blanket.

Look for the following features in a jogging stroller:
- Large and height-adjustable handlebars that are comfortable in your hands;
- Wheel-locking mechanism and handbrakes if possible;
- Good shoulder harness to keep your baby secure (some joggers have a hammock-style sling for babies under four months);
- Large, bicycle-style tires to provide stability;
- Front screen to keep out bugs and deflect any stray airborne debris;
- A handy place for your water bottle;
- Wheels that can be tuned rather than wheels made of plastic.

There are many brands of jogging strollers available in fact too many to mention. There is a Calgary-based maker of jogging strollers, Chariot Carriers Inc. Chariot Carriers are sold in many bike stores across Calgary as well as Kacz' Kids. Check out their website at www.chariot carriers.com

Paula says...

"If you are nursing and running, you will need a good sports bra for appropriate support. Check out 'Chapter Two: Surviving the First Six Weeks' on 'Nursing Bras' and also try specialty running stores."

CYCLING

There are numerous brands and types of bicycle trailers sold in Calgary. Some baby stores carry them; however, most are sold at bicycle shops. Trailers vary by weight, wheel type, shock absorbers and accessories such as roof racks. Prices can be as high as over $600. Some trailers can carry two children.

It is best to stay on the bike trails in Calgary and to avoid roads and highways. To find out about bike trails in your community, consult the Calgary Pathway and Bikeway Map. It also shows winter routes and out-of-service routes. The map can be purchased for $2 at most bike stores.

Alternatively, you can order it by calling the City of Calgary at 311 or by visiting the city's online store at www.calgaryonlinestore.com. There is a shipping and handling charge of $1. The most recent edition at the time of printing was from 2006.

Some parents choose to purchase helmets for even very small children, since everyone on a bike is travelling at a significant speed. Gyro makes helmets for infants and toddlers that are highly adjustable so the fit is correct. They are available at Bow Cycle and Ridley's.

Paula says...

"We added a lambskin rug (about $35 at IKEA) to our bike trailer to keep our son warm in colder weather."

Calgary-based Chariot Carriers Inc., which manufactures jogging strollers as mentioned above, also makes a bicycle attachment for its strollers. If you are not an avid cyclist but want to head out occasionally, you can rent a trailer for your bike for approximately $25 per day. Chariots outfitted with a bike attachment can be rented from the following locations in Calgary:

Rapid Rent a Ski
Address: 903 Heritage Drive S.W.
Phone: 253-2975
Website: www.rapidrent.ca

Sports Rent
Address: 4424 16 Avenue N.W.
Phone: 292-0077
Website: www.sportsrent.ca

University of Calgary
Outdoor Program Centre Rentals
Location: University of Calgary
Phone: 220-5038
Website: www.ucalgary.ca/opc

ICE-SKATING

Your baby can easily come along with you while you are ice-skating at a public rink. Merely bring along your stroller and push the stroller along the ice as you skate behind. The Olympic Oval public rink is a popular place for skating with your little one. If you have your stroller, you need to take the elevator just east of the Oval to get to the main floor.

ICE-SKATING

CROSS-COUNTRY SKIING

Unfortunately, there are no facilities that offer babysitting services while you cross-country ski, so you'll just have to take your little tyke along with you.

There are a couple of options for carriers for cross-country skiing:
- Mountain Equipment Co-op carries a Canadian-made CH2 Baby Glider pull-style sled with a five-point harness. The seat has a built-in back support and fleece lining for comfort. It costs over $400 and has a maximum load of 44 lbs. It is not recommended for babies under six months.

- Chariot Carriers Inc. makes a cross-country ski conversion kit for its jogging stroller, which costs about $200.

There are several places in Calgary that rent cross-country ski trailers. Mountain Equipment Co-op rents their Baby Glider. However, they only have a couple of them available for rent, so book well ahead. Chariots converted for cross-country skiing can also be rented for approximately $15 a day. See the list above under "Cycling" for where to rent them. The Nordic Centre in Canmore also rents pulks for those skiing there.

DOWNHILL SKIING

One of the joys of living in Calgary is its proximity to world-class skiing. The closest skiing can be found within the city limits at Canada Olympic Park. For information about skiing at Canada Olympic Park, see "Chapter Twelve: Activities" – "Calgary Sites".

At most daycares, they require that you:
- Provide a minimum of 24-hour notice (two-week notice is recommended);
- Bring your baby's or toddler's Alberta Health Care card;
- Provide indoor shoes or slippers;
- Provide your own formula or milk, wipes, baby food, bottles and diapers;
- Do not pack any nuts or nut products for your child since other children could have allergies.
- Check ahead to see if any foods are prohibited.

Daycares for Children Younger than Nineteen Months

Two ski hills have daycare facilities that look after children under nineteen months of age - Fernie and Lake Louise.

A comparison of the two daycare facilities is set forth in the table below:

	FERNIE	LAKE LOUISE
Phone	1-250-423-4655	1-403-522-3555 ext 2118
Website	www.skifernie.com/daycare	www.skilouise.com/daycare
Hours	8:30 a.m. – 4:30 p.m.	8:30 a.m. – 4:30 p.m.
Rates – full day	$56 (0 – 19 months)	$56 (0 – 19 months)
Rates – half day	$25 (3 hours maximum)	Not applicable to infants
Discounts for siblings	None	None
Food provided? ($ cost)	Yes ($6.50)	Yes ($7)
Cancellation policy	24-hour notice or cancellation fee of $25.	48-hour notice, otherwise full charges apply.
Late fee	$7 per 15 minutes late.	$7 per 15 minutes late.
Other	Will not take sick children; eight licensed spots for children under 19 months.	Nine licensed spots for children under 19 months.

Paula says...

"At Mount Norquay you can purchase part-day lift tickets for between two and five hours of skiing or snowboarding. This is great way to save if you only want to do a little bit of skiing."

Tip!
If you are thinking of ski lessons for your little one, you will need to wait until they are over three for any lessons.

Daycares for Children Older than Eighteen Months

Here is a list of ski lodges that provide child care for children over eighteen months, in addition to the two mentioned above

	KIMBERLY	MOUNT NORQUAY
Ages	18 months – 6 years	19 months – 6 years
Phone	1-250-432-0301	1-403-760-7709
Website	www.skikimberly.com	www.banffnorquay.com
Hours	8:30 a.m. – 4:30 p.m.	9 a.m. – 4 p.m.
Rates – full day	$41	$45 (19 – 36 months) $37 (37 months – 6 years)
Rates – half day	$26	$27
Rates – hourly	N/A	$13 (one hr) $18 (two hrs)
Extended stay	N/A	N/A
Discounts for siblings	None	None
Food provided? ($ cost)	Yes ($8)	Yes ($7)

	SUNSHINE	PANORAMA
Ages	19 months – 6 years	18 months – 5 years
Phone	1-877-542-2633	1-800-663-2929
Website	www.skibanff.com	www.panoramaresort.com
Hours	8:30 a.m. – 4:30 p.m.	9 a.m. – 4:30 p.m.
Rates – full day	$60 (includes lunch)	$60* (19 – 36 months) $55* (37 months – 5 years)
Rates – half day	$30	
Rates – hourly	N/A	$12 per hour
Extended stay	N/A	Reduced rates for stays of three or more days.
Discounts for siblings	None	None
Food provided? ($ cost)	Yes (included in price)	Yes ($7)
Other	Discounts are available for three, four and five full days of child care; Must bring a copy of Birth Certificate and Health Insurance Number.	24 spaces available per day; Must bring copy of; Birth Certificate, Immunization History, Health Insurance Number.

* Rates are higher for child care that is not pre-booked.

Slope-Side Accommodation

Slope-side accommodation is another way of making sure that you can hit the slopes early while looking after your little one in comfort. Slope-side accommodation can be found at the following five ski hills: Fernie, Sunshine, Panorama, Kicking Horse and Kimberly.

Elena says...

"We've used the slope-side accommodation option instead of the daycare option. I liked how we could alternate skiing and look after the little one in the comfort of the hotel room without too much hassle."

Fernie Alpine Resort
Phone: 1-866-633-7643 or (250) 423-4655 or Resorts of the
            Canadian Rockies at 256-8473; 1-877-333-2339 to book
            accommodations.
Website: www.skifernie.com/vacations

Fernie accommodation includes hotels, condos, homes and lodges. There is a central reservations phone number listed above. Cribs are available upon request, however, high chairs may not be available at the main resort. All rooms are non-smoking. Fernie has "ski-in, ski-out" accommodation.

Kicking Horse Resort
Phone: 1-866-SKI-KICK (toll free)
Website: www.kickinghorseresort.com (click on
            "Accommodations" and then "The Mountain")

Kicking Horse is a new ski resort with "ski-in, ski-out" condos, hotels and lodges. Please contact the resort for more details about accommodation.

Kimberley Alpine Resort
Phone: 1-877-754-5462 Reservations Line
Website: www.skikimberley.com (click on "Accommodations")

One accommodation option at Kimberley is the Mariott Hotel. This is a condo-style hotel. The Mariott only has one crib, so make sure that you book it ahead of time. There are high chairs available in the breakfast area. All rooms are non-smoking and have full kitchens. The Mariott also has a heated pool and two hot tubs. There are a number of other accommodations available at this resort as well, including "ski-in, ski-out" accommodation.

DOWNHILL SKIING

Panorama Mountain Village

Phone: 1-800-663-2929 (toll free)
Website: www.panoramaresort.com (Click on "Accommodation")

Panorama has a variety of accommodation options ranging from condos to townhouses, including "ski-in, ski-out" accommodation. The central reservations line is listed above. Playpens are available upon request. They also have a lovely warm outdoor pool.

Sunshine Village

Phone: 1-87-SKI-BANFF
Website: www.skibanff.com (click on "Accommodations")

Most "ski-in, ski-out" resorts are outside the National Parks with one exception. Sunshine boasts that they are the only one within the National Parks. Cribs are available upon request and high chairs are found in the restaurant. Non-smoking rooms are available. There are no cooking facilities in the rooms, with the exception of one terraced family suite which has a microwave.

Day Lodges

Finally, you can always just bring your baby and hang out at a day lodge while mom and dad alternate looking after her. Most day lodges are non-smoking so you can comfortably bring your baby along for the day. Few, however, have baby-changing facilities, so you may end up changing your baby on a table or a corner of the floor. Fernie and Lake Louise top the charts for their baby-friendly facilities, as each has change areas in their washrooms. Both of these resorts also provide breastfeeding areas in their daycare facilities. The other day lodges are not conducive to breastfeeding as they do not offer any quiet areas or family washrooms.

FITNESS CLASSES FOR YOU WITH YOUR BABY

To get some exercise in a gym, you have two options: use babysitting services at the gym or sign up for a class designed for moms and dads and their babies. Below you will find information on facilities in Calgary and area that offer programs for you and your baby.

Cardel Place

Location: Nose Creek Sports and Recreation Association
             11950 Country Village Link N.E.
Phone: 532-1013
Website: www.cardelplace.com

Cardel Place recreation facilities offer the fitness classes for parents and babies listed below. For details, check out the program brochure available online.

- Baby & You Walking Workout (summer only) ($68) – This course is eight classes long and takes you and your stroller outdoors. It focuses on cardio fitness and muscular conditioning.
- Baby & You Workout: Post-Natal ($131) – This one-hour weekly course is for new moms who are interested in getting back into shape. It is fifteen weeks long and focuses on improving strength, tone and endurance as well as cardiovascular fitness. Bring your stroller.
- Postnatal Yoga ($80) – This course is offered in partnership with CHR. Babies must not be able to crawl yet. The course consists of six weekly classes. It is intended for moms only.
- Baby & You Aquacise ($58) – This course runs for seven classes and costs $58. Babies must be able to hold their heads up. Infants up to 18 months are welcome.

City of Calgary Facilities
Address: Various locations
Phone: Information 3-1-1, Registration 268-3800
Website: www.calgary.ca/recreation

The City of Calgary's "Recreation in the City Program Guide" contains information on all programs offered by the city, including locations of aquatic and fitness centres and leisure centres, prices, registration and admission specials. See "Chapter Twelve: Activities" – "Calgary Sites" – "Calgary Parks" for where to pick up your free copy of the guide.

Low-income Calgarians can apply for assistance with fees and admissions at City of Calgary recreation facilities and other participating organizations. Phone 3-1-1 for details.

Fitness classes for parents and babies offered at the city's recreation facilities are listed below. For details, please see the City of Calgary's "Recreation in the City Program Guide". A variety of locations and class durations are offered. With the exception of the yoga and Pilates courses, all classes cost between $40 and $66 and are suitable for babies up to twelve months. The yoga and Pilates classes cost between $70 and $90. The StrollerFit course is for either moms or dads, but the rest of them are intended for moms only.
- Mom & Baby Fit Together – In Water: Basic aerobic conditioning, strengthening and stretching exercises in water.
- Mom & Baby Fit Together – On Land: Aerobic exercise in a baby-friendly environment.
- Mom & Baby Fit Together – Strength: Strength training using your baby for resistance.
- Parent & Baby Fit Together – Stroller Fit: Cardiovascular exercise and strength training, including exercises which can be done outdoors with your baby.

- Mom & Baby Fit Together – Yoga: Yoga postures are suitable for new moms with infants up to ten months. This class is difficult to take with a crawling baby, so try to take it within six months of your baby's birth.
- Mom & Baby Fit Together – Pilates: Enjoy the benefits of Pilates with your baby in a casual atmosphere.

East Lake Recreation and Wellness Centre (Airdrie)

Location: Recreation and Wellness Centre
              800 East Lake Boulevard, Airdrie
Phone: 948-8804
Website: www.airdrie.ca (click on "East Lake Recreation and Wellness Centre")

Fitness classes for parents and babies offered at the Recreation and Wellness Centre in Airdrie are listed below. For details, check out the program brochure available online or at the centre.
- Parent and Baby Fit Together ($58) –This course is ten classes long and takes you and your stroller outdoors. It is best when baby is between three and twelve months of age. This is a cardiovascular workout that you can perform while holding your child. It also includes stretching and strengthening exercises that are modified for postnatal moms.
- Strollercize ($78) –This indoor course is ten classes long. It focuses on cardiovascular and toning benefits for new moms. A stroller is required for the class.

Talisman Centre

Address: 2225 Macleod Trail South
Phone: 233-8393
Website: www.talismancentre.com

Built in 1983 to host the Western Canada Summer Games, the Talisman Centre is the second largest public recreation facility in North America. It is managed by the Lindsay Park Sports Society, which is an independent non-profit society.

Here are brief descriptions of fitness courses for parents and babies offered at the Talisman Centre. For details, see the centre's program guide available on its website (look under "Programs") or at the facility.
- You & Me Baby Aquatic Workout – In this class babies sit in special floatable boats while parents work out in water. Babies must be between three months and sixteen months old. There are twelve classes in a course, and the cost is $132 (about $11 per class).
- You & Me Baby Gym Workout – Parents exercise while holding or strolling their babies. The exercises include low-impact aerobics and power walking. Babies must be between three months and one year

of age. As with the aquatic workout above, twelve classes cost $132 (about $11 per class).
- Postnatal Yoga – This course is offered by the Talisman Centre in partnership with CHR. Babies must not be able to crawl yet. The course consists of six weekly classes and costs $70 (about $12 per class). It is intended for moms only.

Vocational Rehabilitation Research Institute
Address: 3304 33 Street N.W.
Phone: 284-2231
Website: www.vrri.org (look under "Recreation")

Vocational and Rehabilitation Research Institute (VRRI) is a registered not-for-profit organization that provides recreation and leisure opportunities to Calgarians. You can pick up VRRI's program guide at the recreation centre or download it from the website.

VRRI does not provide babysitting services; however, it offers a fitness class for moms and babies:
- Mom/Baby Strollercize – This class is designed to help mothers get back into shape without needing a babysitter. Babies must not be overly mobile, i.e. crawling or rolling excessively, so probably less than six months old. You need to bring your baby in a stroller to the class. This is a registered program of between four to six classes and the cost ranges from $20 to $30 ($5 per class).

YMCA
Address: The YMCA has the following facilities in Calgary:
               Bishop McNally: 5700 Falconridge Boulevard N.E.,
                   Phone: 285-7444
               Community: 510, 940 6 Avenue S.W.,
                   Phone: 531-1660
               Crowfoot: 8100 John Laurie Boulevard N.W.,
                   Phone: 547-6576
               Eau Claire: 101 3 Street S.W.,
                   Phone: 269-6701, 781-1692 (Childcare centre)
               Shawnessy: 400, 333 Shawville Boulevard S.E.,
                   Phone: 256-5533
               South: 11 Haddon Road S.W.,
                   Phone: 255-8131
Website: www.ymcacalgary.org

The drop-in fee for non-members is about $11 for an adult and $4 for any child up to age eleven. Annual adult memberships cost between $476 and $620 depending on location, and there is a one-time fee for new members of about $70.

YMCA is now offering a course called Toddler Time and Parent Yoga for children from ten months and up. Your toddler gets involved in arts, crafts and gym time while you enjoy a forty-five minute yoga class. There are between eleven and fifteen classes and the costs ranges between $165 and $225 ($110 and $150 for members).

> **Tip!** *Children over three years old can attend an unparented class swimming or at the gym. Enjoy your own workout while your little one is in their scheduled class.*

Fitness Facilities with Babysitting Services

The following table provides a summary of all the fitness facilities that offer babysitting services. All listed facilities offer drop-in babysitting and provide a maximum of three hours of babysitting in any given day.

	Cardel Place	City of Calgary: Aquatic and Fitness Centres (AFC)	City of Calgary: Leisure Centres	East Lake Recreation Centre (Airdrie)	Talisman Centre	Westside Rec Centre	YMCA
Minimum age					Over three months old only.		Over six weeks old only.
Babysitting rate	$4 per hour.	$2 per hour.	$4 per hour.	$3 per hour.	$5 per hour.	$5 per hour.	$5 per hour.
Advance booking required?	Minimum two hours in advance.	Minimum two hours in advance.	Minimum 24 hours in advance.	Yes	Minimum a week in advance for weekday; First come first served on weekends.	Recommend a week in advance and a minimum of 24 hours in advance.	Recommended
Multiuse passes ?	Yes			Yes	Yes		Yes
Adult admission cost	$10	$5	$9	$7 ($21 family)		$11	$11
Children's admission	Free under 2 years old. $3.50 over 2 years old.			Free under 3 years old.			$4
Notes		Not all AFCs offer babysitting. Admission specials available.	Admission specials available.	Evening babysitting on Monday and Wednesday evenings, subject to demand.	Cancellation child care charges apply.		

CARDEL PLACE

Location: Nose Creek Sports and Recreation Association
              11950 Country Village Link N.E.
Phone: 532-1013
Website: www.cardelplace.com

Adult admission is $10. For children over two years old it is $3.50. Family entry is $21. Multi-use passes are available as well as annual membership.

Drop-in babysitting services are available at specified hours. Check their website for times. The cost is $4 per hour. You can reduce the cost of child care by buying a ten- or thirty-hour pass. You need to book babysitting service at least two hours in advance.

CITY OF CALGARY FACILITIES

Address: Various
Phone: Information 3-1-1, Registration 268-3800
Website: www.calgary.ca/recreation

Here is some information on admission to and babysitting at the city's aquatic and fitness centres (AFCs) and two leisure centers.

Aquatic and Fitness Centres:

Adult admission is around $5.

Drop-in babysitting services are available in approximately half of the AFCs. The cost is just over $2 per hour. Days and times for babysitting services are noted on the city's website or call the AFCs directly. You need to book babysitting service at least two hours in advance.

Leisure Centres:

Regular adult admission is about $9; however, a one-hour swim with a baby (adult plus child under two years of age) only costs $5.

Babysitting is just over $4 per hour at the Southland Leisure Centre; it is $3.50 per hour at the Village Square Leisure Centre. Please note that you need to book babysitting at least twenty-four hours ahead by phone. It is possible to lower your costs by buying multiple passes for babysitting and admission. Also look for admission specials in the city's "Recreation in the City Program Guide" or on the website. For example, you can take advantage of half-price Tuesday evenings, free public swims on statutory holidays at some locations and lower admissions on Sundays at some locations.

EAST LAKE RECREATION AND WELLNESS CENTRE (AIRDRIE)

Location: Recreation and Wellness Centre
             800 East Lake Boulevard, Airdrie
Phone: 948-8804
Website: www.airdrie.ca and click on "East Lake Recreation and
             Wellness Centre"

Adult admission is $7. Admission is free for any children under three years of age. Family entry is $21. Multi-use passes are available as well as annual membership.

Drop-in babysitting services are available at specified hours. The cost is $3 per hour. You can reduce the cost of child care by buying a ten-, twenty- or one-hundred hour pass. You need to book babysitting service ahead.

TALISMAN CENTRE

Address: 2225 Macleod Trail South
Phone: 233-8393
Website: www.talismancentre.com

The day access fee for an adult is $11 and a ten-time pass is $89. Memberships are available for one month, four months and one year for $89, $300 and $640 respectively.

Child care services at the Talisman Centre are provided for children over three months of age, for up to three hours at a time. The cost for infants and toddlers is about $5 each per hour (a bit less if you buy a multiple pass). Please note that the child care services are not offered after 3 p.m. on weekdays or 2 p.m. on weekends. In addition, the service is not provided on statutory holidays. Call the Talisman Centre or consult its program guide for more details. If you want to use the babysitting services on weekday mornings, you will need to reserve at least a week in advance. During other times, the services are offered on a "first come, first served" basis.

WESTSIDE RECREATION CENTRE

Location: 2000 69 Street S.W.
Phone: 531-5875
Website: www.westsiderec.com

Westside Recreation Centre has babysitting services for you while you work out. The day access fee for an adult is $11 and a ten-time pass is $99. Annual memberships are available.

The child care services at the Westside are provided for infants and toddlers for up to three hours at a time. The cost for infants and toddlers is about $5 each per hour (a bit less if you buy thirty-hour passes for $120). On Mondays, Wednesdays and Thursdays child care is available from 8:15 a.m. to 7:30 p.m. On Tuesdays and Fridays the child care centre closes by 5:30 p.m. On weekends they are only open until 1 p.m. It is recommended that you pre-book your space a maximum of one week and a minimum of twenty-four hours prior to the time requested. One day's notice must be given of cancellations or charges will apply. Child care is not available on statutory holidays.

YMCA

Address: Five locations (previously mentioned in this chapter)
Website: www.ymcacalgary.org

The drop-in fee for non-members is about $11 for an adult and $4 for any child up to age eleven. Annual adult memberships cost between $476 and $620 depending on location, and there is a one-time fee for new members of about $70.

Babysitting services are available at the rate of $5 per hour for non-members and $4 per hour for YMCA members. Babysitting is available for infants over six weeks of age for a maximum of two hours and only when an adult is using the facility. Advance booking is recommended.

PERSONAL FITNESS FOCUSED ON MOMS

Over the past two years there has been a dramatic growth in the number of personal fitness coaches for moms who are interested in getting their bodies back in shape after having a baby. Here is a list of some of the services available in Calgary:

Bellies, Babies and Beyond

Phone: 852-4650
Website: www.belliesbabiesandbeyond.ca

This company offers mobile personal training. You can work out at home, or wherever you choose. This way you do not have to worry about child care or travel time. They bring the equipment to you, including stability balls, hand weights, medicine balls and tubing. An initial consultation takes ninety minutes and costs $125. Personal training costs $85 per hour. You can get a group together and reduce the price per person.

They also offer classes such as Fit Babies for newly postpartum moms. The program is twelve classes long and costs $192.

Bikini Bootcamp
Phone: 542-0790
Website: www.bikinibootcamp.ca

This is an eight-week program offered in Calgary, Airdrie and Cochrane. Two weeks before you start the program, they will do an initial assessment (forty-five minutes) to determine your fitness level. This will be repeated two weeks after you finish the program. The programs take place outdoors and cost $375. There are three levels of courses: beginning, intermediate and advanced.

Calgary Adventure Bootcamp
Phone: 246-7386
Website: www.albertabootcamp.com

This program is offered either five days a week or three days a week. The fitness sessions are held outdoors and run for fifty-five minutes. Mom or Dad can bring their baby along in a stroller, which becomes part of the exercise routine. This program is suitable for all fitness levels.

FITMOM Calgary
Phone: 874-4063
Website: www.fitmomcanada.com/calgary/

FITMOM Calgary offers postnatal and beyond fitness classes and personal training. Classes and training are offered across Calgary but not in the neighbouring areas. There are two courses suitable for babies between six weeks and eighteen months:
- FITMOM + Baby: In this course, moms wear babies in a carrier as they perform standing cardiovascular and strengthening exercises followed by an aerobic circuit and floor work to target core muscles.
- FITMOM Stroller: Classes are one hour long and travel through a local park on a challenging circuit program.

All classes run in twelve-week blocks for $192 and are offered on an on-going basis. One-on-one personal training is offered at $75 per session.

Talisman Centre
Phone: 233-8393
Website: www.talismancentre.com

M.O.M. (Makeovers of Moms) – This class is for moms who delivered more than eight months ago and want to get fit again. Do not bring your baby to this course. There are eleven classes in each course and the cost is $121 ($11 per class).

Thrive Fitness

Phone: 605-6204

Website: www.thrivefitness.ca

This company provides both personal fitness training and baby massage instruction. A one and a half hour fitness consultation and appraisal costs $75 and provides an assessment of your lifestyle goals, time constraints and motivators. The personal training sessions cost $65 per hour.

Moms in Motion

Website: www.momsinmotion.com

This is a U.S. based company that has a group that meets regularly in Calgary. They offer training two nights a week. Fees are $100 for ten sessions. There is also a sign-up fee of about $65. Ten percent of the fees go to the Alberta Children's Hospital.

Elena says..

"One cost-effective option for using a personal trainer is to sign up for one through your gym. After just one one- to two-hour session, you will have an exercise program designed for your preferences, fitness level, goals and time constraints. I like to have a session with a trainer every four to six months, which lets me freshen up my program and avoid being unmotivated. These sessions are also excellent opportunities to ask lots of questions and help you feel like you really know what you are doing at the gym!"

CHAPTER TWELVE
ACTIVITIES

SITES IN CALGARY AND AREA

Don't forget to check out www.calgaryattractions.com to find some coupons for discounts into many of the sites in Calgary listed. The following is a listing of some of Calgary and area's sites for you to enjoy.

Bernard Callebaut

Address: 1313 1 Street S.E.
Phone: 265-5777 or 1-800-661-8367
Website: www.bernardcallebaut.com

If you are a big chocolate fan you will enjoy Bernard Callebaut's lovely tour through the chocolate-making factory. Complimentary guides are provided for groups of ten or more. The tour is free and you usually get a chocolate at the end. If you are in a smaller group or by yourself, you can just stroll through the factory with your baby and read the information displays on the walls.

Butterfield Acres Farm

Address:	254077 Rocky Ridge Road (North West corner of Rocky Ridge Road and Country Hills Boulevard)
Phone:	239-0638 or 547-3595 (information line)
Website:	www.butterfieldacres.com

This is a true farm experience complete with outhouses. They have chickens, cows, donkeys, rabbits, emus, geese, ducks, horses, and you can even try milking a goat. The kids love watching and touching the animals. This farm is more suitable for toddlers than babies. Come prepared for inclement weather and wear some sturdy shoes, as the ground can get quite muddy.

Hours: 10 a.m. – 4 p.m.
(Except weekdays in April, May, June and September: 10 a.m. – 2 p.m.)
Open for special events only from October to March.

Prices: A day pass costs $12 for adults; $9 for children who are "able-to-walk".

A season's pass is valid from April through September. The pass costs $30 for one adult and $22 for one child (able to walk). The season's passes pay for themselves within three visits.

Parking: Parking is free.

Baby Notes: Butterfield Acres is installing a new hand washing station, washrooms complete with change tables and a nursing room for mothers. Currently, all washrooms are outhouses (authentic) and there is no place to change or nurse a baby. It is probably best to go back to your car for nursing or changing your baby. Do bring hand wipes with disinfectant.

Other Notes: They have other special events during the year that costs approximately the same as the usual drop-in fee. These are popular so you will need to book ahead:

• Easter Egg Hunt:
  You guessed it, children search for Easter Eggs. They also take home a clay pot with quick-growing seeds. This hunt is recommended for children under the age of six. Remember to dress appropriately for the weather as the hunt takes up to two hours.

• Harvest Pumpkin Hunts:
  These run every weekend in October. Dress in orange and head out on the tractor-pulled hay wagon in search of your pumpkin. Once you have selected your pumpkin, you can decorate it. You need to be on site at least fifteen minutes before your hunt. Dress appropriately for the weather as the Pumpkin Hunt takes up to ninety minutes.

• Party Packages:
  Butterfield Acres has birthday party packages available from $150 and up.

Calgary International Airport

The airport is a great place to go with your kids, particularly if you are not travelling. Kids love watching the planes arriving and being serviced. The space port is great fun and you can get lunch on the top floor. The fountains on the departures level are great for the kids to watch. There is a nursing room on each level with a change table and a comfortable chair. Parking is free if it is under thirty minutes otherwise it costs about $4 per hour.

Calaway Park

Address: 245033 Range Road 33 (West of Calgary off Highway #1)
Phone: 240-3822
Website: www.calawaypark.com

Calaway Park is Western Canada's largest outdoor family amusement park with ninety acres of amusements and a total of thirty rides. Not all rides are suitable for children under twenty-four months. The rides are categorized by height of child, starting at twenty-eight inches tall. Children as young as nine months could theoretically go on the rides with this criterion. Most of the rides for the youngest children are parented.

Hours: In the spring, Calaway Park is open on the weekends only from 10 a.m. to 7 p.m. (11 a.m. to 6.p.m. in the fall). During the summer months it is open daily from 10 a.m. to 7 p.m.

Prices: A day pass for an adult costs approximately $27. If you go after 2 p.m. entry costs only $15. Children under twenty-four months are free. It is also possible to get an annual pass which costs approximately $60. Annual passes are sold for just $30 on the first weekend of the season, which is usually the third weekend in May. They are also sold at Christmas and during the spring through Calgary Co-op grocery stores at a reduced price. The website www.calgaryattractions.com has coupons you can print that provide entry discounts.

Specials: On Father's Day, admission for fathers is free! There is live entertainment daily.

Parking: There is plenty of free parking.

Baby Notes: Baby-changing facilities are available in all washrooms and family washrooms are available. If you need to nurse, go to guest services and they will open the first aid room for you.

Calgary Parks

Did you know that Calgary has over 8,000 hectares of parks in over 3,000 sites and about 900 playgrounds? Parks make wonderful places for a stroll with your baby, by yourself or with your Parents' Club. And, as soon as your baby is able to sit, chances are that she will enjoy the swings at a local playground.

You can find listings of regional and local parks and playgrounds on the City of Calgary website at www.calgary.ca. To find the listings, follow the following links from the home page: "City Living", "Parks and Cemeteries", then "Parks". Here, under "Regional Parks", you will find listings by city quadrant. Under "Local Parks and Playground Locations", you can find a local park or playground close to your home in listings by community.

There is a table listing features of Calgary's regional parks in the City's "Recreation in the City Program Guide". You can pick up free copies of the guide on stands located across Calgary. Copies are available at:
- Calgary Co-op, Safeway and IGA
- City of Calgary aquatic and fitness facilities, leisure centres, arenas, art centres, Devonian Gardens, Inglewood Bird Sanctuary
- Convenience Stores (Mac's, 7-11)
- Calgary Public Library locations
- Community Health Region
- Sports Swap (all three locations)
- Educational institutions

The City of Calgary Parks department operates the Outdoor Resource Centre, located next to the Bow River at the corner of Memorial Drive and 10 Street N.W. The building is shared with the Calgary Area Outdoor Council, which is located on the second floor. The Outdoor Resource Centre, open every day from 11 a.m. to 6:30 p.m., has displays, guides and information on parks, pathways and outdoor recreation opportunities within Calgary and throughout southern Alberta. You can find details on the best picnic places, the pathway system, off-leash areas, cycling, hiking, running, nature walks and bird watching. For more information, call the Centre at 221-3866.

Paula says...

"My favourite park in the summertime is Riley Park (800 12 Street N.W.). It is located just south of SAIT and is best accessed from 14 Street and 8 Avenue. You do need to pay for parking. There is a fabulous wading pool, lots of tall trees for shade and a tremendous play area for toddlers. Bring along a blanket to sit on and mosquito netting to cover your stroller while your baby sleeps. There are washrooms available and a snack bar."

Calgary Stampede

Address: 1410 Olympic Way S.E.
Phone: 261-0101 or 1-800-661-1260
Website: www.calgarystampede.com

The Stampede Park spans 137 acres and is home to the Calgary Stampede each July. If you would like to introduce your baby to farm animals, this is the place to go. Most babies over six months will be interested in looking at the animals as well as people-watching at the busy Stampede grounds. The Stampede Parade typically sees about 350,000 people lining the streets and features over 800 horses in the parade.

Hours: The Stampede runs for ten days starting on the first Friday in July after Canada Day. The Stampede Parade is on the first day of the Stampede.

Prices: General admission is $13, children under six are free. General admission is included with tickets to the rodeo or the chuckwagon races and the evening show. The website www.calgaryattractions.com has coupons you can print that provide entry discounts.

Specials: Check the Stampede brochure (mailed to most Calgary homes before the festival) for the current year's specials. Typically, the first Sunday of the Stampede is Family Day, with free admission before 9 a.m. and a free breakfast served inside the gates. Beware, on the morning of

SITES IN CALGARY AND AREA

Family Day there tends to a big line up to get into the grounds, especially just before 9 a.m.

Parking: The parking near Stampede Park is limited and can be expensive. The best way to get to the grounds is to take the C-train.

Baby Notes: All washrooms have baby-changing facilities except for those in the Agriculture Building. Areas for breastfeeding mothers are available in the South Sky Midway washroom and in the Corral Medical Room.

Calgary Tower

Address: 101 9 Avenue S.W.
Phone: 266-7171 or 508-5814;
             Panorama Dining Room: 508-5822
Website: www.calgarytower.com

The Calgary Tower makes an interesting destination for both parent and baby, especially in the winter. It's also a good setting for a Parents' Club outing. The Calgary Tower houses the Panorama Dining Room below the observation deck and Tops Grill above the deck.

Hours: 7 days a week, 364 days a year (closed Christmas Day), but hours and access are limited during private functions. Elevator rides up are offered from 7 a.m. to 10:30 p.m. in the summer and early fall; these hours change to 9 a.m. to 9 p.m. during the rest of the year.

Prices: A day pass costs approximately $13 and gives you access to the top of the tower for the full day; you can come and go. Children under five are free with a purchase of regular adult admission. A yearly pass costs about $35 and pays for itself by your third visit. The website www.calgaryattractions.com has coupons you can print that provide entry discounts.

Parking: There is an independently-operated Tower Centre Parkade that allows easy access to the Calgary Tower without having to go outside. The entrance is off 10 Avenue or via 9 Avenue just east of the Fairmont Palliser Hotel. Parking is about $4 per hour.

Baby Notes: Both restaurants have high chairs for babies. The washrooms have change tables.

Calgary Zoo, Botanical Garden and Prehistoric Park

Address: 1300 Zoo Road N.E.
Phone: 232-9300
Website: www.calgaryzoo.org

The zoo is a wonderful place to walk with your baby. It's an even better place to meet other parents for a walk around, and not just in the summer. The zoo gets very busy on weekends and holidays in the summer; mid-week is less crowded.

Hours: Gates are open from 9 a.m. to 5 p.m. The zoo closes at 6 p.m. It is open year-round except for Christmas Day. It is least crowded from 9 a.m. to 11 a.m. and 4 p.m. to 6 p.m.

Prices: Regular adult day admission is $16, children under three are free. With the price of regular admission you can leave the zoo and come back in the course of the day. An annual pass for one adult costs approximately $40. You can also renew for multiple years and save. The website www.calgaryattractions.com has coupons you can print that provide entry discounts.

Specials: On days when the weather is not great, you can print a bad weather coupon from the zoo's website before going. It will give you 50% off regular admission. In addition, a guide on the zoo's website shows where coupons are currently available (e.g. which newspapers, entertainment guides, etc.). Look under "Admission", then "Special Offers". The zoo also has special seasonal events (e.g. Easter, Halloween, etc.) that do not cost anything above the regular admission. Check out the website or call for details.

Parking: There's plenty of free parking.

Baby Notes: All washrooms contain diaper changing facilities and a nursing room is available in the Kitamba Café. There are also many benches suitable for nursing and rest stops throughout the zoo. A microwave is available for public use in the Kitamba Café. It is possible to rent a stroller for $3 on a "first-come, first-served" basis. The majority of strollers are available at the North Entrance. The Calgary Zoo is a smoke-free facility with the exception of three designated smoking zones.

Canada Olympic Park

Address: 88 Canada Olympic Road S.W.
Phone: 247-SNOW (247-7669);
             General Information and Guest Services: 247-5452
Website: www.canadaolympicpark.ca

Canada Olympic Park (COP) offers skiing, snowboarding, cross-country skiing, luge and skeleton rides. In the summer, the park is open for mountain biking and the ski lifts operate to take bikers and their bikes up the hill.

I am not suggesting that your baby is ready for the ski hill just yet, but COP offers tours of their Olympic facilities and the Olympic Hall of Fame that you may be interested in. A self-guided tour costs $7 per person, while a tour with a guide is approximately $15. In addition, for $5 you can visit the highest point in Calgary – the viewing deck in the ski jump tower. The website www.calgaryattractions.com has coupons you can print that provide entry discounts.

COP offers a self-serve food court, the Paskapoo Restaurant and Lounge and the Naturbahn Teahouse. The restaurant has a lounge menu with everything under $10. The Teahouse offers Sunday brunches (reservations recommended) and a 360° view of Calgary and the Rocky Mountains. It is located at the top of the hill and you can drive up there.

Hours: In the winter (November to March) COP is open from 9 a.m. to 10 p.m. (shorter hours on Christmas and Boxing Day). Summer hours are 10 a.m. to 9 p.m. (10 a.m. to 6 p.m. on weekends and holidays).

Parking: Lots of free parking. There is also a preferred lot near the entrance, which costs about $5. At the time of printing, they were considering designating some parking stalls for family parking.

Baby Notes: Baby-changing facilities are found in all washrooms. There are no private rooms for nursing and no babysitting facilities. There is a play area near the food court in the main lodge but it is more appropriate for children over three years of age.

Devonian Gardens

Address: 317 7 Avenue S.W. (4th level of TD Square)
Phone: 221-4274
Website: www.calgary.ca/parks
             (Click on "Parks and Locations")

Devonian Gardens is a peaceful indoor park located in downtown Calgary. Spanning three levels in TD Square, it is one of the world's largest indoor parks. It houses 20,000 plants and changes its floral displays approximately eighteen times a year to reflect the changing seasons and holiday occasions. This is a great place to visit with your baby during the winter.

Hours: Every day, 9 a.m. to 9 p.m. with the exception of early closing for special functions.

Prices: Admission is free. A $2 donation is recommended.

Parking: The most convenient option is to park in the Eaton Centre Parkade (located under Sears) since you won't have to go outside. This will cost you a few dollars an hour. You can also park at the Bow Valley Parkade for approximately $3 per hour, but this parkade may be full on weekdays.

Baby Notes: There are washrooms in the gardens, but it is advisable to go to the washrooms in the Eaton Centre (4th floor by the food court) for baby facilities. See also "Chapter Eight: Shopping with Your Baby" – "Malls around Calgary". There's a playground area in the gardens for older kids.

Heritage Park

Address: 1900 Heritage Drive S.W.
Phone: 268-8500
Website: www.heritagepark.ca

Heritage Park makes for an interesting walk with your family or your Parents' Club. The park houses over 150 exhibits on over sixty-six acres of land. At six to twelve months, most babies will enjoy having a close-up look at the horses in the park.

Hours: Open daily from 9 a.m. to 5 p.m. from May to September. Open on weekends only during September and October and closed the rest of the year.

Prices: A day pass for an adult costs approximately $14 and an annual pass costs $30. Children under three years old are free. It is also possible to get a day or annual pass that includes rides on the park's steam train and steamboat, wagon rides and antique midway rides. This option costs approximately $23 for a day pass and $38 for an annual pass. The website www.calgaryattractions.com has coupons you can print that provide entry discounts.

Specials: Free Stampede-style breakfast with regular admission is served "hot off the grill" in Gunn's Dairy Barn between 9 a.m. and 10 a.m. every morning from May to October. On Thanksgiving Monday, which is the last day of the season, the rides at the park are free. There are many other special events at the park. Check the website or give them a call to find out more.

Parking: There is plenty of free parking.

Baby Notes: Baby-changing facilities are available in all washrooms. There are no microwaves in the park, so don't plan to warm anything up.

There are no designated areas for nursing but there are a lot of quiet spots that you can use. The Club Café is great for taking a break or lunch with the children. There is plenty of space for the stroller inside or on the boardwalk and the washroom is roomy and has a baby-change table.

Elena says...

"I found a cloakroom in the Wainwright Hotel with wing-back chairs. This worked well for nursing. However, the room may not be open all the time. Check it out if you are looking for a spot inside to nurse."

Inglewood Bird Sanctuary and Nature Centre

Address: 2425 9 Avenue S.E.
Phone: 221-4500 or 221-4532
Website: www.calgary.ca (follow the links for "City Living", "Parks and Cemeteries", "Parks", "SE" and then "Inglewood Bird Sanctuary")

This thirty-two hectare wildlife reserve offers more than two kilometers of level walking trails through the forest, by the flowing river and alongside a peaceful lagoon. Although most of the trails are not paved, they are suitable for strollers.

The Nature Centre is the gateway to the Inglewood Bird Sanctuary and houses an exhibit hall with information on recent bird sightings, bird migration and local birding spots.

Hours: The sanctuary is open during daylight hours, year-round. The Nature Centre is open 10 a.m. to 5 p.m. daily from May to September; and 10 a.m. to 4 p.m., excluding Mondays and holidays, from October to April.

Price: Admission is free, however, donations are accepted.

Parking: Free parking is available.

Baby Notes: The washrooms in the Nature Centre have baby-changing facilities. There is no microwave available for public use. There is no designated nursing area, but the staff has advised me that they can help find an area inside the centre if you ask.

Other notes: You are not allowed to bring pets, bicycles, in-line skates or bird food to the sanctuary.

Fort Calgary

Address: 750 9 Avenue S.E.
Phone: 290-1875
Website: www.fortcalgary.ab.ca

Fort Calgary is located on a forty acre site in the community of Inglewood. It includes the reconstructed 1875 fort site, an interpretive centre with exhibits depicting Calgary from 1875 to the1940s, a replica 1888 Mounted Police barracks, The Deane House Historic Site and Restaurant, and a riverside park complete with interpretive pathways.

Hours: Open all year, every day from 9 a.m. to 5 p.m. Closed New Year's Day, Good Friday, Christmas Eve, Christmas Day and Boxing Day.

Price: Adult admission is approximately $11, children (six and under) are free. Groups of ten or more receive a 15% discount. The website www.calgaryattractions.com has coupons you can print that provide entry discounts.

Parking: Free parking available.

Baby Notes: Baby-changing facilities are located in all washrooms. There is a microwave available for public use. There is no designated nursing area, but the staff has assured me that they can help find a suitable place for this purpose if asked.

The Saskatoon Farm

Location: South of Calgary, east of Highway #2,
              see website for directions.
Phone: 938-6245 or 1 (800) 463-2113
Website: www.saskatoonfarm.com

Spend an afternoon with your toddler picking saskatoon berries. Saskatoon Farm has rows and rows of saskatoon bushes. Berries are ripe for picking from late July to early August. Pails are supplied to all pickers. There's even a handy place to wash your hands after picking. It is a great event for the entire family. Alberta-hardy fruit-bearing trees, shrubs and a number of landscaping items are available for sale. Drop into the café (indoor and outdoor) for pie or some lunch (or both). Their gift shop is worth a visit; they sell unique gifts and collectables. Don't forget to bring home some jams, syrups and toppings made right at the farm.

Hours: Year round from 9 a.m. to 5 p.m.

Price: All saskatoon berries are sold by the pail.

Parking: Free parking is available.

Baby Notes: There is a change table in one of the washrooms – the washrooms are located by the restaurant. If you need to nurse, ask at the gift shop and they will make their office available to you.

Spray and Wading Parks

There is nothing better on a hot summer day than cooling off in a wading pool or having a bit of fun in the spray parks. Bring a blanket for a picnic, some bug spray, sunscreen, a hat for everyone and head out for a terrific afternoon.

Most of these parks are operated by the City of Calgary and you can find more information on them at www.calgary.ca. Click on "City Hall", then "Business Units" then "Parks" and again, "Parks", followed by "Park Features & Activities" and finally "Parks with Wading Pools and Spray Parks".

Wading Pools:
- Bowness Park, 8900 48 Avenue N.W.
- Canmore Park, 19 Street and Chicoutimi Drive. N.W.
- Olympic Plaza, 228 8 Avenue S.E.
- Rotary Park, 617 1 Street N.E.
- Riley Park, 800 12 Street N.W.
- Somerset Square, 999 Somerset Drive S.W.
- Stanley Park, 4011 1A Street. S.W.

Spray Parks:
- Barclay Mall (Eau Claire Area), 3 Street and Riverfront Avenue S.W.
- Bowness Park, 8900 48 Avenue. N.W.
- Prairie Winds Park, 223 Castleridge Boulevard N.E.
- Shaw Millennium Park, 1220 9 Avenue S.W.
- South Glenmore Park, 90 Avenue and 24 Street S.W.
- Valleyview Park, 28 Street and 30 Avenue S.E.

Hours: Open from May to Thanksgiving weekend (weather permitting).

Price: Free

Parking: Free parking is typically available.

Baby Notes: Don't forget to bring swim diapers for your little ones.

Telus World of Science (Calgary Science Centre)

Address: 701 22 Street S.W.
Phone: 268-8300
Website: www.calgaryscience.ca

While the Calgary Science Centre is primarily focused on activities for children over three years old, it still captivates toddlers with WOWtown and the Creative Kids Museum. If you have an infant and a toddler/pre-schooler, this is a great place to let the older sibling have some fun. You can easily watch from a bench in close proximity to the play area, take a breather and perhaps feed your infant. The sound and music exhibit at the Creative Kids Museum is a lot of fun for toddlers (and parents!).

There is an area within WOWtown, just beside the entrance, that is designed for younger children. It has soft blocks, little houses to crawl into and puzzles.

Hours: Monday to Thursday: 9:45 a.m. – 4 p.m.
Friday to Sunday: 10 a.m. – 5 p.m.
Hours vary by season so check their website to confirm.

Prices: Children under three are free. Children over three are $10 for a day pass. An adult pass costs approximately $13 and a family pass is $39. These prices do not include a show at the Discovery Dome (which is suitable for children ages three to eight). If you are interested in seeing the show, you need to pay an extra $2 per person. The website www.calgaryattractions.com has coupons you can print that provide entry discounts.

If you take advantage of the group rates (ten people) and pre-book, the cost per person drops significantly. You can make group bookings at 268-8311. Alternatively, the annual pass is worth it since it costs only $60 for an adult and $30 for a child. Family annual passes cost $120 and are valid for two adults and up to four children. These pass rates do not include the Discover Dome shows. The passes pay for themselves in just over three visits.

Specials: The Science Centre also has birthday party packages that provide entrance for up to twenty people (kids over three and adults).

Parking: Parking is available at the Science Centre at a rate of $1.25 per hour up to $5 for six hours.

Baby Notes: The women's washrooms have baby-changing facilities and dispensing machines for diapers. There is a family-accessible bathroom located next to WOWtown. This bathroom has areas for nursing and changing and stalls that are big enough to fit entire families. You can bring your own food into the Science Centre and there is also a snack bar. There are no high chairs available. You may also want to bring a change of clothes for your toddler, as there is a great water play area in the WOWtown section and, despite the waterproof aprons, the kids end up getting soaked.

Ultimate Trains (Nanton)

Address: 2121 18 Street, Nanton
Phone: 646-1190
Website: www.ultimatetrains.com

If you don't mind the fifty minute drive from Calgary, Ultimate Trains makes a great outing with your kids that even you will enjoy. They have twenty-two model trains running over bridges, viaducts and trestles in a huge 7,000 square foot garden. Children over the age of one will certainly appreciate staring at the trains. They also have two huge covered areas dedicated to Thomas the Tank Engine play areas. Their shop carries train sets and boasts the best prices for Thomas in Western Canada. Over 20,000 visitors visit this store annually. They also have birthday party packages.

Hours: Sunday to Friday: 11 a.m. – 5 p.m.,
             Saturday: 10 a.m. – 5 p.m.
             Open from May to September.

Prices: Children are $2 each and adults are $4.

Parking: Parking is free.

Baby Notes: They have baby-changing facilities located in the store. There are numerous benches surrounding the outdoor train exhibit if you need to nurse. Ask the staff for a private area for nursing if desired.

PLAYGROUPS

Playgroups generally provide set times and places for parented playtime. Parents have a chance to meet and socialize while watching their kids play with lots of toys and each other. Some programs include a parent education element. Below, I have included information on some playgroups to give you further ideas.

Your Local Community Association or Church

Many local community associations or churches host once-a-week playgroups for preschool children. Costs are reasonable and attending a playgroup allows you to meet with other parents in the community. Coffee is usually provided for the adults. Call your association to find out if it offers such a program. You can find contact information at the Federation of Calgary Communities website, www.calgarycommunities.com. Look under "Communities" and then "Organized Communities" and search for your community association's name. Enquire at your local church. These church-based playgroups are typically non-denominational.

Attachment Parenting Playgroup

Address: Wild Rose United Church, 1317 – 1 Street N.W.
Phone: 253-3954
Website: www.naturalfamilyfair.com (click on "AP Group")
Hours: Thursday: 11 a.m. – 1:30 p.m.
Cost: Free

This playgroup brings together families who are interested in attachment parenting. They have a drop-in play group. They also host a mom's night out once a month.

Brilliant Beginnings Educational Centre

Provider: Melanie Gushnowski (founder)
Address: 207A 19 Street N.W.
Phone: 283-5437
Website: www.brilliantbeginnings.ca
Age group: Newborn to four years old
Cost: Varies by course.

Brilliant Beginnings offers programs for infants and toddlers, parenting support and education, as well as services for children with special needs. Melanie Gushnowski, the founder, has a background in Applied Psychology and experience in children's development. Brilliant Beginnings has classes for babies, toddlers and preschoolers. Classes are limited to eight children each.

* Bright Babies class (0 – 12 months old) ($177): This course is over ten weeks and each class is forty-five minutes long.
* Inquisitive Toddlers class (12 – 24 months old) ($127): This course is over seven weeks and is one hour long.
* Play & Learn class (2 – 4 years) ($127): This course is over seven weeks and is one hour long.

Cardel Place

Location: Nose Creek Sports and Recreation Association
11950 Country Village Link N.E.
Phone: 532-1013
Website: www.cardelplace.com
Age Group: 6 – 18 months
Cost: $44 for seven playgroup sessions

Cardel Place has a program called Babies in Toyland for babies and parents. They provide toys and an opportunity to play with your baby and socialize with other parents. Cardel Place also has fun family nights called Pool Play & Movie. Bring your family and friends and start the evening in the pool. Change the kids into their pajamas and settle in to watch a family movie. Chairs and mats are available to sit on. The movie is free and you just need to pay regular admission to the swimming pool.

Gymboree Play Programs

Locations: Hawkwood Village Shopping Center:
              217 Hawksbrow Drive N.W.
            Midridge Plaza: 227 153 Avenue S.E.
            Strathcona Center: 5555 Strathcona Hill S.W.
Phone: 278-5264
Website: www.gymboreeclasses.com
Age group: 0 – 5 years. There are seven age-related program levels.
Cost: About $60 per month per child which includes one weekly class and three playgyms per week. Playgyms are open playtimes for currently enrolled members. There is also a one-time membership fee of $25 for new families.

Calgary has three Gymboree locations (excluding the Gymboree retail stores). Gymboree offers registered programs and also provides a place where babies and parents can play. The rooms are filled with colourful, soft, babyproof activities. Parents are required to wear socks on the play floor. You can sign up online for a free trial class, or phone Gymboree directly. Note that there is usually only one staff member at each Gymboree location. The programs do not operate on a drop-in basis.

The following programs are for babies and toddlers under twenty-four months:

- Level 1 (0 – 6 months): Level 1 focuses on babies becoming calm, attentive and interested in the world through songs, gentle movement, sensory stimulation, infant massage and parent discussion.
- Level 2 (6 – 10 months): Level 2 explores cause and effect and builds your child's strength with ramps, slides and climbers. Parent discussion time helps you learn about your child's development.

- Level 3 (10 – 16 months): Level 3 focuses on two-way communication. Balance and coordination are encouraged on the playscape. Parents can learn how their child interacts with their peers.
- Level 4 (16 – 22 months): Level 4 focuses on motor planning. Toddlers begin to understand the patterns and actions they need to perform in order to reach a goal.
- Level 5 (22 – 28 months): Level 5 focuses on imaginary themes and creative play to support the development of "symbolic thinking". The gym is transformed from slides, tunnels and climbers into doghouses, fire engines and more.
- Family Gymboree (6 months – 5 years): One adult can bring two children to Family Gymboree classes.

Paula says...

"I found the Family Gymboree great as I could take my youngest child out for an activity without having to get a babysitter for my son."

Gymtastics

Locations: 160, 7260 12 Street S.E.
               B5, 2514 Battleford Avenue S.W. (Currie Barracks)
Phone: 254-9010 (S.E. location) 503-0662 (S.W. location)
Website: www.gymtastics.ca
Age group: Over 18 months to adults!
Cost: About $113 for the GymTots class for twelve weekly-classes, forty-five minutes long.

This gymnastics club starts with programs for children aged eighteen months and carries on through to adults. Their philosophy focuses on the "personal growth of each individual; emotionally, mentally and physically." Self-esteem development is one of their primary goals. Gymtots allows children to learn while having a lot of fun. New skills, such as rolling, jumping and hanging are introduced each week. Free time is available for your child to explore and build coordination skills while being around other kids their own age. This is a parented course. Register for these programs early as the best times tend to fill up quickly. Family drop-in gym times are also available.

Inquiring Minds Playgroup

Address: 1330 15 Avenue S.W.
Phone: 463-9565
Website: www.inquiringminds.ca
Age group: 0 – 4 years
Cost: $35 per month for the first child and $25 per month for
              each sibling.

These playgroups are registration-based programs that run from
September through May. You can register ahead of time or drop in. This is
a parented program, so children must be accompanied by a parent /
caregiver. The cost of the program is $35 per month for the first child
and $25 per month for subsequent children. Non-walking siblings are
free! The drop-in cost is $10 per class for the first child and $8 per class
for subsequent children. Do call ahead to make sure there is space in the
class. Day camps are run during the summer.

Les Copains de Jeux

Address: 4800 Richard Road S.W.
Phone: 685-1314 or 288-9113
Website: www.copainsdejeux.org
Age Group: 0 – 5 years
Cost: $10 for membership, additional cost for playgroup
Hours: Friday: 9:30 a.m. – 11:30 a.m. (September to June)

This is a weekly francophone playgroup for parents, caregivers and children.
They offer a variety of in-house activities as well as outings. This playgroup
runs from September through June each year. Family membership costs $10.

Mother Goose Program

Website: www.nald.ca/mothergooseprogram
Age group: 0 – 5 years
Cost: Free

The Parent-Child Mother Goose Program uses songs, games and
storytelling to encourage language development and literacy skills in
preschoolers. This registered program includes ten weekly one-hour
meetings. Sitting in a circle on the floor with their children, parents learn
rhymes and songs that involve holding, touching, and bouncing their
children. The children are free to participate, run about, play or nap. Each
gathering ends with a lullaby followed by a story and time to visit with
one another. There is also a Papa Bears Mother Goose program for dads.
In Calgary, the program is offered free of charge by the Families Matter
Society at the West Central Community and Family Resource Centre.
Please see "Appendix 2: Even More Organizations and Publications" –
"Organizations" for contact information for these organizations.

Parents and Children Together (PACT)

Location: Varies
Phone: 241-8544
Website: www.pact.9f.com
Age group: 0 – 5 years

This program combines parent education with a playgroup for children.
You can bring all your children under the age of five. PACT focuses on
child-directed play and provides opportunities for parents to learn more
about their preschoolers. The parent discussion groups are facilitated by
qualified Parent Educators. Your first visit is complimentary. This program
has received the Calgary's Child magazine award as one of the best
playgroups in the city for the past eleven years. See "Chapter Three:
Parenting Help" – "Parenting Courses" for details on this program. This is
not a drop-in program. This program qualifies for the Alberta Stay-At-Home
Parent Subsidy. For more information see "Chapter One: Administrative
Issues" – "Alberta Stay-At-Home Parent Child Care Subsidy".

St. David's Time Out

Address: St. David's United Church, 3303 Capitol Hill Crescent N.W
Phone: 945-2706 or 282-6442
Website: www.members.shaw.ca/stdavidstimeout/
Age group: Newborn to preschool age
Cost: Fees depend on the length of session; however, a
              twelve-week session costs $60. There are additional fees
              for some of the classes for the adults. You can try out the
              program for $5 per person (e.g. $10 for you and your baby).

Drop your child off with experienced paid caregivers for two hours once
a week and join a variety of adult classes: crafts, physical activity, etc. (see
the website or call for a list of classes offered for the current session).
Alternatively, you can just choose to hang out, chat and enjoy your time
out. There are three sessions each year: fall, winter and spring, covering
the months from September to June. The children are divided into age
groups, e.g. newborn-six months, six-twelve months, etc.

Twins, Triplets and More Association of Calgary Playgroup

Location: Varies
Phone: 274-8703 (Voicemail)
Website: www.ttmac.org

TTMAC hosts playgroups for parents of twins and multiples on a monthly
basis. The location is listed in the association's newsletter and on its
website. This is a great chance to catch up with other parents of multiples.

YMCA Activities

Phone: For locations and phone numbers see "Chapter Eleven:
          Fitness and Getting Back into Shape" – "Fitness Classes
          and Working Out" – "YMCA".

Website: www.ymcacalgary.org

The YMCA has two playgroup programs:

Reading, Rocking, Running
(YMCA Shawnessy and Crowfoot locations only for this age group.)
Age group: 10 – 23 months
Cost: $77 to $105 for eleven to fifteen one-hour classes
             ($55 to $75 for YMCA members).

This program includes free play with a variety of equipment combined
with stories and songs. It is recommended that your baby be able to walk
for this program (you may want to check the equipment before enrolling
to see if it is suitable for your child).

Kangaroos & Climbers
(YMCA Eau Claire location only for this age group.)
Age group: 10 – 23 months
Cost: $66 to $90 for eleven to fifteen forty-five minute classes
             ($50 to $68 for YMCA members).

This course is designed for children who are able to walk. It allows them
to explore the gym equipment in a safe and supervised environment.
Children will get to try equipment like trestles, bars, slides, ladders
and more.

DROP-IN PLAYCENTRES

Playcentres try to provide a child-safe zone for your little one to play and sometimes include an area for parents to enjoy coffee and pastries. There is no registration required. They are fabulous when it is cold or rainy and you would love to get out for a cup of coffee and a safe place for your baby to play. Even if your child is walking, be sure to stay close to her so that older children don't run her over. Not all playcentres are created equal; those that cater to preschoolers may have toys that are not recommended for children under three years of age. The designs of some playcentres make it difficult to keep track of your little one, so your visit may not be as relaxing as you had hoped. At some locations you can grab something to eat for both you and your little one; at others, you need to bring food along. The following table compares the costs of all the playcentres in Calgary and area:

Facility	Cost	Suitable age group
Airdrie Family Services	Free	0 – 5 years old
bo bébé's playgroup	$4 per hour or $30 for ten-use pass.	6 months – 18 months
Coffee & S'cream	$4 per child. No time limit.	6 months – 6 years old
Jump'N'Java	$4 per child. No time limit.	6 months – 6 years old
Gymaniacs, Cochrane	$8 per child, $5 per child after 1 p.m., $14.50 family rate. No time limit.	9 months – 5 years old
Let's Play	Free for children under one year old; $6 for one to two years old; (10 card pass $50) $9 for children over three years old. No time limit.	6 months – 3 years old
Market Mall Kids at Play	Free for 30 minutes.	Crawling – 5 years old
Playtime	$5.50 per person (includes beverages). No time limit.	Birth – 6 years old
Sip'N'Safari	$4.25 per child, $2.50 after 2 p.m. Free for children who are not crawling yet. No time limit.	Birth – 6 years old
Urban Treehouse, Airdrie	Free for children who are not walking yet. $5 for children walking to four years old. No time limit.	Birth – 6 years old
VRRI	$2 for children ages 1 to 3.	One – 3 years old

Airdrie Family Services – Parent Links and You (P.L.A.Y.)

Address: 211, 125 Main Street N., Airdrie
Phone: 945-3900
Website: www.airdriefamilyservices.ca
Hours: Monday to Wednesday: 9 a.m. – 11 a.m. and 1 p.m. – 3 p.m.
Cost: Free

This facility is run by a non-profit, charitable organization which provides support and services to families in Airdrie and surrounding areas. They are also part of the Parent Links program and have a free toy lending library.

bo bébé's Playground

Address: 208, 70 Shawville Boulevard S.E.
(Shawnessy Village next to Safeway)
Phone: 249-8944
Website: www.bobebe.com
Hours: Monday, Friday and Saturday: 10 a.m. – 4 p.m. (drop-in)
Cost: $4 per hour or $30 for a ten use pass.

This facility is located within a bo bébé store and caters to kids who are at the crawling and just-starting-to-walk stages. The times shown above are for drop-in unstructured playing. They have a few chairs for adults. No food or drink is permitted in the play area.

Coffee & S'cream

Address: 555 Northmount Drive N.W.
Phone: 210-2020
Website: www.coffeeandscream.ca
Hours: Monday to Saturday: 7 a.m. – 7 p.m.,
Sunday: 9 a.m. – noon (Hours may vary seasonally)
Cost: $4 per child

Coffee & S'cream is a coffee shop that caters to parents with small children. It has a play area for kids six months to six years of age with a lot of push cars, slides and climbing equipment. There is also a padded area with toys, books and a play kitchen. Some tables and chairs are provided in the play area where parents can sit and chat or enjoy their coffee while the children play. There are a couple of high chairs and two washrooms with change tables. They recommend that children wear socks or indoor shoes. Coffee & S'cream also hosts information sessions on parenting and birthday parties. Sunday mornings are popular with Calgary dads who enjoy a coffee, watch their kids play and meet a few of their peers.

Jump'N'Java

Address:	3519 18 Street S.W.
Phone:	243-4255 or 1-855-399-5282
Website:	www.jumpnjava.ca
Hours:	Monday to Thursday: 7 a.m. – 6 p.m.,
	Friday: 7 a.m. – 8 p.m.
	Saturday and Sunday: 8 a.m. – 6 p.m.
Cost:	$4 per child

This coffee shop and playcentre is located in Calgary's Marda Loop area. It offers specialty coffee, gourmet tea, wireless internet and a separate play area. It caters to children between six months and six years of age. The floors are laminate and foam, so they are warm for kids. There are tables and chairs for adults in the play area. Jump'N'Java also hosts birthday parties. It is recommended that children wear socks or indoor shoes.

Gymaniacs (Cochrane)

Address:	2, 125 First Street East, Cochrane
Phone:	932-5104
Website:	www.gymaniacs.com
Hours:	Tuesday to Friday: 9 a.m. – 5 p.m.,
	Monday and Saturday: 9 a.m. – 3 p.m.,
	Sunday: 9 a.m. – 3 p.m.
Cost:	$8 per child, $5 per child after 1 p.m., $14.50 Family rate.

This playcentre has been open in Cochrane since 2003. Gymaniacs has over 1,200 sq. ft. of play area for children from nine months to five years old. The floors in the playgym are covered wall-to-wall with thick foam and there are age-appropriate toys for children crawling to walking and running. They have memberships available for $10 that allows you access to the toy rental and give you reduced rates on multi-visit passes and birthday parties. Non-members can buy a multi-pass ten-visit card for $70 or three months of unlimited visits for $180. Saturdays are Daddy & Me days and cost only $5 for the day if your child is with a male caregiver! Drinks and snacks are available for sale, though no food is allowed in the playgyms area. They do not have a private area for nursing; however, they do have a breastfeeding pillow and comfy armchairs available. If you have a toddler and an infant you can sit back to feed your infant with your toddler in full sight while he plays. It is recommended that children wear socks or indoor shoes.

Let's Play

Address: 146, 13226 Macleod Trail S.E.
Phone: 225-4386
Website: www.letsplaycalgary.com
Hours: Monday to Saturday: 9 a.m. – 8 p.m.,
             Sundays and holidays: 10:30 a.m. – 5:30 p.m.
             (Hours change during the Christmas season)
Cost: Free for children under a year old; $6 for one to two
             years old; $9 for children over three years old.

Let's Play is mostly targeted at older kids, however, there is a toddler area for under-three-year-olds. This area has slides, a tree house, blocks and other safe things for young children. Socks are required in the playground. No outside food or drink is permitted but there is a snack bar in the facility.

Market Mall's Kids at Play

Address: In Market Mall, close to the Food Court
Phone: 288-5466 (Guest Services Centre at Market Mall)
Website: www.marketmall.ca (click on "Kids at Play")
Hours: Monday to Friday: 9:30 a.m. – 8 p.m.,
             Saturday: 9:30 a.m. – 7 p.m.
             Sundays and holidays: 10:30 a.m. – 6 p.m.
Cost: Free

This 1,600 sq. ft. play area provides a fun, safe environment for preschool-aged children to climb, jump and play. The playground has an airplane, caboose engine, red racing car, and more. These are all constructed of soft foam that has been hand-carved, encased in a soft coating and airbrushed.

Upon arrival you must register for your child's thirty-minute playtime at the entrance to the playground. Playtimes start on the hour and half-hour. The number of children allowed to play is limited to twenty at a time. During busy times, especially on the weekends, you may have to register thirty minutes to an hour in advance and do some shopping before your playtime comes up. Please note that parents must stay with their children during their registered playtime. If your child is crawling, you will probably want to choose a time that is not very busy since older children tend to move quickly and can run into your little one. This venue is probably best for infants who are very comfortable crawlers or who have started to walk.

Children attending Kids at Play must be less than forty-three inches tall and under the age of five. Proof of age may be requested in order to ensure the safety of preschool children. It is important to note that all children and parents are required to wear socks inside the playground. You will not be admitted without socks but socks can be purchased at the Old Navy located across from the playground.

Playtime (Toy and Party Rentals)

Address: 390 Northmount Drive N.W.
Phone: 258-0223
Website: www.playtimerentals.ca
Hours: Sunday: closed
             Monday to Saturday: 10 a.m. – 5 p.m.
Cost: $5.50 per person (adults and children) (half price on
             Tuesdays, free for children under one year old.)

This recently-opened company is located in the neighbourhood of
Highwood. They have a playcentre as well as a toy rental business. It is
spacious and most of the floor is covered with foam. They have an entire
wall filled with puzzles for children. There are couches and four very
comfortable armchairs located on one wall facing the playroom. You can
relax and keep your children within sight. Beverages are complimentary
for adults and children. Each parent also receives a complimentary hot
towel wrap for their face. Ahhhh!

Sip'N'Safari

Address: 950 Queensland Drive SE,
Phone: 225-4446
Website: www.sipandsafari.com
Hours: Monday to Friday 9 a.m. – 5 p.m. Saturdays: 10 a.m. – 2 p.m.
Cost: $4.25 per child. After 2 p.m., it costs $2.50 per child.
             Children who are not crawling are free.

Sip'N'Safari is a playcentre that recently opened in Calgary. They have a
very large play area for children from six months up to age six. A full
menu of frothy coffees is on hand as well as some light meals, snacks, and
a kids' menu. There is an activity room where children can work on crafts
and puzzles without being distracted by other kids playing with the larger
equipment. They have a private nursing room and a change room.
Sip'N'Safari hold classes and also run birthday parties.

Urban Treehouse Playcentres Inc. (Airdrie)

Address: 960 Yankee Valley Boulevard S.E., Airdrie
Phone: 945-0676
Website: www.theurbantreehouse.com
Hours: Tuesday to Saturday: 9 a.m. – 8 p.m.
             Sunday to Monday: 9 a.m. – 4 p.m.
Cost: Free for children who are not walking yet.
             $5 for children walking to four years old.

This is a decadent playcentre for both children and parents. With over
2,500 square feet of play area, leather chairs and your favorite frothy
coffees available, you are sure to enjoy this playcentre as much as your

little one. They have an area for infants who are not yet walking with ExerSaucers and bouncy chairs. The large 'Shoots and Ladders' tree house, water play area, theatre and art studio are geared towards kids three and older. There are change tables in both of the bathrooms and the ladies' washroom features a chandelier above the change table. Both parents and children are required to wear socks for entry. If you forgot socks, they sell them at the front desk for $2! Outside food is not permitted but you can pick up some things at the on-site cafe. They also host birthday parties.

The Vocational and Rehabilitation Research Institute (VRRI)

Location:	3304 33 Street N.W.
Phone:	284-2231
Website:	www.vrri.org (look under "Recreation")
Hours:	Varies by season.
	Typically two mornings a week 9 a.m. – 1 p.m.
Cost:	$2 for children ages 1 to 3 years.
	$2.50 for children 4 years and up.

VRRI provides an open drop-in gym for children on two weekday mornings. Play equipment including a mini trampoline, crash mat, balls, scooters and balancing equipment are set up. Open gym times overlap with family swim times. Unfortunately there are no comfortable leather chairs for parents or any frothy coffees available. This open gym time provides your family with a lot of fun for a very reasonable price. VRRI also hosts birthday parties.

MOVIES

If you were a movie buff B.C. ("Before Children"), there's no reason to stop now! Major movie theatres have special weekly screenings of new release movies for parents and babies at regular admission prices. These screenings have special features such as lowered volume levels, adjusted lighting levels and change tables located at the door of the theatre. Cineplex has a program called "Stars and Strollers", and Empire Theatres has "Reel Babies". For details check out these websites:
* www.cineplex.com/Theatres/StarsAndStrollers.aspx
* www.empiretheatres.com/promotions/reel_babies.asp

These programs target parents with babies less than one year of age. I found that they work very well while your baby is still immobile and sleeping a lot, i.e. in the first few months. After that, if you can time a nap strategically, it can still work, but it gets progressively harder after six months of age. At that stage I recommend getting a babysitter and going out without Junior. Taking turns with your better half works too, if you can keep mum about that surprise ending.

Movies are a great activity for mothers of multiples, although you may need to bring bottles since it is impossible to feed two babies while you are sitting in a theatre seat. Bring help if you can and get there early as there are few spots where you can park your double stroller within reach.

Elena says...

"As an aside, the movie tickets from the first time you went to the movies with your new baby make a neat addition to your baby's time capsule box, should you be so organized as to create one. I've marked mine with 'The first movie Daniel ever slept through'. See 'Chapter Fifteen: Mementos' – 'Time Capsule'."

DINING OUT, IF YOU DARE

Are you feeling brave and ready to venture out for a meal with baby along? Here are a few pointers that will make dining out a bit more pleasurable for you and your baby. It is easiest when your baby is portable, nursing or bottle-fed only and not quite mobile. So, really, it is easiest to head out for a culinary experience before your baby is six months old. Most restaurants are not baby-friendly, unless they specifically call themselves a family restaurant. There typically won't be a baby change table and you can forget about a quiet place for nursing.

Choosing a restaurant:
- Choose a restaurant with a baby-changing facility at the very least and a high chair (if baby is sitting up).
- Search www.calgaryrestaurants.ca for restaurants and peruse the menus online. Make your selection.
- Choose a restaurant whose floor is easily cleaned, i.e. not cream or white carpet!
- Avoid tablecloth restaurants. Your baby will try to do magic tricks with the tablecloth but has a few years yet to perfect it!

Choosing a reservation time:
- Choose an early dinner reservation. This way you will receive faster service and not have so many other customers peering over at you if your baby is making a ruckus.

Choosing a table:
- If your baby is awake, sit in the busiest part of the restaurant. People walking by, chefs sautéeing, orders being made - all of these are a feast for baby's eyes.

Preparation, preparation, preparation!

- Feed your baby before you go out. With luck, the drive in the car will lull your baby to sleep and you can dine in peace with your little one snoring away in their bucket seat. Breastfeeding at the table is a bit difficult to do discreetly. A trip back to the car may provide you with some privacy. Few restaurants have a place for private nursing.

- Bring toys, books or other items for distraction. (Try a brand-new inexpensive toy that they have never seen before. This should easily distract them for ten minutes.)

Ordering:

- If you checked the online menu before you left the house, this shouldn't take too long.

- Get in and get out, fast! Now is not the time to linger over the eloquent wording of the menu and peruse all of your options. Select your meal, order quickly and tell your server that you are in a hurry. It is easier to take some time at the end of the meal over a decaf cappuccino than try to wolf down something exquisite that your poor tongue never gets a chance to taste.

- If your baby or toddler is awake, order for them immediately and ask for the food to be chilled prior to bringing it to the table. Ask to have bread brought to the table right away.

Paula says...

"If you want a nice relaxing meal while dining out, call a babysitter and enjoy your night."

FESTIVALS AND SPECIAL EVENTS

The following events are suitable if you have a toddler or older. If you aren't yet at that stage, keep them in mind for future years:

Aggie Days

Location: Typically at the Roundup Centre
Phone: 261-0312
Website: www.stampedeagriculture.com
              (search for "Aggie Days" under "Event Search")

Once a year, the Calgary Exhibition and Stampede's Agriculture Education Committee hosts a five-day program called Aggie Days. This is usually located in the Round-Up Centre at Stampede Park. The first three days are specifically for schools to attend and the final two days (Saturday and Sunday) are open to the public. Cost is about $5 per person and children are free. The event is held in conjunction with the Stampede's Roughstock program. The displays provide information on Alberta's agricultural industry. Some of the centres include cow milking, flour milling, grain farming, sheep-shearing, equine presentations, blacksmithing, beef cattle, working stock dogs, and poultry production. Your little one will have an opportunity to see and touch the animals. Hand wash stations are available near the animals.

Airdrie Festival of Lights

Location: Airdrie Nose Creek Park
Phone: None
Website: www.airdriefestivaloflights.com

Airdrie has a great festival of lights that runs from November 24 to December 31 each year from 6 p.m. to 9 p.m. each evening. The festival is located at Airdrie's Nose Creek Park which is just a ten-minute drive north of Calgary. There is lots of free parking at the park and in the surrounding area. They have light displays, bonfires and hot chocolate, and you can ride on a miniature train. Try out the skating pond as well.

Entrance is free but a $5 donation per family is suggested. About 55,000 visitors attend the festival annually.

To get there from Highway 2, travel west on Highway 567. Turn left at the traffic signal onto Main Street. Drive south and you should be able to see the glow from the park. The entrance to the park is adjacent to Nose Creek Valley Museum.

Calgary Children's Festival

Location: EPCOR Centre and Olympic Plaza
Phone: 294-7414
Website: www.calgarychildfest.org

Each year Calgary plays host to the International Children's Festival, typically held in late May or early June. While the program is mostly directed at children ages three and up, children under two can attend for free.

The open-air activities at Olympic Plaza include face-painting, roving performers, a craft tent and a lot more. The EPCOR Centre hosts a variety of shows. Evening shows start at 7 p.m. so that you can get babies home at a reasonable time. On Saturdays the shows do not start until 10:30 a.m. Tickets cost less than $10 since many of the festival's costs are covered by sponsors. Each of the shows is rated by the recommended age group. Tickets can be purchased at Ticket Master.

You can park your stroller at the "Lost and Found" tent. A quiet space for nursing is provided. Just ask the staff at "Lost and Found" to direct you to the nursing area. Diaper changing facilities are located in the centre court of the EPCOR Centre.

Calgary Child's Annual Free Family Fun Fair

Location: Typically at the Olympic Oval
Phone: 241-6066
Website: www.calgaryschild.com

This is a one-day event that is typically held on the first Saturday in May at the Olympic Oval. It is a free to the public and is geared towards babies, children and their parents. Donations are accepted for the benefit of the Children's Cottage crisis centre. You can meet parenting experts in person and find out about Calgary's resources and services. Bring comfortable shoes, as the Oval has a concrete floor. There is usually a petting zoo and music and dance performances on the main stage. To access the Olympic Oval with a stroller, you will need to take the elevator just east of the Oval to get to the main floor.

Calgary Maple Festival

Location: Symons Valley Ranch (corner of Symons Valley Road and 144 Avenue N.W.)
Phone: 232-5477
Website: www.acfa-calgary.ca or www.oyeoye.ca

This is a one-day, Quebecois-themed cultural festival that typically takes place in mid-March or early April. If you have ever been to a cabane à sucre, you will be delighted with the Calgary Maple Festival. Tickets are $15 for adults and $10 for children under eleven years old. The ticket includes a buffet, one taffy on the snow, all activities on the site and some great musical shows. Parking is free.

Calgary Zoo Lights

Location: Calgary Zoo
Phone: 232-9300
Website: www.calgaryzoo.org

Zoo Lights is a great opportunity to see more Christmas lights than you could ever imagine. Even the youngest children will be fascinated. Keep your child's attention span in mind and dress for the weather. Cold nights are a great excuse to stop for hot chocolate at the Kitamba Café. Fire pits throughout the zoo are great for warming up if the night is chilly. Strolling carolers sing Christmas carols. Check out the Calgary Zoo website for admission costs and hours of operation.

Family-a-Fair (Formerly Mom and Tots' Fair)

Location: Typically at the Roundup Centre
Phone: 201-1771
Website: www.momandtotsfair.ca

This is Alberta's largest show for parents. It is typically held in the Round-Up Centre on the Stampede Grounds over a weekend in March. The fair has many booths providing information on services and resources in Calgary and area. Entertainment is provided for the children. This includes Butterfield Acres' petting zoo, bouncers and a children's centre for bigger kids. There is a mother's room available if you need to nurse.

Saturday Morning at the Symphony (SMATS)

Location: Jack Singer Concert Hall and Lobby
Phone: 571-0849 (CPO Box Office)
Website: www.cpo-live.com (click on "Outreach & Education",
              then "Kids & Families", finally "SMATS")

This is an informal forty-five minute session where musicians and guest artists interact with the audience and perform short pieces. Each lobby demonstration focuses on different instruments: strings, brass, percussion and woodwinds. What a great way to introduce your kids to instruments and wonderful music! After the session, you can enjoy a dress-rehearsal performance of an upcoming CPO concert. SMATS is at 10 a.m. followed by the concert (rehearsal) at 11 a.m.

Twelve Days of Christmas

Location: Heritage Park
Phone: 268-8500
Website: www.heritagepark.ca (click on "Special Events", then
              "Twelve days of Christmas")

This event is held at Heritage Park in Calgary and runs from late November until just before Christmas. It operates 9 a.m. to 4 p.m. on weekends only. Check the website for exact dates. Wagon rides, story time, the Santa Express, shopping and a breakfast buffet are available for your enjoyment.

CHAPTER THIRTEEN
TOYS, BOOKS AND GAMES

Paula says...

"I must say I have one vice in life - children's toys! Our family's initial philosophy was that we would only have enough toys to fill one toy box. Then we moved to only two toy boxes. Now we have removed our entire dining room suite and converted the room into a play area. The kids love it and their friends like hanging out here. As for dining, we are not exactly eating gourmet any longer and we simply move the kitchen table to the living room when we have friends over."

The toy industry in North America is a huge market and you, as new parents, are probably wondering how to choose toys and where to buy them. When you are investing in toys for your child, it is helpful to do some research on safety and on how various toys have been reviewed and assessed.

TOYS
Toy Safety

Health Canada regulates all toys sold in Canada. Any toys sold must meet the safety requirements outlined in the Hazardous Products Act and the Hazardous Products (Toys) Regulations. Health Canada describes the key risks as:

- Children under three years of age tend to put things in their mouths.
- Small toys, balls or toy parts pose a choking hazard to young children.
- Toys with long or stretchy cords that can become wrapped around a child's neck present a strangulation hazard.
- Loud toys can damage a child's sensitive hearing.
- Sharp edges or points on a toy can cut a child.
- Toy packaging, such as plastic bags and plastic wrap, foam, tape or ties, can suffocate or choke a child.
- Ride-on toys can tip and can move very quickly, causing children to run into objects or fall down stairs.

- Latex balloons have caused a number of deaths. Balloon or pieces of broken balloon can be inhaled and block a child's airway.

Health Canada's website can be found at www.hc-sc.gc.ca. Click on "Consumer Product Safety", then "Children's Products" and finally click the upper box on "Toys and Related Products". The Health Canada website has a great sheet of tips on toy safety. Health Canada suggests that you store toys for older children separately from those for younger children and ensure that you adhere to the age labels on the toys.

You can report a product-related injury or a safety-related issue with a product to the Product Safety Office:
Regional Product Safety Office, Health Canada
Location: Harry Hays Building, Room 282
              220 4 Avenue S.E.
Phone: 292-4677

Please note that baby walkers have been banned in Canada since 2004. Anyone with a baby walker is advised to destroy and discard the product so that it cannot be used. The Board that reviewed this product determined that baby walkers can be fatally dangerous since infants do not have the skills, reflexes or cognitive ability to use them safely.

ADDITIONAL INFORMATION ON TOY SAFETY

The Child and Family Canada website also contains a toy safety summary. It can be found at www.cfc-efc.ca. Click on "Come and see our library of over 1,300 documents!" Then choose the category "Safety". You will see a list of safety document summaries. Scroll down until you find one entitled "Toy Safety".

The Children's Safety Association of Canada similarly publishes a toy safety summary. It can be found on their website at www.safekid.org. Click "In the home" followed by "Toy Safety Checklist". They have posted a number of other safety summaries on the website as well.

Toy Recalls

It is important to know if any of the toys in your house have been recalled, particularly if there is a health concern. Health Canada provides up-to-date information on toys that have been recalled. Their website can be found at www.hc-sc.gc.ca. Click on "Consumer Product Safety", then "Advisories, Warnings & Recalls". Scroll down until you find the link for "Check for Juvenile Product Recalls", and you will find a list of all toys and products that have been recalled since 1995.

TOYS

Rather than sporadically checking this site, you can subscribe to Consumer Product Safety news on Health Canada's website. At the same location indicated above, updates are e-mailed to you with new information, consumer advisories and warnings, juvenile product recalls, and consultation documents regarding consumer product safety. This is a free service.

Toy Reviews and Assessments

There are two non-profit North American parent groups and a number of private companies that review toys. The Canadian Toy Testing Council and the U.S.-based Parents' Choice Foundation are non-profit and focused on helping parents make better toy choices. Two of the larger private companies that review toys are the Oppenheim Toy Portfolio and Dr. Toy. Each has a website with best toy listings and has published books on how to make toy selections.

THE CANADIAN TOY TESTING COUNCIL

The Canadian Toy Testing Council has been around since 1952 as a non-profit, volunteer organization. Toys are tested by Canadian children in everyday settings to review design, function, durability and play value.

The council rates each toy by awarding Three Stars, Two Stars, One Star, Novelty or Not Recommended. Ratings and reviews of each toy tested are published online in their "Toy Report". You can find this report on the website www.toy-testing.org under "Toy Reports". Toys are listed by appropriate age range and alphabetically.

This Council also reviews and evaluates Canadian children's books to promote child literacy.

PARENTS' CHOICE AWARDS™

You have probably seen some toys boasting a "Parents' Choice Awards™ Program" sticker, and wondered who these parents are and what is this all about. This American program is run by a non-profit organization called Parents' Choice Foundation. Its purpose is to "search out and recommend products that help kids grow – imaginatively, physically, morally and mentally – fairly priced products that are fun, safe and socially sound." They have six award levels, Classic, Gold, Silver, Recommended, Approved, and Fun Stuff. Parents' Choice also has an online study guide called "What Makes a Good Toy? How to Choose a Good Video/DVD". You can find this online publication at www.parents-choice.org and click on "About Parents' Choice" and then "About the Foundation". Scroll down and you can find the link highlighted in blue towards the bottom of the page.

Parent's Choice website has the following suggestions as to what makes a good toy:
- It can be played with in many ways.
- It challenges a child to do, think or feel.
- It contributes to the development of a child's physical, mental, social and emotional skills.
- It is attractive and well made, with pleasing shapes, colours, textures, or sounds.
- It is fun and fits a child's talents, interests, abilities, and size.
- It fits in with your own tastes, knowledge, and pocketbook.
- It is safe.

OPPENHEIM TOY PORTFOLIO

The Oppenheim Toy Portfolio reviews thousands of toys every year and publishes a website and a book. Their recommendations are based on kids', parents' and educators' reviews. Their most recent book was published in 2007:
- Joanne Oppenheim, *Oppenheim Toy Portfolio: The Best Toys, Books and DVDs for Kids, 2007 Edition* (Oppenheim Toy Portfolio Inc, 2006)

The website www.toyportfolio.com lists some of their award-winning toys online. The toy lists are divided by age groups and a photograph of each toy is provided. Toys also receive awards if they are suitable for children with special needs.

Oppenheim Toy Portfolio also publishes a list of children's books that it recommends by age.

DR. TOY

Dr. Toy is actually Dr. Stevanne Auerbach, who has a background in child psychology, education, special education and child development. Dr. Auerbach administers an annual program that designates Best Classic Toys, Best Vacation Products, 100 Best Children's Products and Smart Play Products of Excellence. The winners in each of these categories are listed on her website at www.drtoy.com. Click on "Awards List". Her 100 Best Children's Products of 2006 have been broken down by topics such as 10 Best Toys and 10 Best Educational Products. Appropriate age range for each toy is referenced.

Dr. Auerbach's most recent book was published in 2006 and is available at the Calgary Public Library:
- Stevanne Auerbach, *Smart Play Smart Toys: How to Raise a Child with a High PQ* (*Play Quotient)* (Institute for Childhood Resources, 2006)

ADDITIONAL BOOK REFERENCES

There are other books available on how to choose toys for your children:
- Lauren Bradway, *How to Maximize Your Child's Learning Ability: A Complete Guide to Choosing and Using the Best Games, Toys, Activities, Learning Aids and Tactics for Your Child* (Authors Choice 2001)
- Doris M. Johnson, *Children's Toys and Books: Choosing the Best for All Ages from Infancy to Adolescence* (Scribner Book Company, 1982)
- Marianne Szymanski, *Toy Tips: A Parent's Essential Guide to Smart Toy Choices* (Jossey-Bass, Incorporated Publishers 2004)

Paula says....

"It is interesting how two things are always a huge hit for my kids: the tags on the toy and the box it came in. My sister brought over a huge TV box made into a house complete with cardboard shingles. Both my children still play with it today even though an apparent hurricane (our three year old) removed all the shingles."

Jill says...

"We're not sure whether each multiple should have an identical toy or not. Perhaps this depends on the toy and the children. We used two ride-on cars and duplicated some favourite baby toys, but otherwise accepted the fact that a sibling's toy is always more interesting!"

Developmentally appropriate toys

Toys are an important part of childhood development. Babies explore cause-and-effect, problem-solving, and development of large motor skills through play and toys. My favourite toys are those that don't buzz, beep or require batteries.

You can find guidelines respecting children's developmental stages in the first three years by going to the www.calgaryhealthregion.ca website. Click on "Programs and Services" and go to the "3 Cheers for the Early Years" section. Under the "3 Cheers for Parents" tab, you will find information on development under "Everyday Miracles" and information on age-appropriate toys under the "Play" link at the top of the page.

The book *Why Motor Skills Matter*[9], written by a paediatric physiotherapist, lists recommended toys for specific age categories. The following is a summary from the book:

[9] Tara Losquadro Liddle, *Why Motor Skills Matter: Improve Your Child's Physical Development to Enhance Learning and Self-Esteem* (McGraw-Hill, 2004)

Suggested Toys in Why Motor Skills Matter by Age Range

- 0 – 3 months: Baby mirror placed in the crib, mobiles, small rattles that are easy to grasp, play gyms with overhead toys, soft toys such as soft blocks, plush toys, stacking cups and blocks, toys for belly play.
- 4 – 6 months: Activity center, textured books/pop-up books, balls, cause-and-effect toys, soft toys, textured teether toys, stacking rings, picture books made out of cloth, cardboard and plastic.
- 7 – 12 months: Cause-and-effect toys, toys your baby can ride for balance, push toys to encourage walking, activity tables to pull up on and play, cubes and cups for stacking, stacking rings, dolls, plush animals, books (flap books, peek-a-boo books, alphabet books, picture books), musical instruments, musical tapes and bubbles.
- 1 – 3 year old: Toy strollers to push, ride toys, pull toys, bath toys, crayons, puzzles, balls of various sizes, nesting cups, shape sorter, foam puzzles, interlocking blocks, wood pegs, lock boxes, toys that imitate things that you do and simple matching games.

Toy Libraries and Toy Banks

Using a toy library lets you provide your child with a variety of toys without spending a small fortune and dedicating two-thirds of your living space to toy storage. Renting toys can be a particularly good idea if you want to try out a toy before buying it or if you need extra toys for a special occasion such as a birthday party.

	Quadrant/ Area	Annual Membership	Cost	Notes
Airdrie Family Services	Airdrie	None	Free	
Bethany Chapel Toy Lending Library	S.W.	None	Free	Open September through June Fridays only, from 9:30 – 11:30 a.m.
Gymaniacs	Cochrane	$10	Varies	
Playtime Toy and Party Rentals	N.W.	None	Varies	Suitable for children older than 6 months.
Toylend Inc.	S.E.	$12	Varies	Suitable for children older than 6 months.
Families Matter Resource Centers	N.W. and S.E.	None	Free	Open September through June.
Okotoks Toy Library	Okotoks	$65	Varies	
West Central Community and Family Resource Centre	S.W.	$5	Free	This is a toy bank rather than lending library. You can take toys or donate toys.

TOYS

214

Airdrie Family Services Toy Lending Library

Address: 211, 125 Main Street N., Airdrie
Phone: 945-3900
Website: www.airdriefamilyservices.ca
Hours: Monday to Friday: 8:30 a.m. – 4:30 p.m.
             Tuesdays: Open until 8 p.m.
             (shorter hours in July and August)

There are no fees for using this toy lending library. Airdrie Family Services also has a resource library that keeps the same hours.

Bethany Chapel Toy Lending Library

Address: 3333 Richardson Way S.W.
Phone: 249-8605
Website: www.bethanychapel.com
Hours: Fridays only from 9:15 a.m. – 11:30 a.m. from September through June.

They provide coffee and a play area for the children; at the end of the playgroup you may borrow a toy for one week.

Gymaniacs

Address: 2, 125 First Street East, Cochrane
Phone: 932-5104
Website: www.gymaniacs.com
Hours: Tuesday to Friday: 9 a.m. – 5 p.m.,
             Monday and Saturday: 9 a.m. – 3 p.m.,
             Sunday: 11 a.m. – 3 p.m.

Gymaniacs' rental catalogue can be found on its website. It includes climbers, playcentres, ride-on toys, Leap Pad products, portable DVD players and inflatable bouncers as well as strollers, playpens and booster seats. You need to become a member for $10 before you can rent toys. You can rent most items for one week or for just a couple of days. The bouncers are one- or two-day rentals only. Prices range from $4 to $50 per week depending on the item.

The Okotoks Toy Library

Address: 118 Elma Street, Okotoks
Phone: 938-7884
Website: www.okotokstoylibrary.com
Hours: Monday, Tuesday, Wednesday, Friday: 10 a.m. – 1 p.m.,
             Thursday: 6 p.m. – 8 p.m.,
             Closed on weekends

At the Okotoks Toy Library, you need to obtain an annual membership for either $65 or $30 plus six volunteer hours. Your membership includes an entrance to an annual Christmas party and to Easter and Halloween preschool events. Members can sign out a few toys for up to two weeks and rent toys for parties at a rate of $8 for three days. They also rent cake pans ($5) for birthday or event cakes. You need to return the toys in a clean condition and late fines are levied if toys are not returned on time. A catalogue of items is posted online.

Playtime Toy and Party Rentals

Address: 390 Northmount Drive N.W.
Phone: 258-0223
Website: www.playtimerentals.ca
Hours: Sunday: closed
             Monday to Saturday: 10 a.m. – 5 p.m.

This business has recently opened. No annual membership is required and the standard rental period is one week. You don't need to clean the toys – the staff sanitizes everything. For children in their first year, you can choose from infant toys and accessories, stacking toys, activity centres, push toys, doll houses, climbers and bouncers and pull- and ride-on toys. Most of these are suitable for children six months and older. Prices range between $3 per week to $200 per day (for bouncers). They also provide a delivery service; ask for details. Reserve your toy ahead of time so that you are not disappointed.

Toy Banks in the Families Matter Resource Centres

Phone: 205-5178
Website: www.familiesmatter.ca (look under "Our Programs",
             then "Family Resource Centres")

Families Matter operates three toy banks in its Family Resource Centres (see below) that lend toys at no cost to families with children aged birth to five years. For more information, call Families Matter.

You can donate your used toys to the Bowness Montgomery Family Resource Centre for use in the toy bank.

Bowness Montgomery Family Resource Centre (A Family Pride Parent-Link Centre)

Address: 4615 85 Street N.W.
Phone: 288-1446
Hours: Tuesday and Thursday: 9 a.m. – noon, open year round.
             Toy donations are accepted at this location.

Ranchlands Family Resource Centre
Address: 14 1840 Ranchlands Way N.W.
Hours: Wednesday: 9 a.m. – noon, open September to June.

Keeler Elementary School Family Resource Centre
Address: 4807 Forego Avenue S.E. (Forest Heights)
Hours: Monday, Tuesday, Thursday, Friday: 9 a.m. – noon,
             open September to June.

Toylend Inc.
Address: Home-based business in McKenzie town
             (call for directions)
Phone: 616-2229 or 874-6446
Website: www.toylend.ca
Hours: Saturday: 10 a.m. – 4 p.m.
             Monday to Friday: 10 a.m. – 6 p.m.
             Evenings, Sundays and holidays by appointment only.

This is a new Calgary home-based business. Annual memberships may be purchased for $12. Rental charges are additional and vary by toy. The rental period is typically between three days and a full week, but they will accommodate longer or shorter rentals. A refundable deposit is required on large toy rentals and you may need to book two to three weeks ahead of time to ensure availability of the toy of your choice. For children in their first year, you can choose from infant toys and accessories, stacking toys, activity centres and push- and ride-on toys. Most of these are suitable for children six months and older.

West Central Community and Family Resource Centre
Address: 3507A 17 Avenue S.W.
Phone: 543-0555
Website: http://members.shaw.ca/westcentralcrc
             (look under "Programs")

This centre provides places for parents to meet new people and have a coffee while their children enjoy craft time and toys. Parents can also borrow free toys from the toy library and keep them for a couple of weeks. Please call the centre for hours and locations.

Gifts

No doubt you will receive toys as gifts during the early years. Should the topic of gifts arise, ask givers to look for age-appropriate toys or books. Most toys have an age listing somewhere on the package. Remember that toys containing small parts are dangerous for children younger than age three. Also, some toys are very loud. You can always ask for a "classic" toy without electronics!

Calgary and Area Toy Stores

If you love toy shopping, then you are in luck! Calgary has a fantastic number of stores that can provide you with just the right toy. Community sales are also a terrific source of gently-used toys, sold at a fraction of the price of new. Sears, Superstore, Zellers and Wal-Mart also have a good selection of great-value toys. Here's a list of some other toy stores that you might be interested in dropping in on:

Toys "R" Us
Location: Three locations in Calgary
Website: www.toysruscanada.ca

Toys "R" Us carries a great selection of toys and some stores now have a baby section called Babies "R" Us. This area is devoted to infants and toddlers, uses dimmer lighting than in the rest of the store and has a fully equipped baby change area and a private area with a comfortable chair for nursing. If you don't feel like heading out to shop, you can shop online at www.toysrus.ca and even sign yourself up for a baby registry!

There are a number of independent specialty toy stores in Calgary that are worth a visit:

Castle Toys
Address: 101, 5718 1A Street S.W.
Phone: 258-1100
Website: www.castletoys.ca

This store has been around for over twenty-five years and carries a number of high quality toys. Their stock ranges from toys for infants to items for teenagers. Brands carried for infants and toddlers include Melissa & Doug puzzles, Brio, Manhattan Toys, WOW toddler toys, Lamaze and a number of others. They sell gift cards, so you could always encourage gift-givers to purchase one for you! Castle Toys has a baby-change area in the washroom, but does not have a private nursing area. The aisles are a little bit narrow for strollers. Warning: if you bring your kids into this store, you may never be able to get them home again.

Gracie and Gruff

Macleod Trail Location
Address: 9309 Macleod Trail S.W.
Phone: 692-6644
Bankers Hall Location
Address: 315 8 Avenue S.W. (second floor)
Phone: 264-6678
Website: www.gracie-and-gruff.com

This store gets its name from its two original founders. The Macleod Trail store is 3,000 sq. ft. and has a gazebo for your kids to hang out in while you are making your selection. Story time is scheduled in English on Tuesdays at 10:30 a.m., Saturdays at 11 a.m. and 1 p.m., and in French on Saturdays at noon. They carry a large selection of toys for infants to twenty-four month olds. Gracie and Gruff sell gift cards which are great when you are stuck for a gift idea! The Macleod Trail location has a baby change area in the washroom, but no private nursing area. They also have a place to sit and have a cup of coffee. Bring the kids and stay awhile!

Discovery Toys

Location: Home based consultants and online
Website: www.discoverytoysinc.com

Discovery Toys carries toys specifically designed for infants by developmental stage. You can shop online or find a local consultant. To shop online, go to the website and click on "Shop online". Toys are listed by relevant age group. If you prefer to talk to someone about the toys, you can log onto the website and click "Find a Consultant", followed by "Canada", and enter your home postal code. The website will direct you to local Discovery Toys representatives, who host their own websites. Contact a representative directly and they will help you purchase products or even host a party for you and your friends.

Kidsource

Address: 6019 1A Street S.W.
Phone: 253-4567
Website: www.kidsource.ca

This store is located near Chinook mall and mostly focuses on toys with an educational bent. They carry toys for infants, toddlers and older children. Most of the store is dedicated to teachers, who can order items for their classrooms. An extensive brochure is available for preschools and elementary schools to order classroom supplies. The staff is knowledgeable about all products. The washroom does not have a dedicated baby-change area, but you can use the large counter. Unfortunately, there is no private nursing area available but if you ask they will provide you a comfortable chair in their staff room. Kids can play in the designated area while you are browsing the aisles.

Grand River Toys (Online)
Phone: 1-800-567-5600 (toll free)
Website: www.grandrivertoys.com

This is an Ontario-based online store that offers an amazing quantity of toys. The list of toys can be searched by age, price or brand. Postage is charged at a flat rate of $15 to Alberta. The catalogue is definitely worth browsing.

Scholar's Choice
Spring Hill Village Shopping Centre
Address: 178, 8060 Silver Springs Boulevard N.W.
Phone: 286-2262
The Boulevard Shopping Centre
Address: 16061 Macleod Trail S.E.
Phone: 254-2604
Website: www.scholarschoice.ca

Scholar's Choice has two retail locations in Calgary. A catalogue is available with a wide range of brands for infants and toddlers. Educational toys are the focus and most of their sales are to teachers. You can order online and also sign up for a membership card for $10. This card entitles you to 10% off most products, as well as many other services. The Spring Hill Village location has a baby change facility, but does not have an area for nursing. The Boulevard Shopping Centre location does not have a baby-change facility. If you need to nurse your child while you are there, ask the staff and they will bring a comfy chair into the large washroom.

ToyDreams Inc.
Address: 310, 55 Strathcona Boulevard S.W.
Phone: 217-7300
Website: www.toydreams.ca
            (website was not active at the time of print)

This store is located in Strathcona and is beautifully arranged. They carry toys suitable for infants and toddlers, as well as older children. The products are impeccably displayed on glass shelves. ToyDreams does not have a washroom for use by the public or an area for nursing. There is a public washroom in the Sobey's next door.

Child at Heart Children's Store
Sunnyside/Kensington Location
Address: 940 2 Avenue N.W.
Phone: 270-4542
Britannia Plaza Location
Address: 817A 49 Avenue S.W.
Phone: 243-3070
Website: www.childatheart.ca

These two boutiques are adorned with brand name shoes and clothes, eclectic toys and baby accessories. The Sunnyside location is next door to the Heartland Café and has an intimate feel. While it does not have a baby-change area you can head next door to the café. Mothers often use the bench in the store for nursing. The Britannia location is significantly larger than the Sunnyside one, and is located next to Owl's Nest Bookstore. This location does not have a washroom for use by the public; however, they have two dressing rooms with comfortable chairs that you can use for nursing. They sell gift certificates. Ten-percent discounts are available to parents of twins and multiples and to teachers who present a teacher's card. Parents of twins and multiples are identified by their saggy-baggy eyes and the fact that they are weaving on their feet!

BOOKS

Books are a vital part of your child's development. Reading to your baby will help develop a strong bond between you and your child and also encourage her interest in books.

Selecting books for your baby and toddler

It is tough to figure out what books to get for your kids and at what stages. You can even read a book on how to select books for your children!
* Anita Silvey, *100 Best Books for Children* (Houghton Mifflen Company, 2004).

Tips on Selecting Books from the staff at
Monkeyshines Children's Books:
Zero to Six Months
* Books with photographs can be better than those with illustrations for young infants; particularly if they include photographs of other babies. Black and white is best for the youngest infants. Cloth books and textured pages are also great for this age group as they can be scrunched and eaten and still survive.

Six to Twelve Months
- At this stage, rhyming books are good for developing language skills. Bath books are fun as well.

Twelve to Eighteen Months
- Interactive books are interesting for this age group, especially lift-the-flap books.

Eighteen to Twenty-Four Months
- At this age, books can start to be more illustrative with longer story lines. New sibling books may be of interest if a new baby is on the way.

Children's Book Reviewers

There are two toy reviewers that also evaluate children's books.

The Canadian Toy Council reviews Canadian children's books to promote child literacy. They publish a report on their website www.toy-testing.org, (click on "Great Books").

Oppenheim Toy Portfolio publishes a list of children's books recommended by age. Log onto their website www.toyportfolio.com. Select the age range and scroll down past the list of toys and you will find a list of recommended books by topic.

Local Bookstore Recommendations

Some local Calgary children's bookstores have recommended the following titles to start your child's library:
- Allan Ahlberg, *Each Peach Pear Plum* (Viking Juvenile, 1999)
- Eric Carle, *The Very Hungry Caterpillar* (Philomel Books, 2002)
- DK Publishing, *My First Word Board Book* (DK Publishing, 2004)
- Mem Fox, *Time for Bed* (Red Wagon Books, 1997)
- Dorothy Kunhardt, *Pat the Bunny* (Golden Books, 1998)
- Iza Trapani, *The Itsy Bitsy Spider* (Charlesbridge Publishing, 1998)
- Bill Martin Jr., *Brown Bear* (Henry Holt and Co., 1996)
- Margaret Wise Brown, *Good Night Moon* (HarperCollins, 2005)

Sources of Books

The Calgary Public Library is a fantastic and endless source of books for your children. The twelve dollars you will pay for membership is well worth it.

CALGARY PUBLIC LIBRARY

Address: Seventeen locations (for addresses and phone numbers
             see White Pages or the website below)
Website: www.calgarypubliclibrary.com

Discover a love for the Calgary Public Library during your parental leave!
The library provides excellent resource materials, books for babies and
CDs and videos relating to your baby's first few years. You can search for
materials and place them on hold on the library's website or by calling
one of its branches. The holds will be delivered to the library location of
your choice.

Membership costs $12 per year and children's memberships are free. You
can get your own Calgary Public Library card at any branch by paying the
registration fee and presenting two pieces of identification. One of your
pieces of identification must show your current Calgary address (such as a
driver's license, tax receipt, or utility bill). You must renew each year by
showing identification with your current Calgary address, and by paying the
registration fee and any outstanding fees. The membership is non-transferable
and only the person to whom it is issued can use the library card.

The Calgary Public Library now offers bags filled with pre-selected books,
CDs or videos/DVDs for babies, toddlers and preschoolers. The bags are
located by the checkout desk and marked by age group. This makes it a lot
easier to pick up library books when you have only a few minutes.

Paula says...

*"We have four baskets of children's books that we
rotate on a weekly basis. This helps keep the kids from
getting bored with the same books. I also buy books
from the local library. Look for a table near the entrance
with books for sale. Prices typically range from $0.50 to $1
per book. A bargain indeed!"*

BOOKSTORES

I love browsing through the children's section in any bookstore. The
following is a list of bookstores that I have enjoyed:

Chapters/Coles/Indigo
There are multiple locations in Calgary and area. Most stores have a
children's book section and a weekly storytime. Call ahead for details. You
can order online at www. chapters.indigo.ca.

McNally Robinson Booksellers for Kids

Address: 120 8 Avenue S.W.
Phone: 538-1797
Website: www.mcnallyrobinson.com

This independently-owned store is located downtown on Stephen Avenue Mall. It features a wonderful selection of children's and parenting books in the basement. They carry a number of imported specialty baby games, books and toys. Prairie Ink, the café on the top floor, provides evening music. Story time is held every Friday morning at 10:30 a.m. and the staff will read to all ages that show up. They do not have a nursing room but the chairs in the story time area are comfy and quite private. Baby-changing facilities are located in the women's washroom. An elevator is available for strollers.

Monkeyshines Children's Books

Address: 113, 2215 33 Avenue S.W.
Phone: 240-1723
Website: www.monkeyshinesbooks.com

This is the only bookstore in Calgary that is just for children, and it is located in Marda Loop area. The owner was a preschool teacher. The staff is highly knowledgeable about all of their products and you will receive personalized service. Monkeyshines also sells a number of toys and hosts a story time on Thursday mornings at 10:30 a.m.

Paula says...

"I came across a custom-made book called 'Blanket Full of Love: Book and Blanket Gift Set' by Starrytime's Custom Kids Books & Keepsakes. This company specializes in books and baby blankets that feature your child's name, personal traits and a personal dedication. The story is a real tear jerker and makes a great gift for others as well as for your own child. You can purchase the book ($55) or gift set ($100) directly through www.starrytime.com (click on 'Products' and then 'Retailers'). You can also order the book through Monkeyshines."

Owl's Nest Bookstore

Location: 815A 49 Avenue S.W.
Phone: 287-9557
Website: www.owlsnestbooks.com

Owl's Nest is an independent bookstore owned by a Calgary couple. It is located in Britannia just up the road from Sunterra. The area for children's books and toys is next to a section for adults. They have a washroom, but do not have a change area. If you need to nurse your infant, simply ask the staff and you can use the staff room. They also advertise free delivery within eight kilometers of the store.

Usborne Baby Books
Website: www.usborne.ca

Usborne Books offers a great range of books for babies, infants and older children. Go to their website to find a sales representative near you or just order online.

GAMES TO PLAY WITH YOUR LITTLE ONE

"The best inheritance a parent can give his children is a few minutes of his time each day." O.A. Battista

As a new parent, you might be struggling to figure out games and activities that you can do with your infant and toddler. There are a number of books available to help you play with your baby. Here are some that are available at the Calgary Public Library or your local bookstores:

Zero to twelve months
- Linda Acredolo, *Baby Minds: Brain-Building Games Your Baby Will Love* (Creative Publishing International 2001)
- Sheila Ellison, *365 Games Smart Babies Play* (Sourcebooks Inc., 2005)
- Wendy Masi, *Baby Play (Gymboree)* (Creative Publishing International, 2001)
- Susan Ann Stelfox, *Baby Be Loved: Growing and Learning Together During the First 24 Weeks* (Mason Publishing, 2001)
- Miriam Stoppard, *Baby's First Skills* (DK Publishing, 2005)
- Penny Warner, *Baby Play and Learn* (Meadowbrook Press, 1999)

Twelve months and older
- Sheila Ellison, *365 Games Smart Toddlers Play* (Sourcebooks Inc., 2006)
- Wendy Masi, *Toddler Play* (Gymboree Play & Music) (Barnes & Noble, 2004)

Any age
- Wendy Masi, Gymboree – *The Parent's Guide to Play (Gymboree Play & Music)* (Firefly Books, 2006)
- Penny Warner, *Quality Time Anytime: How to make the most of every moment with your child* (Meadowbrook Press, 2002)

CHAPTER FOURTEEN
COURSES

There are hundreds of courses available for and about babies, from sleep courses to baby sign language. This section reviews available courses by topic rather than provider. This way, you will be able to find all of the options available in your area of interest.

Course prices change often and so it is likely that, when you register, the cost of your course will be different than what is printed here. I have included prices only to give you an indication of what to expect.

COURSES ON GETTING YOUR BABY TO SLEEP

If there is one thing that gets new parents' attention while they are sipping coffee and straining to stay awake, it is suggestions on how to get their child to sleep through the night. There are many schools of thought on this topic. Approaches run the gamut from Family Bed (Dr. Sears), to Cry It Out (Ferber technique), to Teaching-in-Small-Steps and Living-With-It. You may start with one approach and end up with another, but at the very least, you'll feel as if you have a plan and are working towards a goal. I suggest that you do your research and decide which technique you are most comfortable trying and what works for your family.

> **Tip!** When people talk about their child sleeping through the night they mean that the child has slept continuously for five hours or longer.

COURSES ON GETTING YOUR BABY TO SLEEP

Course	Provider	Information about the course	Cost	Age Range
Sleepy Time for Infants	Brilliant Beginnings Phone: 283-5437 www.brilliantbeginnings.ca	This course covers strategies to help your baby sleep through the night.	$43 per person, $64 per couple.	Prenatal to 12 months.
Sleep Like a Baby	Calgary Health Region Phone: 781-1450 www.birthandbabies.com	Learn about normal newborn sleep patterns and how to handle your own exhaustion.	$25 per single, $40 per couple.	Birth to 3 months.
Sleep Workshop for Tired Parents	Calgary Health Region Phone: 781-1450 www.birthandbabies.com	The sleep course is offered every few months and explores options for helping your baby sleep. You'll meet other parents who are in the same state of exhaustion as you. The course reviews approaches you can take and helps you develop a plan for change. This is a very popular course, so book even before your baby is six months old.	$25 per single, $40 per couple.	6 to 12 months.
Sleep from the Start	Raymond Parenting Phone: 242-3533 www.raymondparenting.com	Learn how to avoid sleepless nights by encouraging self-calming skills (for baby) from the beginning.	$60 per family (includes parents, caregiver, grandparents).	Prenatal and Postnatal.
Sleep from Now On	Raymond Parenting Phone: 242-3533 www.raymondparenting.com	Helps correct your child's sleep problems and avoid the risks of sleep deprivation.	$85 per family (includes parents, caregiver, grandparents).	Over 12 lbs and up to four years.

Paula says...

"In retrospect, we should have sleep-trained our kids at a younger age. We were surprised at how little time it actually took and wondered why we hadn't start sooner. During the worst of my sleep-deprivation, I developed an ability to sleep absolutely anywhere, while my husband suffered from insomnia! I'm glad those days are behind us."

A number of books have been written on the topic of sleep. Here are a few suggestions:

- Richard Ferber, *Solve Your Child's Sleep Problems: New, Revised, and Expanded Edition* (Fireside, 2006)
- Rebecca Huntley, *The Sleep Book for Tired Parents* (Parenting Press, 1991)
- Harvey Karp, *The Happiest Baby on the Block: The New Way to Calm Crying and Help Your Newborn Baby Sleep Longer* (Bantam, 2003)
- Elizabeth Pantley, *The No-Cry Sleep Solution* (McGraw-Hill, 2002)
- William Sears, *The Baby Sleep Book: The Complete Guide to a Good Night's Rest for the Whole Family* (Little, Brown and Company, 2005)
- Shelly Weiss, *Better Sleep for Your Baby and Child: A Parent's Step-by-step Guide to Healthy Sleep Habits* (Robert Rose, 2006)

COURSES ON BABY SIGN LANGUAGE

Baby sign language appears to be in style these days, and a vast number of providers are available. There is some debate over the merits of baby signing.

Paula says...

"We started signing with our son when he was six months old and he started signing back to us by nine months old. His signing vocabulary expanded to over ninety signs by the time he was two and was limited only by our knowledge of signing. As his spoken words increased he stopped signing. Now he, at forty months, signs with our daughter, eighteen months, who has started sign language."

Jill says...

"We attended an evening baby sign language course, but ended up using only the most powerful sign: 'more'."

COURSES ON BABY SIGN LANGUAGE

Course	Provider	Information about the course	Cost	Age Range
Baby Signing	Brilliant Beginnings Phone: 283-5437 www.brilliantbeginnings.ca	Fun and interactive techniques to teach you and your child how to use sign language to communicate. All classes are taught by "Hands First Baby Sign" instructors.	$122 for six week course.	
Baby Talk	Calgary Health Region Phone: 781-1450 www.birthandbabies.com	This course is quite popular. You will learn over thirty signs from American Sign Language as well as how to teach them to your child. It is a good idea for both parents to attend so that you both know and do the signs.	$60 per single. $90 per couple.	Over 6 months.
Baby's Wants And Needs	Hands First Baby Sign Phone: 253-8358 www.handsfirst.ca	Learn sixty signs with your baby.	$115 for six week course, 45-minute sessions.	6 – 18 months.
Baby Signs	Tiny Talk and Walk Phone: 479-TINY (8479) www.tinytalkandwalk.ca	This course is taught by a mom who used signing with both of her children and a certified instructor with Sign2Me Presenters Network. Learn thirty to sixty signs with your baby including songs and nursery rhymes.	$75 for four one-hour lessons.	Baby Signs: 6 – 18 months. Toddler Talk: 2 – 3 years old.
Sign Babies	Wee Hands www.weehands.com	Enter your postal code to find classes near you.	$70 for four lessons.	Infant/toddler signing classes.
Wee Sign	Wee Sign Phone: 755-1757 www.weesign.ca	Contact Wee Sign to find a local instructor.	$120 for six lessons.	Infant or toddler lessons.

COURSES ON POSTNATAL YOGA

Course	Provider	Information about the course	Cost	Age Range
Postnatal Yoga	Calgary Health Region Location: Varies Phone: 781-1450 www.birthandbabies.com	Six-week course. Yoga stretching, muscle toning and breathing exercises. This is for moms only!	$80	Up to about 7 months.
Toddler Time and Parent Yoga	YMCA Eau Claire Phone: 269-6701 www.ymcacalgary.org	Eleven or fifteen-week courses. Kids have gym and craft time.	$165 – $225 ($110 – $150 members)	From 10 months and up.
Postnatal Yoga	The Yoga Shala Calgary Address: 1511 19 Street N.W. Phone: 210-3000 www.yogashalacalgary.com	Seven week course for moms.	$90	
Postnatal Hatha Yoga	Now and Zen Location: Varies Phone: 269-2940 www.nownzen.net	Eight-week course.	$153	Babies up to 5 months.
Post-natal Yoga	The Yoga Studio North West: Crowchild Square South West: Wellington Square www.yogastudiocalgary.com	Five-week course.	$75	2 to 9 months.

COURSES ON NUTRITION

Course	Provider	Information about the course	Cost	Age Range
Picky Eating No More!	Brilliant Beginnings	Two hour parenting workshop.	$43 for one, $64 for couple	Toddler
Feeding Your Baby	Calgary Health Region Phone: 781-1450 www.birthandbabies.com	This course is a must! A registered dietician presents information on feeding your baby in the first year. It covers everything from introducing solids to allergies. Take the course when your baby is about four to five months old.	Free	Over 6 months.
Snacktivity – Picky Eaters	Crowfoot YMCA Phone: 547-6576 www.ymcacalgary.org	Teaches you how to help your child to eat well and be active for healthy growth.	Free	Over 14 months.

COURSES ON SAFETY, FIRST AID AND CPR

Course	Provider	Information about the course	Cost	Age Range
Infant CPR	Calgary Health Region Phone: 781-1450 www.birthandbabies.com	Paramedics usually teach this course.	$42 per person, $57 per couple.	Infants
Safety First	Calgary Health Region Phone: 781-1450 www.birthandbabies.com	This is an all-day course that teaches how to babyproof as well as first aid basic response to childhood emergencies and CPR. Don't bring your baby to this course.	$60 per person, $100 per couple.	Any age.
Standard Child Care First Aid and CPR	Talisman Centre Phone: 233-8393 www.talismancentre.com	Recognized by Alberta Social Services and recommended if you work with children.	$90	Any age.
Family Safety Course	Chrysalis Education Phone: 475-7805 www.chrysaliseducation.ca	This is designed for new or expecting parents, and any other interested family members. You will learn first aid and CPR techniques specifically geared towards infants and children. Topics include choking and CPR. This course does not provide certification.	$60 per person.	Infants and children.

COURSES ON INFANT MASSAGE

Course	Provider	Information about the course	Cost	Age Range
Shantala™ Baby Massage	Brilliant Beginnings Phone: 283-5437 www.brilliantbeginnings.ca	All classes taught by a certified Shantala™ massage instructor.	$38 for 90 minutes of instruction.	
Infant Massage	Calgary Health Region Phone: 781-1450 www.birthandbabies.com	Be sure to bring your baby to this one.	$60 for four weekly classes.	Birth to crawling (7 months).
Shantala™ Baby Massage	Chrysalis Education Phone: 475-7805 www.chrysaliseducation.ca	Introductory courses are available in your home.	$38 for intro. level; $50 for advanced 90-minute course.	
Shantala™ Massage	Thrive Fitness Phone: 605-6204 www.thrivefitness.ca	Private lessons or group lessons.	$70 for a private session; $38 for a group; 90-minute course.	

CALGARY PUBLIC LIBRARY CHILDREN'S PROGRAMS

The library's "Children's Program Guide" is published four times a year and has details of children's programs running at each of the seventeen Calgary branches. This information is also available on the library's website: www.calgarypubliclibrary.com. The library has a registration-based program and a drop-in program.

Baby Story Time is a free registration-based program that runs at some branches. To register, both you and your baby must have a valid library card. Baby Story Time is a half-hour program offered over the course of three weeks, and is intended for children from six to twenty-three months. You and your baby will enjoy songs, rhymes and stories. Staff also introduce library resources and ways in which you can share books and language with very young children.

Drop-in Baby Story Time does not require pre-registration. Check the program guide or the website for details.

MUSIC CLASSES

There are many organizations that offer music classes for your baby. Some use the Suzuki method while others employ the Kindermusik method. There are also some classes that combine music with play, movement or drama. Here's a table with a quick overview of some of the courses available in Calgary. You can find more details on each organization below.

MUSIC CLASSES

ORGANIZATION	AGE GROUP (months)	PRICE	NUMBER OF CLASSES	PRICE PER CLASS	NOTES
bo bébé	0 – 24	$90	8	$11	
Creative Kids	0 – 30	$150	10	$15; $15 one-time administration fee.	Additional children may receive discounts.
Gymboree	6 – 28	$60 per month	4 to 5 per month	$12-15; $25 one-time membership fee.	Access to drop-in playtime.
Kindermusik	0 – 18	Varies by instructor			
Kindermusik (Cardel Place)	6 – 18	$125	5	$17*	Includes a music CD library worth $40.
Mount Royal College	0 – 36	$276	17	$16	You will also need to pay $2 for parking.
Suzuki Talent Education Society	0 – 36	$234	18	$13; $65 per year membership fee.	

*After the value of the music library is taken into account.

bo bébé's Music and Play

Location: Shawnessy Village bo bébé store
Phone: 249-8944
Website: www.bobebe.com

This program offers parented, instructor-led classes for babies and toddlers as well as drop-in play times without instruction. For information on drop-in play times, see "Chapter Twelve: Activities" – "Drop-in Playcentres".

Edu-Play is a one-hour, structured play session offered on Tuesdays, Wednesdays and Thursdays in eight-week sessions. Cost is $90 for the course and a one-time registration fee of $20.

Classes focus on music and nursery rhymes and the classroom is filled with soft building shapes, tunnels, rainbow bridges, a bumble bee island and a large variety of toys. Every class finishes with parachute play and the bubble machine.

Creative Kids' Active Music™

Location: Nine locations throughout the city.
Phone: 238-3133
Website: www.creativekidsclasses.ca

Two of the music programs are for babies and toddlers:
• Duets class for newborns to fourteen month olds.
• Semitones for twelve to thirty month olds.

The classes incorporate creative movement, drama and action songs. They use props such as percussion instruments, puppets, hoops, scarves, hobbyhorses and streamers. Ten weekly forty-five minute classes cost $150. There is also a $15 administration fee for first-time registrants. There are discounts for siblings and you can often enroll two siblings in the same class. Instructors have backgrounds in music education. This program qualifies for the Alberta Stay-At-Home Parent Subsidy. For more information see "Chapter One: Administrative Issues" – "Alberta Stay-At-Home Parent Child Care Subsidy".

Gymboree Music Classes

Locations: Hawkwood Village Shopping Center,
                      217 Hawksbrow Drive N.W.
                      Midridge Plaza: 227 153 Avenue S.E.
                      Strathcona Center: 5555 Strathcona Hill S.W.
Phone: 278-5264
Website: www.gymboreeclasses.com

Calgary has three Gymboree locations. Gymboree offers music classes and provides a place where babies and parents can play. The rooms are filled with colourful, soft, babyproof activities. Children indulge in scarf activities, baby dances and ball games. They explore safe and age-appropriate instruments and enjoy lullabies. Parents are required to wear socks on the play floor. This is not a drop-in program.

- Music 1 (6 – 16 months): This class builds a repertoire of songs that support the development of a child's melody, pitch and rhythm.
- Music 2 (16 – 28 months): This class focuses on rhythm, beat, tempo, and melody and builds a foundation of musical skills to grow on.
- Family Music (6 months – 5 years): One adult can bring two children to this class.

The sessions are $60 per month which includes drop-in playtime access. There is a one-time $25 membership fee for new families. You can sign up for a free trial class online or by calling Gymboree directly.

Gymboree also runs play sessions. See "Chapter Twelve: Activities" – "Playgroups".

Kindermusik Village™

Location: Varies
Website: www.kindermusik.ca

Kindermusik (meaning children's music) is an early childhood music and movement program that was developed in Germany in the 1960s and introduced in the USA in 1974. Nearly 5,000 licensed educators around the world teach Kindermusik. The Kindermusik Village™ course is intended for newborns to eighteen-month-olds, and involves singing, moving, listening, interacting socially and playing simple instruments. See the website for locations of licensed teachers in Calgary, Airdrie, Okotoks, Chestermere and Cochrane as well as for more details on the Kindermusik method.

Kindermusik is also offered at Cardel Place for children ages six months to eighteen months. Classes are forty-five minutes long. Five classes cost $125 per child. This program qualifies for the Alberta Stay-At-Home Parent Subsidy. For more information see "Chapter One: Administrative Issues" – "Alberta Stay-At-Home Parent Child Care Subsidy".

Mount Royal College Conservatory - Music with Your Baby
Location: Mount Royal College and VRRI
Phone: 440-6821
Website: www.mtroyal.ca/conservatory

This program is designed for children from birth to thirty-six months. A semester consists of seventeen forty-five minute classes held once a week. Cost per semester is about $276. Parents sing traditional folk and nursery songs and share the rhythm of language through chants and verse. The program follows the Suzuki method of introducing young children to music and language. The classes fill up quickly, so register well in advance. At the end of each semester there are family concerts which are not to be missed. You will need to pay $2-3 for parking for each class. This program qualifies for the Alberta Stay-At-Home Parent Subsidy. For more information see "Chapter One: Administrative Issues" – "Alberta Stay-At-Home Parent Child Care Subsidy".

Jill says...

"If you have multiples, enlist a friend or relative or pay for a babysitter to come with you to activities requiring a one-to-one adult to child ratio such as the Mount Royal Music classes. They are just as much fun with multiples as they are with one baby."

Suzuki Talent Education Society - Early Childhood Program: Music for Parent and Baby
Location: 7102 14 Avenue S.W.
Phone: 243-3113
Website: www.suzukitalented.org

The society offers weekly classes aimed at children from birth to thirty-six months. Children and parents learn together in classes that incorporate songs, stories and rhyming activities. There are eighteen classes in a semester and the cost is $234 per semester. In addition to tuition, a membership fee of $65 per year is payable. The classes follow the Suzuki method (see the website for more information on this method). This is the same method used in the Mount Royal Conservatory's Music with Your Baby program.

ART CLASSES WITH YOUR BABY

As your baby enters her second year, you may want to introduce her to art. There are two places in Calgary that provide art programs for children aged two or younger.

Gymboree Art Programs

Locations:	Hawkwood Village Shopping Center:
	217 Hawksbrow Drive N.W.
	Midridge Plaza: 227 153 Avenue S.E.
	Strathcona Center: 5555 Strathcona Hill S.W.
Phone:	278-5264
Website:	www.gymboreeclasses.com
Age group:	18 months – 5 years.
Cost:	About $60 per month per child, which includes one weekly class and three playgyms per week. There is also a one-time membership fee of $25 for new families.

• Art 1 (18 – 24-month-olds) This class introduces your toddler to a world of colour, form and texture. Building activities explore collage, tactile station, painting, song, story-time and movement.
• Family Art (6 months – 5 years) This is a course for families; one adult can bring two children.

Creative Kids' Hands-On Art Classes

Location:	Nine locations throughout the city.	
Phone:	238-3133	
Website:	www.creativekidsclasses.ca	
Cost:	Ten weekly forty-five minute classes cost $150. There is also a $15 administration fee for first-time registrants. There are discounts for siblings and you can often enroll two siblings in the same class.	
Age Group:	Crafters:	18 months – 3 years
	Mosaics:	18 months – 5 years

The Hands-On Art classes provide ideas and materials for your child's imaginative art work. Instructors have backgrounds in art education. This program qualifies for the Alberta Stay-At-Home Parent Subsidy. For more information see "Chapter One: Administrative Issues" – "Alberta Stay-At-Home Parent Child Care Subsidy".

SWIMMING WITH YOUR BABY

Once your baby can hold his head independently, you can enroll him in a parented swimming class. "Swimming class" is a euphemistic term for introducing your baby and toddler to water. On a per-class basis, swimming is one of the cheapest activities for you and your baby. Most pools are salt water, but call to confirm with the swimming pool.

There are a few different swimming programs for you and your baby in Calgary. Each program's courses for babies under one year old are designed to introduce your baby to water through songs and play. As your baby becomes a toddler they will learn front and back floats with a lifejacket. The differences in the programs are more apparent at advanced levels.

Here's a list of the swimming programs offered in Calgary:
- **Learn to Swim** by Red Cross is offered at the following facilities: City of Calgary facilities, University of Calgary, VRRI, Cardel Place, East Lake Recreation and Wellness Centre (Airdrie).
- **Swim for Life** by the Lifesaving Society is offered at the City of Calgary facilities.
- **SEARS I Can Swim** developed by Swimming/Natation Canada is offered at the Talisman Centre.
- YMCA has its own **YMCA National Swimming Program**.

You can also take your baby and toddler to the pool for a drop-in swim. Some facilities have wading pools which are better suited for young children than regular pools. Check the program brochures for the organizations listed below to find out about times and admission prices for drop-in swims.

Elena says...

"Daniel and I both enjoyed going to the warm indoor wading pool at the City of Calgary's Foothills Pool on Sunday afternoons at the special admission cost. To avoid disappointment, I always called ahead to make sure the pool was not closed that day for maintenance and to confirm the hours."

You will need to dress your baby in swimming diapers to access most pools. These can be purchased anywhere regular disposable diapers are sold. In addition, some facilities require swimming pants over swimming diapers (see below).

Swimming Courses

On the following page is a table summarizing available swimming classes; more detail is provided below. All classes are thirty minutes long unless otherwise noted.

ORGANIZATION	PROGRAM AND LEVEL	AGE (MONTHS)	NUMBER OF CLASSES	COST	COST PER CLASS	POOL TEMP	NOTES
East Lake Recreation and Wellness Centre (Airdrie)	Learn to Swim – Starfish/Duck	4 – 36	5 – 8	$24–35	$5	32–34 °C	Babies and toddlers require either Gabby's swimwear or swimming diapers.
Cardel Place	Learn to Swim – Starfish/Duck	6 – 36	7 – 8	$27–44	$4–$6	27–29 °C; 31 °C (tots')	Babies and toddlers require Gabby's swimwear over swimming diapers.
The City of Calgary	Learn to Swim – Starfish/Duck	6 – 36	5 – 8	$29–35	$4–$6	Varies	Babies and toddlers require plastic pants over swimming diapers.
The City of Calgary	Swim for Life – L'il Tots 1	6 – 36	5 – 8	$29–35	$4–$6	Varies	Babies and toddlers require plastic pants over swimming diapers.
Big Hill Leisure Pool (Cochrane)		6 – 36	6	$40	$7	33.3°C	
Talisman Centre	SEARS I Can Swim – Preschool Ducklings/Dinos	3 – 36	7 – 10	$35–51	$5–$7	29.9°C	
University of Calgary	Learn to Swim – Starfish/Duck	4 – 36	8	$44	$5.50	28.9°C	
VRRI	Learn to Swim – Starfish/Duck	6 – 36	5 – 6	$38–45	$7.50	34.5°C	In fall and winter the classes are 45 minutes long. Summer classes are 30 minutes long and cost less on a per-class basis.
YMCA	YMCA National Swimming Program – L'il Dippers, Splashers, Bubblers	3 – 36	10 – 15	$60–90	$6	31°C	Fall and winter courses have 10 to 15 classes. Summer courses have fewer classes.
Westside Rec Centre	Learn to Swim	4 – 48	9	$43	$5	30°C	
Cardel Place	Gym and Swim	12 – 36	6	$54	$9	27–29 °C; 31°C (tots')	Babies and toddlers require Gabby's swimwear over swimming diapers.
YMCA	Gym and Swim	10 – 24	10 – 15	$100–$150	$10	31°C	Fall and winter courses have 11 to 15 classes. Summer courses have 7 to 11 classes.

SWIMMING WITH YOUR BABY

Big Hill Leisure Centre (City of Cochrane)

Location: Big Hill Leisure Centre
Phone: 932-2774
Website: www.cochrane.ca (Click on "Town Courses, Programs and Pool Schedules")

This pool offers the Red Cross' Learn to Swim program. Classes are for children between three months and three years of age and are called Parents and Tots. Six classes cost $40. The pool temperature for lessons is 33.3°C. Please note that children under three must wear swimming diapers.

This program qualifies for the Alberta Stay-At-Home Parent Subsidy. For more information see "Chapter One: Administrative Issues" – "Alberta Stay-At-Home Parent Child Care Subsidy".

Cardel Place

Location: Nose Creek Sports and Recreation Association
             11950 Country Village Link N.E.
Phone: 532-1013
Website: www.cardelplace.com

Cardel Place offers the Red Cross' Learn to Swim program. The following courses are suitable for babies and toddlers:
• Starfish level: Suitable for babies aged four to eighteen months. Cost varies by course length. Eight classes cost $34.
• Duck level: Suitable for children between the ages of eighteen months and three years. Cost varies by course length. Eight classes cost $34.
• Gym and Swim class: Suitable for children between one and three years old. This program starts in the gym and then moves to the pool for activities. Six classes cost $54.

The temperature of the main pool is between 27 and 29 °C. (Their Tots' pool is 31°C but courses are not taught in this pool.) Babies and toddlers are required to wear both a swim diaper and Gabby's swimwear. You can purchase both there. Swim diapers are available for $3 and the Gabby's swimwear is available for $7.

City of Calgary Facilities

Location: Various
Phone: Information 3-1-1, Registration 268-3800
Website: www.calgary.ca/recreation

Some City of Calgary aquatic facilities offer the Red Cross' Learn to Swim program, while others provide the Lifesaving Society's Swim for Life program. Regardless of the program, the classes are for six- to thirty-six month olds. Five to eight classes cost between $29 and $35.

Please note that children under three must wear swimming diapers AND plastic pants (the pants can be purchased on location for a few dollars).

You can find details on locations and times in the City of Calgary's "Recreation in the City Program Guide" or on the City's website. Free copies of the guide are widely available on stands across Calgary (see "Chapter Twelve: Activities" – "Calgary Sites" – "Calgary Parks").

Low-income Calgarians can apply for assistance with fees and admissions at Calgary recreation facilities and other participating organizations. Call 3-1-1 for details.

Jill says...

"We enjoyed the warm wading pool and the wave pool at the City of Calgary's Southland Leisure Centre. I used lifejackets which are available for rent. There are also family-friendly change rooms in the assisted change area. I took my smaller side-by-side stroller out to the pool deck after wiping the wheels off."

East Lake Recreation and Wellness Centre (Airdrie)

Address: 800 East Lake Boulevard, Airdrie
Phone: 948-8804
Website: www.airdrie.ca (click on "East Lake Recreation and Wellness Centre")

Airdrie's pool offers the Red Cross' Learn to Swim program. The following courses are suitable for babies and toddlers:
- Starfish level: Suitable for babies aged four to eighteen months.
- Duck level: Suitable for children between the ages of eighteen months and three years.

The temperature of the leisure pool is between 32 and 34 °C. Babies and toddlers are required to wear either a swim diaper or Gabby's swimwear over top of a swim diaper. You can purchase both there. Swim diapers are sold for $2 and the Gabby's swimwear is available for $10.

Talisman Centre

Location: 2225 Macleod Trail South
Phone: 233-8393
Website: www.talismancentre.com

The SEARS I Can Swim program offered at the Talisman Centre was developed by Swimming/Natation Canada, which is the national governing body of competitive swimming. The temperature of the pool is 29.9°C.

* Preschool Ducklings is for children aged three months to one year, and is a parented course. Seven to ten classes cost between $35 and $51.
* Preschool Dinos is for children aged one year to three years, and is a parented course. Seven to ten classes cost between $35 and $51.

Talisman guarantees success! If your child does not improve their swimming capability they will refund your course fee.

University of Calgary

Location: Campus Recreation Main Office, room KNA-101 of the
              Kinesiology Building (for registration)
Phone: 220-7749 during registration hours (8:30 a.m. – 4:30 p.m.)
Website: www ucalgaryrecreation.ca/acquatics/swimming-child-youth

The University of Calgary Kinesiology Faculty offers the Red Cross' Learn to Swim program.

* The Starfish level of the program is for children aged four months to eighteen months, and is a parented course. Eight classes cost $44.
* The Duck level is for children between eighteen months and thirty months, and is a parented course. Eight classes cost $44.

There is lots of room for stroller parking on the pool deck. Playpens are available for use in the ladies' and men's locker rooms. This helps to keep your child from straying too far while you are changing. They also have baby-change tables in both washrooms. A swimsuit over plastic pants, pool pants or a swimming diaper is required and a sleeper is recommended for extra warmth. The website above provides information about the courses and online registration. The temperature of the pool is turned up on Saturdays to 28.9 °C.

The VRRI Recreation Centre

Location: 3304 33 Street N.W.

Phone: 284-2231

Website: www.vrri.org (look under "Recreation")

The Vocational and Rehabilitation Research Institute (VRRI) is a registered not-for-profit organization that provides recreation and leisure opportunities to Calgarians. The VRRI's salt-water pool is the warmest in Calgary at 34.5°C. You can pick up VRRI's program guide at the recreation centre or download it from its website. The VRRI offers the Red Cross' Learn to Swim program.

- The Starfish level is for children six months to three years of age.
- The Duck level is for children between the ages of eighteen months and three years old.

Winter courses have five to six, forty-five-minute classes. In the summer, courses have seven or eight, thirty-minute classes and cost less on a per-class basis. Babies must wear swimming diapers (plastic pants are not required). Five to six classes cost from $38 to $45.

Westside Recreation Centre

Location: 2000 69 Street S.W.

Phone: 531-5875

Website: www.westsiderec.com

The Westside Recreation Centre is run by a registered not-for-profit society. The facility has the largest indoor leisure ice facility in North America and a cardio-fitness facility as well as a wave pool, Tots' pool and lap pool! Typically, classes for children under twenty-four months take place in the wave pool (without waves, of course). The wave pool is kept at 30°C. The centre offers three programs: Red Cross' Learn to Swim, Lifesaver and their own program.

- The Treasures of the Sea program is a Westside program for children six to eighteen months old.
- The L'il Tots program is a Swim for Life program for children between the ages of eighteen months and four years old.
- The Wet Adventures program is a Learn to Swim program for children between the ages of six months and four years old.

Courses have nine thirty-minute classes and costs $43. Babies must wear swimming diapers and swimming pants.

YMCA

Location: Five locations (see "Chapter Eleven: Fitness and Getting Back Into Shape" – "Fitness Classes and Working Out" – "YMCA")

Website: www.ymcacalgary.org

The YMCA National Swimming Program offers a swimming class for three- to eighteen-month-olds called L'il Dippers – Splashers. The class is designed to introduce young children to a water environment, initiate movement skills and help them develop a sense of comfort and confidence in the water. The pool temperature is 31°C.

Fall and winter courses have ten to fifteen classes. In the summer, shorter programs (seven to eleven classes) are available. Fees for YMCA members are lower than those shown in the table above. Schedules vary from once a week to three or five times a week depending on the course. Check out the YMCA program brochure, which is available on the website or at YMCA facilities, for times, locations and prices. A word of warning: member registration begins earlier than registration for the general public. If you are not a member, be sure to register as soon as possible as these courses tend to fill up quickly.

Babies must wear "appropriate swim pants capable of retaining fecal material" (or a disposable swimming diaper, in which case plastic pants are not required). You can buy swimming diapers at the front desk for $3 each.

In addition to swimming classes, YMCA offers the following course: YMCA's Gym and Swim. This course is designed for children aged ten to twenty-three months who are able to walk. It provides structured and free play activities in the gym and pool. Songs, stretching and safety education are included in the gym component. Pool time includes songs and safety education as well as water orientation, games and free play with pool toys. Ten to fifteen one-hour classes once a week cost $110 to $165 ($80 to $120 for members).

This program qualifies for the Alberta Stay-At-Home Parent Subsidy. For more information see "Chapter One: Administrative Issues" – "Alberta Stay-At-Home Parent Child Care Subsidy".

CHAPTER FIFTEEN
MEMENTOS

BABY ANNOUNCEMENTS

It is possible to spend a small fortune on baby announcements. They can be elaborate or very simple. You can include a photograph or not. You can purchase pre-made cards and fill in the blanks, spend a few hours making your own custom cards, or even have a print shop complete them for you. You can also simply send out an e-mail with a picture of the baby and relevant details. Some people place an announcement in the local paper. The choice is up to you.

Information provided in a baby announcement usually includes:
* Baby's full name (including all middle names)
* Date and time of birth
* Place of birth
* Baby's weight and length at birth
* Names of parents and siblings

Try to issue announcements as close to the birth as possible. Some people get the cards ready ahead of time, and then simply fill in the specifics and mail them out right after birth.

Paula says...

"I waited about three months until the fog seemed to clear and I had a little more time available."

Elena says...

"I, on the other hand, found that buying, filling and sending out the cards in the first week brought some illusion of order to my newly hectic life."

There are many options available in Calgary if you decide to custom-make your baby announcements. Staples, Office Depot and Michaels all have a great selection of materials for making cards yourself. You can bring a favourite photo to London Drugs and they will make announcement cards. There are also many small digital print shops throughout Calgary that will help you design and print custom cards. Check the Yellow Pages for these.

Finally, look at birth announcements as a great reason to reconnect with friends or relatives you may not have written to in a long time. And don't forget to keep a copy of the announcement as a souvenir or an item for your child's time capsule!

SCRAPBOOKING

The first year has so many changes and milestones in store for your baby that you will want to keep mementos of this year to remember it by. Scrapbooking has become very popular with new parents. A scrapbook makes a fantastic gift to your child when he or she grows older.

You can include almost anything in your baby's first-year scrapbook. Here are a few suggestions: milestones, growth spurts, and pregnancy and ultrasound pictures. Be sure to include lots of great photos. You can do things in a chronological or random order. You can organize the material by activities, e.g. sleeping, eating and playing. Be as simple or elaborate as you want; it is all about having your own style.

Scrapbooking supplies are available at stores such as Michaels, Scrapbooker's Paradise (two locations, north and south), Memories (in Canyon Meadows), Shoppers Drug Mart and Zellers. There are also some home businesses that provide fabulous scrapbooking products. They include Creative Memories, Stampin Up! and Close to My Heart.

There are, of course, many resources on the Web. For example, you can find some ideas on the Michaels' website at www.michaels.com (Click on "Scrapbooking". Under "Find Great Ideas" select "Baby Layouts"), and Hewlett-Packard has a scrapbooking community website: www.hp.com/go/scrapbooking .

If you have never made a scrapbook before, you can take a class or read a book on scrapbooking. Instead of buying a book, you can borrow one from the Calgary Public Library. Scrapbooker's Paradise offers beginner classes for a small fee and you can use most of their tools for free when you sign up for a membership. Many community associations run scrapbooking groups, so look through your local community paper for information or call your association. The home businesses listed above also provide lots of valuable ideas and how-to's. They show you how to use their products and can give you one-on-one help to get you started. In addition, they run workshops where you can meet other scrapbookers.

Finally, there are some pre-made beginner kits available that come with instructions or page layout recommendations. They are really easy to use and you can finish them off in a couple of hours.

Scrapbooking is a wonderful creative hobby that you can continue doing as your children grow. Happy scrapbooking!

TIME CAPSULE

Most parents like the idea of making a time capsule for their baby, but don't get around to acting on it. Making a time capsule for your baby can be very easy, and you can get a lot of help from friends and family. Simply ask baby shower guests, visitors or even guests at your baby's first birthday party to bring items for the time capsule. Then find a durable metal box with a label and add a few things yourself. Here are some ideas of what to include:

- Postage stamps issued around your baby's birth.
- Magazines from the month of your baby's birth. Special magazine issues (e.g. "Time Magazine") reviewing the year of your baby's birth are a great choice.
- A grocery store flyer with current prices in it.
- A set of coins and paper bills issued in the year of your baby's birth. You can buy coin sets from Canada Post outlets or check out the Royal Canadian Mint website at www.mint.ca (look under "Shopping", "Gift Finder" and select "Baby" in the "Occasion" box).
- A copy of your baby's birth announcement card and a list of the people to whom it was sent.
- Your baby's hospital bracelet and one of those tiny hospital baby hats.
- A sample of your baby's first diaper size (unused, of course!). You will be amazed at how small they were by the time your child is a toddler.
- The sleeper they came home from the hospital in or an equally small one.
- Your favourite baby outfit from the first year along with a picture of your baby wearing it.
- A pair of your baby's first tiny socks.
- All the cards you received from friends and relatives.
- Favourite photos.
- Handprints and footprints.

Elena says...

"I wanted to get some new-looking paper bills for Daniel's time capsule. I called my bank and asked if they could find some almost new bills for me. I found that the mention of a new baby evoked a great response."

PHOTOGRAPHY

Babyhood is brief, so many of us try to capture this time with innumerable home photographs. In addition, you may want to have professional photos of your new family taken. There are too many photographers available in Calgary and area to list in this section, so I've decided to list only those whom my friends or I have come across. Don't limit your options to those listed below. Set your budget first and then choose a photographer to match. Remember that a private photographer can cost considerably more than a portrait studio like Sears or Wal-Mart but the quality can be significantly higher. One word of advice: make sure you set a budget BEFORE you choose shots for printing. Finally, remember to make an appointment at a time when your baby is likely to be alert and content.

Kids Photo
Location: Market Mall, near the Food Court
Phone: 239-6505
Website: www.kidsphoto.ca

This portrait studio specializes in bringing personalities to life in their photographs. Bring your own props and changes of clothing if you like. Photo sessions are thirty ($50) or sixty ($80) minutes long. One-hour sessions are suggested if you want to change outfits or photograph young babies. A few days after the shoot, you can preview the photos and make your selection. The prints will be ready about ten days after the preview. Kids Photo has a kids club membership which includes three half-hour photo sessions and three 8x10 portraits for $100. You must take the three photo sessions within two years.

Sears Portrait Studios
Website: www.searsportrait.ca

The website provides a studio locator: enter your postal code and it will produce a list of the studios closest to you, complete with phone numbers. The sitting fee is $16 and you will pay $11 per sheet of photos printed. Look for coupons before you go. They often come in the mail before Christmas and there are even some on the website (click on "Offers").

Wal-Mart Portrait Studios
Website: www.walmart.ca

PCA Portrait Studios operate licensee studios in Wal-Mart stores. Search the Wal-Mart website for locations of stores with portrait studios: go to "Storefinder" from the main page, click "PCA Portrait Studio" and search for the nearest location.

Bellies & Babies by Nicole
Phone: 276-1015
Website: www.nicolejoshi.com

Nicole Joshi uses colour as well as black and white photography for pregnancy, baby and family photography. Sittings are free for first-time clients.

Bowes Photography
Phone: 585-5677
Website: www.bowesphotography.ca

Danna Bowes will come to your home to take your family's portraits. She serves Calgary, Airdrie, Cochrane, Okotoks, Strathmore, Chestermere and the surrounding areas. She specializes in prenatal, newborns, babies, children and families.

Brenda Castonguay Photography
Phone: 714-9252
Website: www.toviewmore.com

Brenda Castonguay uses black and white photography to capture intimate and interactive portraits of newborns, infants and children in a casual and fun atmosphere. She won the Calgary's Child Magazine Parent's Choice Award in 2001 and 2002.

Julie Marwood Photography
Phone: 245-2138
Website: None

Julie Marwood has a studio in her home and specializes in black and white baby photographs. She is a mom herself and really understands how to pose your baby at different ages.

Kristen Shima Photography
Phone: 948-4730
Website: www.kristenshima.com

Kristen Shima's photography is worth reviewing; log on to her website to have a look. She uses colour to capture the mood and is great at playing with light. She won the Calgary's Child Magazine Parent's Choice Award – Honorable Mention in 2006.

PHOTOGRAPHY

Mom2Boys Productions

Website: www.mom2boysproductions.com

Mom2Boys productions create DVD video montages from your own photos and videos. A collection of your favourite photos and videos are set to your favourite music. This is a great idea as a memento of your baby's arrival or her first birthday.

BP BIRTHPLACE FOREST

The BP BirthPlace Forest program plants trees each year to represent Calgary's newborns. The Forest was started in December 2000 and is sponsored by the City of Calgary Parks, BP Canada Energy Company, Golden Acre Garden Centres Ltd. and the Calgary Health Region. This program helps to green the community and educate the public on the importance of the urban forest while creating a living legacy. Plantings take place once a year in September. Registration of newborns is free and if your baby has siblings, you can register them in the family forest for $25. To register your baby, download a registration form from www.calgary.ca (just search the website for "Birthplace Forest"). At some hospitals, the form is included in your paperwork. You can also contact the City of Calgary at 3-1-1 or 268-2489 (if calling from outside the city), or send an e-mail to birthplaceforest@calgary.ca.

CHAPTER SIXTEEN
CHILD CARE OPTIONS

The intent of this section is to provide an introduction to child care options in Calgary. Rather than providing detailed information on Calgary's child care institutions, I offer guidance on where to look for further information.

Families with lower income are entitled to financial assistance with child care expenses. See "Alberta Child Care Subsidy Program" later in this chapter.

Alberta Children's Services has a great booklet entitled "Choosing Child Care: A Guide to Licensed and Approved Child Care in Alberta." It lists a broad range of supports and resources to help you choose child care. This booklet is available at public health clinics and the Alberta Children's Services office (phone: 297-6100) in Kensington.

There are many books available to help in your quest to find the right care for your child. Here are a few:
- Brenda Sissons, *Choosing with Care: The Canadian Parent's Practical Guide to Quality Child Care for Infants and Toddlers* (Addison-Wesley, 1992)
- Suzanne Laird, *Choices in Child Care: What's best for Your Child?* (Detselig Enterprises, 1992)
- Judith Berezin, *The Complete Guide to Choosing Child Care*, the National Association of Child Care Resource and Referral Agencies in Cooperation with Child Care, Inc. (Random House, 1992)

Child care options in Calgary include daycare centers, drop-in centres, family day homes, and live-in or live-out nannies. Below is some information on each of these options as well as on babysitting.

BABYSITTING

It can be a challenge to head out for a nice evening and leave your precious little one behind with a babysitter. It usually feels much easier when the babysitter is a direct family member; however, here are a few things that might ease the transition for your evening away.

There are certified babysitters! The following programs in Calgary provide such certification:

- Red Cross offers a Babysitting Certification program through the University of Calgary, Kinesiology Client Services (formerly Campus Recreation). This course teaches prospective babysitters about their responsibilities, safety, first aid, injury prevention, infant or child CPR and how to be a caring babysitter who gets along with parents and children. The classes are ten hours long and must be attended to be eligible for babysitting certification. The course is for people over eleven years old and costs approximately $65. You can find out about the course details at: www.ucalgaryrecreation.ca/activekids/babysitting-certification or by calling 220-7241.

- The YMCA offers a Babysitting Certification Course for twelve- to seventeen-year-olds. Check out their program brochure. This program was developed by the Alberta Safety Council. The program is twelve hours long and costs $60.

- Talisman Centre also offers a Babysitter Course or Camp which is for youth over eleven years old. The course is ten hours long and the camp involves forty hours of training over four days. Both cost $55. Contact Talisman Centre at 233-8393 or www.talismancentre.com to register.

- For adults, there is an Infant CPR course offered by the CHR as well as a Safety First course offered by the Red Cross through CHR. Even if you have a friend or relative over to babysit, it is a good idea to ensure that he or she has had some safety instruction or infant CPR.

Babysitters are currently paid in the range of $7 to $15 per hour and you are generally expected to pick them up and drive them home. Depending on your circumstances, you might be able to exchange babysitting services (or another favour) with friends. Some daycare staff also babysit.

Since your babysitter may not be familiar with your house, it is a good idea to keep a reference sheet available so that she can find items in an emergency. See "Appendix 1: Reference Sheets" for a template that I use for our babysitters.

Canadiansitter.ca
Website: www.canadiansitter.ca

This website provides an easy-to-use database of qualified and educated babysitters. The sitters are university and college students who are looking to gain experience and earn extra money while continuing their education. Sitters join the database for free and parents pay $40 for a three-month membership or $80 for a one-year membership. You may carry out a free trial search to find sitters in your area. You are given unlimited access to the database during the membership period and you pay the sitter directly for the job, so there are no other costs. The interesting thing about this website is that parents can enter feedback on the sitter's work. You can read the feedback online in the sitter's profile.

Professional Babysitting Services

There is only one company in town that provides babysitting services:

Post Natal Helpers Ltd.
Phone: 640-0844 (24-hour answering service)
Website: None
Hours: Try to accommodate all client requests, depending on staff availability
Cost: $18 per hour (minimum four-hour charge)

We already mentioned this company in "Chapter Three: Parenting Help". It provides in-home temporary child care services, including some emergency care for sick children.

Babysitting Co-ops[10]

Towards the end of your baby's first year or earlier if you are comfortable with it, you may want to join a babysitting co-op. These are comprised of parents who exchange babysitting services. The advantage is that you will have an adult (as opposed to teenaged) babysitter and you won't have to spend money. The downside, of course, is that you have to do your share of babysitting duties.

There may already be a babysitting co-op in your area, so check with your local community association. Some churches also organize them. Alternatively, you can organize your own. Here are some things to keep in mind if you decide to go the last route:

The number of participating families should be large enough to get a sitter, but small enough so that you know everybody and feel comfortable with them. Generally, look for about ten participants.

There should be a short and simple list of rules, such as: (1) the sitter is the mother unless otherwise agreed; (2) meals are to be discussed before each sit; (3) the sit is at the sitter's house during the day and at the parents' house in the evening ... etc.

You will need to keep track of babysitting hours. This is usually done with tokens issued in one-hour and half-hour denominations. At the beginning, a certain number of hours (around thirty) are allocated to each member in tokens.

[10] Based on the following article: Judy Arnall, "BabySitting Co-ops Are a Great Resource!", *Calgary's Child,* September – October 2004, 71

Second and subsequent children usually "cost" less to babysit (e.g. half-hour token for each babysitting hour).

You may want to set up a rotating secretary position. The secretary keeps track of token counts, takes sitter requests and calls around to fill them, starting with the members with the lowest token counts. Alternatively, you can use e-mail to keep the token count list current and available to all.

It is a good idea to meet monthly to discuss any problems or issues that come up. Make this a fun social evening and use it as a chance to get to know your potential sitters better!

LOOKING FOR CHILD CARE AFTER PARENTAL LEAVE
Out-of-Home Child Care Options

Alberta Children's Services defines three types of out-of-home child care options for very young children – daycare centre, day home, and drop-in centre – as follows:

- **Daycare centre:** provides care for seven or more children under the age of seven years for more than three consecutive hours in a day. Each adult supervisor may care for up to three children under thirteen months of age or up to four children between thirteen and nineteen months of age.
- **Drop-in centre:** provides care for seven or more children for more than three consecutive hours in a day; no child can be cared for more than forty hours in one month.
- **Family day home:** offers care in the provider's home for up to six children under the age of eleven years. Each adult supervisor may care for up to two children under two years of age, three children under three years of age or six children under eleven years of age.

Each daycare or drop-in centre must be licensed by the local Child and Family Services Authority (CFSA). This means that the facility must meet a set of minimum standards in order to receive and to maintain the license. These standards are intended to ensure that the health, safety and developmental needs of children are being met. The CFSA #3, which covers Calgary and area, licenses and monitors child care facilities in Calgary. Please see their contact information below under "Child Care Subsidy Program".

On the other hand, day homes can be licensed (approved) or unlicensed (independent). Approved day homes work under contract with, and are monitored by, day home agencies, which in turn operate under contract with the regional CFSA. Other day homes operate independently and are, in essence, private babysitting facilities. Information on unlicensed day homes can be found through private advertising. Check the Internet or your local bulletin boards (e.g. at your community centre) for information. The rest of this section addresses licensed or approved day homes.

Prices for full-time daycare vary from about $650 to over $1,000 per month for children under eighteen months and slightly less for children over eighteen months. Day home prices vary between $450 and $715 per month and are again slightly less for children over eighteen months.

WHEN TO START LOOKING FOR A DAYCARE CENTRE

Waiting lists for daycare centres vary significantly. Some Calgary downtown daycares have one- to two-year waiting lists, which means that you need to get on the waiting list before your child is born! Of course, you can use other arrangements while you are waiting for an available spot at your daycare of choice. Some daycare centres outside of downtown have immediate availability while others have waiting lists several months long. Some employers, especially those located downtown, have arrangements with daycare centers so that their employees are given priority. Therefore, if you are considering daycare as a child care option after your parental leave, familiarize yourself with what is available and call around to ask about waiting lists as soon as possible. Ideally, you should do this in the last trimester of your pregnancy! Most daycares will tell you to call again a few months before or the month before your child needs to start. But some popular daycares will put you on a waiting list right there and then. Get on several waiting lists, because you never know whether any particular daycare will have space when you need it. Once you are on the waiting list, it is important to call periodically to ensure you stay on it.

Paula says...

"A number of friends tell stories of having lost their spot because of a mislaid waiting list, a computer crash, or an error. In each of these cases, they did not receive a spot at the daycare and had to find alternative child care arrangements. Call the daycare often and even try to get a written acknowledgement of where you are on the list."

While you should do some preliminary research and get on waiting lists well in advance, daycare visits can be done a few months before you actually need to enroll your child.

WHEN TO START LOOKING FOR A DAY HOME

As with daycare centres, there is no fixed rule as to how far ahead you should start looking for a day home. Most day home agencies I contacted recommended starting four to five months before you need child care. Some agencies keep waiting lists while others don't.

HOW TO LOOK FOR A DAYCARE CENTRE OR A DAY HOME

To locate child care centres or approved day homes you can use Alberta Children's Services' (ACS) website (see below), the phone book, your community association, friends, or hire a consultant. For a good start, ask friends or relatives for references or go through the Yellow Pages listings under "Daycare Centres".

If you are looking for a daycare centre, write out a list of daycares in the area suitable to you. Then start checking them out by:
* looking at their websites, if available; and
* calling to ask about ages they accept (many do not accept children under eighteen months), prices, availability, waiting lists and part-time options.

Tip! *If you are interested in part-time childcare at a Daycare Centre, you may need to team up with another parent and share one spot between both families.*

Arrange to visit several daycares and use the checklist from the Alberta Children's Services website (see below) during your visit. You'll start to get a feel for the level of service, care and philosophy behind each child care centre. Be sure to review recent licensing inspection reports during your visit. These are reports made by inspectors from the CFSA. At least two reports should be completed each year.

* The Calgary Health Region, Environmental Health Program also performs inspections on a semi-annual basis. You can ask the daycare for a copy of the report. If it is not available, you can contact the Calgary Health Region at 943-8060 and get a copy of the Health Inspection Report for approximately $15.

* The Fire Department, 287-4299, inspects fire and safety equipment as well as access to fire exits, evacuation procedures and fire safety and planning in child care facilities. This inspection is done once a year.

Ask for references, ideally from parents whose children have been there for longer than a few months.

If you are looking for an approved day home, contact one of the day home agencies. The agencies monitor and support their approved day homes and help parents find suitable placements. You can find them in the phone book under "Daycare Centres", on the ACS website (see below), or on the website for the Alberta Association for Family Day Home Services (see below).

Listed below are some of the resources you can use to find an appropriate out-of-home child care arrangement for your child.

Alberta Children's Services
Phone: 1-866-714-KIDS (Parent Information Line)
Website: www.child.gov.ab.ca/whatwedo/childcare

Look under "Finding Quality Child Care" on the ACS's website. You will find links to two information booklets prepared by the ACS and called "Choosing a Day Care Centre: a Guide for Parents" and "Choosing a Family Day Home: a Guide for Parents". You can call Calgary and Area Child and Family Services Authority (CFSA) and see if there are any booklets available for pick-up at their office (look under "Alberta Child Care Subsidy Program" below for address and phone number). The booklets on choosing a daycare centre are also available at many of Calgary's daycares.

You can search daycare and approved day home listings on the ACS website by postal code or just get a listing for all of Calgary. Alternatively, you can get a list of licensed child care facilities from the CFSA (see contact information below under "Alberta Child Care Subsidy Program").

ACS provides financial assistance with child care costs to eligible low-income families through its Child Care Subsidy Program. See below for more information.

Alberta Association for Family Day Home Services
Phone: No central number
Website: www.cfc-efc.ca/aafdhs

For a listing of day home agencies, see the "Membership List" on the website. You will find links to some agency websites and general information about approved day homes.

Childcare SOLUTIONS

Phone: 874-5466
Website: www.childcaresolutionscalgary.com

Childcare SOLUTIONS is owned and operated by Krista Phillips, who is a private consultant working in association with Childcare Referral Agencies to assist both parents and child care providers. The company offers parent consultations, information packages and guides, and assisted visits to child care providers. The service packages offered cost $65 and up. The owner has sixteen years of experience in the child care field.

211 in Calgary and Cochrane

Phone: 2-1-1
Website: www.211calgary.ca

This free Calgary and Cochrane telephone referral service is staffed with information and referral specialists who, among other things, can help with finding child care in Calgary and Cochrane. Please see "Chapter Three: Parenting Help" – "Parenting Help Lines and Websites" for more information.

Busy Family

Phone: (905) 709-2756 or 1-800-905-3333
Website: www.busyfamily.com

This company provides online customized research on personal and family care providers in Canada. Membership costs $75. Some employers provide membership as part of their benefits package, so be sure to check with your employer. Busy Family uses a team of trained researchers to identify licensed service providers across Canada and to telephone-verify detailed information about each provider twice a year. Busy Family does not accept fees of any kind from listed service providers. Consultants are available to support your search if you have special needs or if you can't find what you are looking for online. They report on each service provider's professional or program specialties, years of experience, staff qualifications, costs and fees, admission requirements, ethnic or religious program affiliations, languages spoken and more.

Child Care Online

Website: www.childcare.net

You can check out Child Care Online, an Ontario-based website for parents and caregivers. For a small fee, they provide books or download information on how to look for child care and how to monitor your child care provider. This website has a section on Alberta, however, it currently contains very little information.

> **TIP!** *Part-time daycare is tricky. Some centres do not offer this option at all. If it is offered, you will usually need to be matched up with another child to share the spot. This can take awhile. In the meantime, you may have to pay for the full-time spot to hold your place.*

THE ALBERTA CHILD CARE SUBSIDY PROGRAM

The Child Care Subsidy Program has been established to help eligible Alberta families pay child care costs for preschool children enrolled in a licensed daycare centre or an approved family day home. For more information see "Chapter One: Administration" – "Alberta Child Care Subsidy Program".

The Kin Child Care Program is available for relatives providing childcare outside the family home. Funding is available for compensating your relative who is providing childcare. Contact the Child Care Subsidy Office for more information on the Kin Child Care Program.

In-home Child Care Options: Nannies

In-home child care arrangements can be made with either live-in or live-out nannies. Parents who choose to use a nanny do not have access to the ACS's Child Care Subsidy Program; however, you can still deduct your child care costs as part of your income tax calculation. These private arrangements for live-in or live-out nannies are neither regulated nor monitored by Calgary Family Services Authorities. Parents alone are responsible for monitoring care.

In-home child care provides more flexibility than daycare or day homes. You can save time by avoiding the drive to and from daycare and getting the sleepy kids ready to go in the mornings. Your work schedule is also not affected if your child is ill. The cost of a live-in nanny is comparable to some downtown daycare options when you include the cost of monthly downtown parking, and if you have more than one child, it may even cost less.

There are drawbacks to employing a nanny, live-in or live-out. You become an employer, so the paperwork is considerable. You will also need to withhold taxes, CPP and EI premiums from your nanny's paycheque and remit these funds to the government. In-home child care is more expensive than out-of-home child care when you are considering care for one child. With a live-in nanny, you also need to be comfortable with another person living in your home, as you relinquish some privacy and assume some added responsibilities for the caregiver. You may even need to schedule your vacations around your nanny's vacation!

There are two ways to find a nanny: either complete the legwork and paperwork yourself, or use an agency.

HIRING A NANNY DIRECTLY

If you have decided to obtain in-home care for your child, the next step is to determine whether you wish to have a live-in or a live-out nanny. The cost of a live-out nanny is typically 20% to 50% more than the cost of a live-in nanny. The difference is to cover the cost of living for a care-giver who resides outside of the home.

Domestic Nanny (Live-in or Live-Out)

A domestic nanny is someone who resides in Canada and has landed immigrant, permanent resident or citizenship status. A live-out domestic nanny is the most expensive form of in-home care. However, with this option, while you are still an employer with all of the attendant paperwork hassle, your house is still your own and you don't need to go through a lengthy immigration process. Few live-out domestic nannies are available on a part-time basis.

If you are hiring a live-in nanny, remember that you need to look for someone who is not only skilled in child care, but is also someone who is compatible with your lifestyle. Having sufficient suitable living quarters will be the key to having a successful live-in nanny arrangement.

Since you are not using an agency, you will have to advertise in the local paper, use word of mouth, enquire through your church or community association or contact some of the schools in Calgary that have child development programs. It is a good idea to put together a job description that will form the basis of the contract. Screen the applicants, interview them and then finally make an offer to the successful candidate. The process will probably take one to three months. Make sure you give yourself enough time to find someone appropriate rather than rushing into an arrangement that you are not comfortable with. Having a contract between you and the nanny is the key to having a clear understanding of job expectations.

Paula says...

"I found one part-time nanny by placing handwritten advertisements at Mount Royal College. I put one beside the office for the childcare program and one beside the office for the social work program."

If you have not been successful in hiring someone locally, then you may apply to hire someone through the Live-In Caregiver Program administered by Citizenship and Immigration Canada.

International Nanny (Live-In)

Hiring an international live-in caregiver is a multi-step and time-consuming process. The International Live-in Caregiver Program is a very specific immigration program and its rules only apply to those who are part of the program. This program does not apply to landed immigrants or citizens. It is wise to begin the process at least six months before the date on which you expect your caregiver to start work.

Citizenship and Immigration Canada (CIC) posts general information about the Live-in Caregiver Program for both employers and employees at www.cic.gc.ca/english/work/caregiver/index.asp. However, the best guidelines are found on the Human Resources and Skills Development Canada (HRSDC) website at www.hrsdc.gc.ca (under "Individuals" click on "Jobs", then "Hiring Foreign Workers" and finally "Hiring Foreign Live-in Caregivers"). I suggest that you read the posted information very thoroughly.

Here's a brief summary of the steps involved in the process of hiring an international nanny:

1) Find an international caregiver.

This can be done on your own, through newspaper ads or the Internet or with the help of an agency. The CIC website (see above) provides recommendations on using an agency. You can also post a job on the employer section of the Government of Canada Job Bank website (www.jobbank.gc.ca/Intro_en.asp). To do so, it is necessary to create an account. There are many pieces of information to fill in, but you will eventually end up with a very useful list of required skills and responsibilities for your caregiver. Remember, your caregiver's job is to care for your child, not to clean your house. It is reasonable to expect a live-in caregiver to do her share of dishes, etc.; however, housekeeping duties are to be no more than fifteen hours per week, and the caregiver may not be asked to do outside work such as shoveling snow or even pet care.

2) Negotiate the contract.

There are a number of minimum terms that must be included in the contract. The details will need to be included in the work permit application. A sample contract can be found the CIC webpage about the Live-in Caregiver Program (see above).

3) Check with HRSDC.

You will need to obtain a "Labour Market Opinion" (LMO) from HRSDC, which is a letter that states there is a shortage of domestic help in the caregiver field. You will need to show that you have made efforts to hire locally. An advertisement run for one Saturday in the classified ads may be sufficient. You will be required to submit any responses in your application to HRSDC. The form for an application for a LMO can be found on the HRSDC website (see the address and links above). At the time of writing, LMO's were taking over three months due to the labour shortage in the Calgary market! Once you receive a confirmation letter from the HRSDC, send it along with the contract to your caregiver.

4) Apply for a Business Number.

You need a business number in order to remit taxes, CPP and EI payments for both you and your caregiver. Go to www.businessregistration.gc.ca.

5) Apply for a work permit.

Your caregiver must do this at the embassy in his or her home country. Details are available on the CIC website at www.cic.gc.ca. You can also find relevant informationon the local embassy website. The fees vary. Depending on your arrangement with the caregiver, you may need to cover these processing fees. A criminal check and health check may also be required at this stage.

Paula says...

"In our case we reimbursed our international live-in caregiver for the processing fees that were incurred. These amounted to about $700."

Paula says...

"We've had nannies who didn't show up, didn't show up on time, quit without any notice, ones without any initiative, ones who had no idea what to do with a child, some who wanted additional pay for working before noon, one who ate all our chocolate, nannies whom other parents tried to snag at the playground, one who had chronic fatigue... You think you have chronic fatigue, what about me? All I can say is, good luck, and I hope you find a good nanny."

NANNY PLACEMENT AGENCIES

Nanny placement agencies do not do all of the work for you. They find candidates but you still have to check their references and interview them. Agencies tend to charge placement fees ($650 – $800 for local and $200 for international nannies) but often provide a guarantee that starts on your employee's first day of work.

There is a list of agencies in the Yellow Pages under "Nannies". Ask around and get recommendations from friends. Agencies vary widely in terms of services offered. Don't necessarily pick the cheapest agency. Ask the staff for the names of a few families who have used the agency. Find out what other services the agency provides. Ask if the agency's caregivers are bonded and also how extensive their background checks are. A thorough background check should include criminal records, driving violations and credit history. Ask about the replacement or refund policy or guarantee if the initial caregiver doesn't work out. Depending on the agency, replacement offers are good for periods ranging from thirty days to a year.

There is a web-based Canadian organization called Canadian Nanny, which has a database of nannies and families looking for them. The Canadian Nanny website is www.canadiannanny.ca. Access to the database costs $60 for sixty days. Nannies are not screened; however, you can see resumes of nannies looking for work in your area. You are also able to view feedback from other parents on the nannies.

TYPICAL COSTS

Under the International Live-in Caregiver Program nannies are paid a minimum starting gross wage of about $1,525 per month based on 44 hours per week. The cost of room and board can be deducted at a rate of $370 per month. However, since you are an employer, you will also need to contribute to CPP and EI, which costs about $95 per month. The net monthly cost for a live-in nanny is about $1,300 per month. You will also need to provide vacation time or vacation pay of 4%. Any work over 44 hours per week requires payment at overtime rates as per the Employment Standards Code of Alberta.

Domestic live-in nannies expect a starting gross wage of $1,700 or more per month based on 44 hours a week. Wages are based upon experience and duties performed. Again, room and board can be deducted. Employer contributions are about $110-$170 a month, so the net monthly cost is $1,500 and up.

Live-out nannies are considerably more expensive, as they must cover their own living expenses. Starting gross wages range from about $2,100 to $3,100 monthly based on the same 44-hour week. Wages are higher if a large amount of housekeeping is required or if there is an obligation to drive. Employers also need to compensate their nanny for mileage and gas if she is required to use her own vehicle. Taking CPP and EI contributions into account, the net monthly cost ranges from about $2,250 to $3,300 per month.

Part-time nannies demand starting gross wages of between $12 and $16 per hour. Part-time nannies are typically harder to find, as most nannies prefer full-time employment.

IMPORTANT GOVERNMENT WEBSITES FOR YOU AS AN EMPLOYER

Live-in Caregiver Program
Website: www.cic.gc.ca/english/work/caregiver/index.asp

Human Resources Development Canada
Website: www.hrsdc.gc.ca

Here you will find links to regional HRDC offices across the province and the centralized foreign worker department.

Alberta Ministry of Labour – Employment Standards Act
Website: www.gov.ab.ca/hre (search for "Employment Standards")

Canada Customs and Revenue Agency
Website: www.cra-arc.gc.ca

Information on source deductions and remittances of income tax, CCP and EI.

Worker's Compensation Board of Alberta
Website: www.wcb.ab.ca

This website provides information on premiums and benefits, how to register as an employer and the responsibilities of employers and employees.

Alberta Health Care Insurance Plan
Website: www.health.gov.ab.ca/ahcip/AHCIP.html

Look here for information on health care eligibility and how to register.

INNOVATIVE CHILD CARE IDEAS

If you and your friends have children approximately the same age, you can always try to work out some arrangement between two or three families for child care.

Co-operative Child Care

If you are considering working part-time, you may be in good company. If two families are interested in part-time work, you can alternate looking after the little ones. For example, if four adults are interested, then three adults could work four days a week and one adult could work three days a week. Recognize that looking after two children is a lot more work than caring for one, and that having about a three-month age difference between the children is helpful in accommodating nap schedules. You will need to have two napping areas, but you can probably share a high chair. Also, it may be easier for the children to have their "daycare" at the same house all the time, rather than alternating.

Sharing a Nanny

If you are returning to work on a part-time basis, but would like to have a nanny look after your little one, there may be an opportunity to share a nanny with another family who also only needs a nanny part-time. This way your baby gets one-on-one care on the days that you are working and stays in familiar surroundings. You will need to ensure that your schedule does not change too much since you will need to coordinate with the other family.

CHAPTER SEVENTEEN
BIRTHDAY PARTIES

Celebrating your baby's first birthday is a wonderful event for you. Your baby, on the other hand, won't really know what is going on and won't care whether you throw a huge party or limit it to a few family members.

The guest list grows quickly when you start inviting children and their parents. If you decide that the party will be too big to hold at home, there are many places where you can host a party for children and parents. Remember that your child will not be able to last very long at their first birthday party, and plan accordingly.

FIRST-BIRTHDAY PARTY LOCATIONS

Here are some options for a first birthday party outside your home:

Your Community Association Hall
If your local community association hosts a playgroup, you may find that they will also rent the space and provide a janitor, toys, coffee maker and a kitchen for an afternoon for about $160. You can invite many children to come and have fun with the toys and after a quick clean-up, you can simply head home. Information about your community association is available online on the Federation of Calgary Communities website at www.calgarycommunities.com. Search under "Communities", then "Organized Communities" and look for your community association by name.

Gymboree
Gymboree hosts birthday parties for about $120. The parties are two hours in length. See more on Gymboree under "Chapter Twelve: Activities" – "Playgroups" – "Gymboree".

Coffee & S'cream

This playcentre hosts two-hour birthday parties and tends to book up well in advance. "Exclusive use" parties are available only on Sundays and cost $100. You may invite a maximum of twenty children or forty guests and you can bring your own food and cake. The attached coffee shop stays open during the party. "Non-exclusive use" parties are available the rest of the week. The back of the play area is made available to a maximum of eight children. For $6 per child, Coffee & S'cream will provide the use of the play area, a juice box and a place setting for each child. For $2 more per child, children will receive ice cream. Again, you can bring your own food and cake. See more on Coffee & S'cream under "Chapter Twelve: Activities" – "Drop-in Playcentres" – "Coffee & S'cream".

Creative Kids

Creative Kids hosts music parties for kids (ages 1-8). The parties are packed with dancing, instruments, singing, musical games and props. There are three party packages available: Adventure (one hour party); Bonanza (two hour party); and Celebration (two hour party including cake, drinks, decorations and goodie bags for all children). Parties start at a base price of $175; additional charges are levied for more children, additional staff or goodie bags. Book at least a month in advance to ensure your desired date and time for your baby's party. For more information on Creative Kids see "Chapter Fourteen: Courses" – "Music Classes".

Jump'N'Java

This playcentre also offers birthday parties on Sundays. The base package costs $6 per child and includes a two-and-a-half-hour stay, a reserved party area, parents' and kids' tables, tablecloth, plates, forks, napkins and a gift table. There are a few other packages available, and you can also arrange a thirty-minute visit from "Barney". Please call Jump'N'Java directly for details. See "Chapter Twelve: Activities" – "Drop-in Playcentres" – "Jump'N'Java" for contact information.

Let's Play

Let's Play offers two party packages and four party rooms to choose from: Princess, Jungle, Pirate and Dinosaur. Exclusive use of the party room is provided for 30 or 45 minutes and costs from $10 to $13 per child. Children can play in the toddler or other areas for the remainder of the day. See "Chapter Twelve: Activities" – "Drop-in Playcentres" – "Let's Play" for contact information.

Playtime

Playtime hosts intimate (fewer than twenty people) birthday parties. It offers two hours of exclusive use of the playroom for a cost of $125. Drinks are included in the price (coffee, juice, pop) and you can bring your own food and cake. Playtime staff will clean up after your party. See "Chapter Twelve: Activities" – "Drop-in Playcentres" – "Playtime" for contact information.

Gymaniacs (Cochrane)

All party packages are 1.5 hours in length, but it is possible to extend to two hours for an incremental cost. Gymaniacs provides you with exclusive use of the facility. You can bring your own food or drink and have between twelve and fifteen children. Prices range between $85 and $160 for non-members: members receive a discount. This is for one-year-old and two-year-old parties. Give them a call for party specifics. See "Chapter Twelve: Activities" – "Drop-in Playcentres" – "Gymaniacs" for contact information.

Sip'N'Safari

Sip'N'Safari offers two birthday packages depending on the number of children. A package for ten children or fewer costs $120 and a package for between eleven and twenty children costs $160. Each one includes two hours of playtime and exclusive use of the play area. Adults receive unlimited brewed coffee and children are provided with a drink and a craft to take home. You can bring your own cake, although all food brought onto the premises must be nut-free. They do not allow latex balloons. You can choose from a selection of party platters for $25 each and they can also provide pizza upon request. The advertisement says that you can leave your mess behind. I'd take them up on that one! See "Chapter Twelve: Activities" – "Drop-in Playcentres" – "Sip'N'Safari" for contact information.

The Urban Treehouse (Airdrie)

This playcentre offers two party packages; you can choose either a basic package or a full-service party package that includes a choice of theme and creative programming. Themes include Fairies and Princesses, Bugs, Glamour girl, Pirates and more. The party packages are based on eight children, including the birthday child. You will receive invitations, a party room, party supplies, drinks, a party throne (oh, I wish they had one for the mom!) and full use of the playcentre. Prices range from $125 to $250. Additional children can be added to the party for extra cost. You will need to provide a deposit to reserve the date. See "Chapter Twelve: Activities" – "Drop-in Playcentres" – "The Urban Treehouse" for contact information.

SECOND-BIRTHDAY PARTY LOCATIONS

In addition to the locations listed above, there are a few other places worth mentioning for second birthday parties.

Creative Kids

Creative Kids has two types of parties available for children aged two and older: Music-based (1 – 8 years old) or art-based (2 – 8 years old). As mentioned above, music parties are packed with dancing, instruments, singing, musical games and props. Art parties involve guests designing a giant birthday card, decorating their party hats, sculpting with clay and doing other crafts. There are three party packages available: Adventure (one hour party): Bonanza (two hour party): and Celebration (two hour party that including cake, drinks, decorations and goodie bags for all children). Parties start at a base price of $175 (Music) and $200 (Art); additional charges are levied for more children, additional staff or goodie bags. Book at least a month in advance to ensure your desired date and time for your baby's party. For more information on Creative Kids see "Chapter Fourteen: Courses" – "Music Classes".

Gymtastics

Gymtastic's southeast location offers birthday parties (Address: 160, 7260 12 Street S.E., Phone: 254-9010).

Birthday parties include one hour of supervised gymnastics time (including an age-appropriate warm-up), games, parachute games, face painting and more. After the gym time, you are allowed one hour in the party room, which has kitchen facilities to accommodate a party of any size. Parties can be hosted on Friday afternoons or Sundays for $190.

Vocational and Rehabilitation Research Institute (VRRI)

VRRI hosts two-hour and three-hour birthday parties for between $100 and $140 for a basic package. The first hour can be spent either in the gym or the pool and the last hour is spent in a party room. You can bring your own food or VRRI can cater the party for you. The package is for up to eleven children. Book at least eight weeks in advance. You can also customize your party with either a sport theme or a play theme. See "Chapter Fourteen: Courses" – "Swimming with Your Baby" – "VRRI".

YMCA

The YMCA hosts birthday parties, however activities vary from branch to branch. Give your local YMCA a call for details. See "Chapter Fourteen: Courses" – "Swimming with Your Baby" – "YMCA" for contact information.

Telus World of Science (Calgary Science Centre)

The Calgary Science Centre hosts birthday parties every weekend. Party packages cost $180 for non-members and $165 for members. You can invite up to twenty people to your party (only those over the age of three are counted). Children under three are free and additional guests over the age of three can be invited for $5 each. You and your guests will enjoy access to the Science Centre for the entire day and you will be provided access to a private room for one hour. You can bring your own food, cake and drinks. A party host will greet you when you arrive and show you to your room. The staff can keep your birthday cake and drinks in the fridge. Your guests can leave presents and coats in a big wheeled tub, which will be brought to your party room at the allotted time. Call the Centre at 268-8300 and press 4 to book your birthday party. By the way, the staff does all the cleaning up!

University of Calgary Gymnastics Centre

If you have a number of children two years old or older, consider renting the gymnasium for an hour. Birthday party packages are available for limited hours on weekends. Your little mites will be given access to the gym with an instructor for an hour and access to the party room for an additional hour. A one-to-one parent-to-child ratio is required and you cannot leave siblings unattended. You must bring your own food and beverages and clean up afterwards. All of this comes at a price of $80. To book the facility, call the Gymnastics club at 220-7749. Cochrane has a similar facility.

Ultimate Trains (Nanton)

An amazing labyrinth of tracks and twenty-two trains is your treat at the end of the trek south to Ultimate Trains. Party packages cost $20 (no, this is not a typo!). The package covers a birthday t-shirt for the child, entrance for six children and two adults (additional people at $2), and an opportunity to have the birthday child photographed standing inside the layout. You can order food from Nanton to be delivered to the birthday party and they will set up your picnic table anywhere in the gardens. The entire birthday party can come and go all day long. Pop over to the Nanton Lancaster Air Museum if you are interested. Call the day ahead to book your birthday party at 646-1190. Remember, while the retail store is open all year, the outdoor play area is only available from May through September. See "Chapter Twelve: Activities" – "Calgary and Area Sites" – "Ultimate Trains".

BIRTHDAY CAKE

Tip! The Okotoks Toy Library rents cake pans for just $5. See "Chapter Twelve: Toys, Books and Games" – "Toy Libraries and Toy Banks".

There are a lot of "first birthday" cake recipes available. Some of them avoid ingredients that you may not have yet introduced to your baby, such as cows' milk or eggs. Others avoid too much sugar. There is a website called www.coolest-birthday-cakes.com if you are searching for ideas. Some of the photos are of diaper cakes!

Paula says...

"Whatever recipe you choose, I recommend that you do a trial run on the recipe beforehand to ensure that the cake is edible. I found one cake recipe that was completely inedible. Thankfully, I tried it out ahead of time. Declan agreed! I ended up getting a plain sponge cake (purchased very inexpensively from Safeway) and using whipping cream as the icing."

Calgary Businesses Specializing in Birthday Cakes

Sugar Shack Cakes

Location:	Calgary N.W.
Phone:	278-1285
Website:	www.sugarshackcakes.ca

If you are looking for low-calorie, this is not the place! If, however, you are looking for a unique cake for a birthday party then it is the place. This company is owned and operated by a mompreneur from her home. Cakes are available for pick-up before 5 p.m. and can be delivered within Calgary's northwest on Friday afternoons or Saturday mornings. Prices vary by size. Have a look at the website to see the variety of cakes and sizes.

Cakeworks
Phone: 571-2253
Location: 126, 3132 26 Street N.E.
Website: www.eatcake.ca

Cakeworks is a Calgary-based company that started at five cakes a week and has grown to two hundred cakes a week. You can order your cake online and either have it delivered or pick it up yourself. The cakes come in too many types and shapes to list.

> **Tip!** *Upon request, Calgary Co-op will make six-inch sponge cakes that are perfect for babies to dive into on their birthday.*

CHAPTER EIGHTEEN
PRESCHOOLS

You are probably wondering why a book designed for babies and toddlers would include a section on preschools. There has been a dramatic rise in the number of births in Calgary since 2004. In 2004, Calgary had approximately 66,200[11] children under four years of age. By 2010 the City of Calgary estimates that that number will increase to 91,300. Yes, that is a forty percent increase in the population of little munchkins in this city. Can you say Baby Boom? This means that you may have to register your child for preschool before your child is preschool age. During my research, one preschool told me that they have already started to receive registrations for infants who wish to attend the school up to two years in the future.

AT WHAT AGE DOES PRESCHOOL START?

Preschool starts at ages three and four. There is no law requiring you to send your child to preschool. It is completely optional. The goal of preschool is to help develop fine and gross motor skills, as well as social skills. Preschool can also help your child with the transition into kindergarten.

WHEN SHOULD YOU START LOOKING AT PRESCHOOLS?

Starting to research preschools after your child's first birthday may seem extreme, however, it may prove to be necessary in the coming years in Calgary. Starting early will give you time to find the right school and to register your child well in advance. Since programs and teachers can change, check to make sure that your choice of school is still valid closer to the date. At the very latest, you should start your research a couple of months prior to the registration deadline.

Some program registrations are ongoing, which means that you can register your child anytime during the school year. Most preschool programs, however, have a one-day registration, normally held in February or March for the following September. As a rule, you will need to stand in line for several hours. Dress warmly; bring a cup of coffee and a lawn chair. Don't forget to bring any registration forms that need to be filled out ahead of time and the following pieces of information:

- photocopy of your child's Birth Certificate
- immunization record (available from your public health clinic at no charge)
- Alberta Health Care number for your child
- names and phone numbers of emergency contacts for your child
- lots and lots of cheques

Paula says...

"We arrived at a preschool registration at 5:45 a.m. for a 9 a.m. registration only to find that we were third in line. The first in the queue had been there by 2 a.m. I had heard of other queues starting up to eight hours ahead of time. Whatever you do, get there early, dress warmly and bring a warm drink and some reading material. Long gone are the days when we would stand in line for concert tickets like this!"

REGULATION OF PRESCHOOLS

Preschools are licensed and governed by Alberta Social Services (Social Care Facilities). Child Care Regulation sets out the minimum standards that must be met in child care facilities prior to a license being issued. These standards are intended to ensure that the health, safety and developmental needs of children are being met.

Child and Family Service Authorities (CFSAs) license, monitor and enforce standards of care under the Child Care Regulation. Calgary and area is regulated under Region 3 of the Child and Family Service Authorities. Their website can be found at www.calgaryandareacfsa.gov.ab.ca; click on "Child care". You can also contact your nearest CFSA office for information on assessing and choosing quality child care or preschool or to register a complaint about a regulated child care facility or preschool. CFSA offices are listed below.

Child and Family Services Authority Regional Authority Office
Address: #300, 1240 Kensington Road N.W.
Phone: 297-6100

COMMUNITY-BASED OFFICES WITH CHILD CARE LICENSING SERVICES:

Bowness Multi-Service Team
Address: Suite 200, 7930 Bowness Road N.W.
Phone: 297-2600

South of McKnight Multi-Service Team
Address: #101, 5112 47 Street N.E.
Phone: 297-8084

High River Multi-Service Team
Address: P.O.Box 5147, 129 4 Avenue W.
             1st Floor, Provincial Building, High River
Phone: 652-8360

All preschool programs must meet stated criteria in order to receive and maintain a license. You can find additional information on licensing in a publication entitled "Licensing Standards and Best Practices in Childcare Manual" produced by Alberta Child Services. The most recent edition was printed in 2004. It can be found online on the Alberta Children's Services website at www.child.gov.ab.ca. Click "What we do" and then "Childcare". Scroll down to the "Licensing Standards and Best Practices in Childcare Manual." The manual is lengthy, but it sets out important guidelines for both preschools and daycare facilities. The guidelines address topics such as how much space is required for children at each age and the required staff-to-children ratios.

The manual indicates that, for 2007, the minimum primary staff-to-children ratio in nursery schools is 1:12 for children three to five years old and 1:15 for children over five years old. These ratios are the same as those required for drop-in daycare centres.

One interesting fact to note is that Alberta Children's Services does not require preschool teachers to have any qualifications. There are requirements for daycare teachers, but not for preschool teachers. Preschool instructors tend to be highly trained, but exact qualifications are at the discretion of the preschool.

Preschools are classes are run either two or three half-days a week, depending on the age of the children. Programs are offered either in the morning or the afternoon and are usually not more than three hours in length. Some private programs run preschool five days a week and some are scheduled for full school days.

WHAT KINDS OF PRESCHOOLS ARE OUT THERE?

There is a wide range of preschool philosophies. Here are a few terms and schools of thought (pun intended) that it be helpful for you to understand:

- **Montessori Program**
  This type of program originated in Italy in the early 1900s, and was designed by a physician called Maria Montessori. Only some schools are affiliated with the two major accrediting organizations. Affiliation is not a requirement for Montessori schools. In Montessori programs all tasks and activities are reality-oriented. Children work independently on different tasks and teachers are called guides. Children are free to choose their own activities in the classroom. Each of the two major accrediting organizations maintains a website:
  Association Montessori Internationale (AMI) www.montessori-ami.org
  The American Montessori Society (AMS) www.amshq.org.

- **Play-based Programs or Learning-through-play Programs**
  In these programs, children learn through hands-on activities. Teachers are seen as facilitators rather than instructors. One U.S. preschool provides a great summary of play-based preschool philosophy on its website: www.adventurecenterchildcare.com.

- **Reggio Emilia Program**
  This program is named after a city in northern Italy where educators, parents, and children began working together after World War II. The program is family-centered and offers infant-toddler and preschool levels. It is not based on a formal model like Waldorf and Montessori, with defined methods, teacher certification standards, and accreditation processes. Teachers see themselves as a provocation to and a reference point for the children. The following website contains extensive information about Reggio:
  http://ceep.crc.uiuc.edu/poptopics/reggio/reginfo.html. Information can also be found on a Calgary preschool's website:
  www.bethanychapel.com/playschool.htm

- **Traditional Learning Programs**
  These programs reflect what you and I probably experienced when we were in school. They set high expectations for academic excellence and provide whole group instruction. Classes are highly structured and orderly.

- **Waldorf program**

  Waldorf schools reflect a play-based philosophy that was developed in Germany. Teachers incorporate storytelling and fantasy into the curriculum. Toys are meant for open-ended imaginative play. Children learn social skills from the teacher modeling good social behavior. The day is scheduled to include group and individual activities. Directed activities include crafts and painting.

  More information can be found at www.waldorfearlychildhood.org. Other websites of interest include www.bobnancy.com and www.awsna.org. Teachers receive training at the Steiner Institute, named after the founder of the Waldorf method.

WHERE DO I FIND A LIST OF PRESCHOOLS?

In 2007 there were 153 licensed preschools in Calgary. There is list of all licensed preschools on the Alberta Children's Services website at www.child.gov.ab.ca. Click on "What We Do", followed by "Child Care"; scroll down and click on "Nursery School Lookup" and follow the directions. Contact information is listed for each school.

Calgary's Child magazine also features a preschool edition every February. It is printed too late for some preschool registrations. This publication provides a short summary of most of the programs and their contact information. You can find the latest preschool listing online at www.calgaryschild.com. Click on "Guides" and then scroll down until you find the "2007 Preschool Guide".

TYPICAL COSTS

Community preschool programs vary considerably in price. Two-days-a-week programs cost between $90 and $215 per month ($810 – $1,935 per year) and three-day programs range from $100 to $235 per month ($900 – $2,115 per year). You will also need to pay a one-time administrative fee (typically less than $80).

Private schools may require a mandatory family bond. This is, in essence, an interest-free loan to the school (usually around $10,000). You receive your principal back when your family's last student leaves the school. Private preschool tuition fees vary between $3,000 and $4,000 per year for half-day programs and are approximately $6,000 per year for full-day programs. Private schools levy additional fees such as family registration, assessment, and enrollment fees.

HOW TO CHOOSE A PRESCHOOL

Factors that Paula suggests when considering a preschool for your little one:
* Comfort with school philosophy
* Comfort with teacher's style
* Proximity to your home
* Smaller class size
* Lots of books available
* Low teacher-to-student ratio
* Larger-sized classroom
* Available spot in preferred class time (morning or afternoon)

The following website has some suggestions on selecting schools: www.guidetoschools.ca. Click on "Resources" and then on "Click here to view the school checklist".

Calgary's Child magazine also ran an article entitled "Choosing the Right Preschool". It can be found on its website www.calgaryschild.com. Select "Education" then scroll through the articles until you find "Choosing the Right Preschool".

SELECTING A PRESCHOOL

by Pat Tarr, Ph.D. Associate Professor, Faculty of Education, University of Calgary

As an academic who has been involved in early childhood education for over thirty years, I am concerned that children are becoming more and more pressured to achieve academic success at younger and younger ages. I have heard preschool teachers say that when parents shop for a preschool, they are most impressed by those that send home teacher-prepared crafts and worksheets, or that provide other evidence that the preschool is preparing the children for kindergarten. Earlier preparation does not mean greater academic success. In the desire to ensure academic success, the importance of play in children's growth and development seems to be getting lost. Research has consistently shown that children learn best through play and that play provides children with the necessary foundation for success later in life, both academically and socially. Being successful in the future will require individuals to be imaginative, flexible, creative, and to have good interpersonal, communication and collaborative skills, all of which are learned through play.

Lilian Katz, a prominent early childhood educator, has often said that we "overestimate young children's academic ability and underestimate their intellectual ability". By this she means that we are misdirected when we try to teach young children academic skills prematurely, or skills that are removed from meaningful contexts. In doing so, we overestimate their ability to make sense of these experiences or to be able to use them in new contexts. For example, reading expert Frank Smith claims that phonics instruction before children are readers can confuse children and create reading problems rather than solving them. Likewise, counting to 100 and reciting the alphabet may be impressive coming from a young child, but this ability to memorize is no indication that the child has any conceptual understanding of 100 or why it is important. Play opportunities create meaningful contexts for children that can naturally involve literacy and math experiences, such as creating menus for a restaurant or money for a store. We underestimate children's intellectual skills when we provide pre-solved problems for them to do (such as step-by-step crafts), ignore their questions, or impose an adult approach on them. Young children are deep thinkers and theory-makers who are capable problem posers and problem solvers given a supportive environment.

Anyone who has closely observed a young child intent on solving a self-initiated problem knows that it is a myth that young children have short attention spans. We can easily teach them to be disengaged with programs that have many transitions from one activity to another, or by providing them with learning experiences in which skills are taught removed rom any meaningful context. Providing extended time for free play and investigation supports children's engagement in their learning. It also supports the acquisition of social skills as children negotiate both their roles in and the direction of their play. Fantasy and role-playing provides opportunities for them to act in roles that are beyond their current level of development and so supports their growth. This kind of play also provides children with opportunities to develop their imagination, and to reflect on and consolidate their experiences. You will see them playing out themes that deal with good and bad, fears, and familiar roles. This is a normal and important part of their development.

The arts are also important to young children's development. Through drawing, painting, clay work, children can express their ideas and develop fine motor skills essential for later writing. Such activities should be open-ended so that each child's work is a unique record of their expression rather than a lesson in following directions. Through block play children develop mathematical and scientific concepts. Through physical activity children develop a sense of their body and large motor skills, and being active helps children focus more closely when engaged in quieter activities.

Researchers are also becoming increasingly concerned that as children are spending more time in scheduled activities or in front of computers they are losing valuable connections with nature; outdoor play encounters and investigations in and about the natural world are also an important part of early childhood experiences.

I truly believe that parents and teachers can best support young children's future academic development by providing them with opportunities to play with others, to spend time exploring the natural world, to have time to "do nothing", to think and to dream. Yes, read to them, play with language and words, and engage in meaningful activities that involve mathematical concepts in the contexts of real experiences such as setting the table.

Often, we believe that preparation means doing now what will be expected from children in a year or two. I have been in early childhood settings where three-year-olds were expected to sit for a long circle time because they would have to do it in kindergarten. This thinking puts children in double jeopardy because in spending a long time in circle they are missing out on more meaningful and developmentally appropriate experiences. If they have difficulty sitting still, they may receive negative messages about their behavior. We can best support young children by living fully now, taking into account their wonder and curiosity, and by listening carefully to their interests so that we can support their learning with materials and experiences that strengthen them as meaning-makers.

Paula says...

"One of the programs we looked into required us to provide a full profile of our child's strengths and weaknesses. We thought that the words "He's three!" summarized everything they needed to know."

CHAPTER NINETEEN
AFTERWORD

The first years of life are so special; I hope that you and your baby or toddler are able to take advantage of some the services and activities that are mentioned in this book.

If you have a comment you would like to share, please write to:
Playgroup Books
Suite 119, 2137 33 Avenue S.W.
Calgary, Alberta T2T 1Z7

Alternatively, you can send an e-mail to info@babyguidetocalgary.com or log onto www.babyguidetocalgary.com to send your feedback. Thank you for reading this book, and all the best to you and your family!

Paula

CHAPTER TWENTY
ABOUT THE AUTHOR
AND CONTRIBUTORS

AUTHOR:
Paula McGarrigle

Paula is married and has two children: Declan, born in 2004, and Ailish, born in 2005. Paula was raised in Ireland and immigrated to Canada in 1981 as a teenager. She attended the University of Alberta where she obtained degrees in Biology and Chemical Engineering, and Queen's University where she obtained an MBA. None of this education prepared her for entry into parenthood. Paula currently works full-time in the Canadian Wind Energy Industry. Paula also plays violin locally and is an avid photographer. Paula and her family enjoy playing violin together, walking in the community and playing in the park.

ABOUT THE CONTRIBUTORS
Dr. Evelyn Jain

Dr. Evelyn Jain is a family physician and lactation specialist. She teaches at the University of Calgary, Faculty of Medicine as a Clinical Assistant Professor. Through her breastfeeding clinic in Lakeview she has helped thousands of mothers solve their breastfeeding problems and establish a wonderful fulfilling breastfeeding relationship with their babies. She is well-known internationally for her lactation teaching to physicians and Lactation Consultants, and she has developed many teaching and media aids for professionals and parents regarding breastfeeding, including the video and DVD: "Infant Tongue Tie: Impact on Breastfeeding". Dr. Jain is a mother and a grandmother.

Jill Olson

Jill is married and has three daughters: Julie, born in 2004, and twins Sarah and Chelsea, born in 2006. She obtained a degree in Mechanical Engineering from the University of Alberta in 1986 and has worked in the oil and gas industry since 1988 – taking breaks to have children. Jill and her husband, Doug, are avid skiers and hikers, fitting in some mountain biking, backpacking and camping (mostly before children). They have a lot of practice on the local playgrounds with their children. They will mark the day on the calendar when their children are able to ski along with them (and probably faster). ("Not likely!" says Doug!)

Elena Rhodes

Elena is mother to Daniel, born in 2004, and Anna, born in 2005, and a consulting actuary. She moved to Calgary from Tyumen, Siberia in 1995 and graduated from the University of Calgary in 2000. She currently balances her work and family life by working part-time. On her non-working days, Elena and her kids take advantage of the many activities that Calgary has to offer to families with young children. Elena and her husband, John, love hiking, skiing, snowshoeing, backpacking and camping (summer and winter!) and look forward to enjoying these activities with their children.

Nicola Sadorra

Nicola's joy and toughest job is being mother to Zachary and Maya. Her loving husband, Jack, helps to keep her balanced. Raised in Edmonton, Nicola earned degrees in Psychology and Physical Therapy at the University of Alberta and McGill respectively. Nicola worked in the U.S. where she gained specialty training as a Paediatric Physical Therapist. Back in Calgary, Nicola supplements her part-time work as a Physical Therapist with a new business, Tiny Talk and Walk, providing gross motor and sign language instruction to families and childcare facilities. When Nicola isn't working, she likes to camp, hike, bike and ski with her family.

Dr. Wendy Street-Wadey

Dr. Wendy Street-Wadey is a native Calgarian and mother to a preschool-aged daughter, Julia. Wendy attended the Faculty of Dentistry at the University of Western Ontario and graduated with a Doctorate of Dental Sciences (DDS) in 1988. After graduation, Wendy worked in private practice in Northern Ontario for one year, and then returned to Calgary, where she ran her own practice in the Chinook Centre Professional Tower until the birth of her daughter. Since the early 1990's Wendy has been a part-time clinical instructor for the dental assisting program at SAIT. Dr. Street-Wadey is a member of the Calgary Society for Advanced Dentistry Study Club, the Calgary and District Dental Society, the Alberta Dental Association, the Canadian Dental Association, and is an honorary member of the Rotary Club of Calgary Fish Creek.

Dr. Pat Tarr

Pat Tarr is an Associate Professor in the Faculty of Education where her specializations in early childhood and art education come together in her research around the Reggio Emilia Approach to education. She has a special connection to very young children, having taught in a parent-toddler preschool program for six years at the University of British Columbia. Pat is also a mom and grandmother.

APPENDICES

APPENDIX 1:
REFERENCE SHEETS AND CHECKLISTS
REFERENCE SHEET FOR YOUR BABYSITTER

Baby's full name:
Date of birth:
Current age:
Current weight:

Parent contact information
Name:
Cellphone numbers:
Where we are tonight:
Location, contact names and numbers:

Emergency: CALL 911
Poison Control Center: 944-1414
Our address:
Our home phone number:

Health information
Alberta Health Care number:
Allergies:
Any medical conditions:
Family doctor:
Clinic address:
Phone:

Household information
Fire extinguisher location:
Main fuse box location:
Electricity emergency: Call ENMAX at
Gas emergency: Call DIRECT ENERGY at
Gas supply shut off is located...
Water emergency: Call ENMAX at
Main water shutoff is located....

Other
Nearest hospital:
Directions:
Local police:
Local taxi:

MONITORING SLEEPING PATTERNS

By monitoring your baby's sleep, you will be able to discern emerging patterns. That way, you can plan your day a little better, knowing when naptime starts and ends.

Mark with a dash when the baby goes to sleep and when he awakes. Draw a line between the two dashes. Cat naps of less than thirty minutes should be marked with a "*" sign. Also keep track of meal times: BK = Breakfast, L = Lunch, S = Snack, D = Dinner, B= Breastfeed or Formula.

Time	Day 1	Day 2	Day 3	Day 4	Day 5
1 a.m.					
2					
3					
4					
5					
6					
7					
8					
9					
10					
11					
12					
1p.m.					
2					
3					
4					
5					
6					
7					
8					
9					
10					
11					
12					

MONITORING FEEDING AND BODILY FUNCTIONS FOR THE FIRST SIX WEEKS

During the first six weeks you may have many appointments with public health nurses, your baby's physician or with breastfeeding specialists. All of them will ask about your baby's feeding and bodily functions as part of assessing her well-being.

Paula says...

"I found I was so tired that I had difficulty recalling pees and poops, so I put together this handy sheet. This allowed me to record what was happening and then respond to enquiries. I could also remember which side I had nursed from last time and whether or not I had given Ovol."

Jill says...

"This is even more critical with two or more babies. Tired parents may need to make sure that each child has been fed!"

You can also expand this table to keep track of when you give your baby any medications or vitamin supplements prescribed by his doctor.

DATE	TIME	BR /SUPP	VOID	STOOL	FIRST BREAST	SECOND BREAST	GAS RELIEF DROPS	VITAMIN D DROPS	VOLUME DRANK (mls)	DURATION	SEEDY STOOL	NOTES
		BR /Supp	Y N	Y N	L R	L R	Y N	Y N			Y N	
		BR /Supp	Y N	Y N	L R	L R	Y N	Y N			Y N	
		BR /Supp	Y N	Y N	L R	L R	Y N	Y N			Y N	
		BR /Supp	Y N	Y N	L R	L R	Y N	Y N			Y N	
		BR /Supp	Y N	Y N	L R	L R	Y N	Y N			Y N	
		BR /Supp	Y N	Y N	L R	L R	Y N	Y N			Y N	
		BR /Supp	Y N	Y N	L R	L R	Y N	Y N			Y N	
		BR /Supp	Y N	Y N	L R	L R	Y N	Y N			Y N	

BR: Breast

Supp: Bottle Supplement

PACKING LIST FOR TRAVELLING

Getting out of the house for a quick trip to the mall is tricky with a new baby; packing for an overnight trip is even more difficult. So, my husband and I put together a packing list to be sure that we had everything we needed when we went traveling. We have modified our list from time to time, but here's a basic list that you can start with.

Category	Item	Number/day	Total Number	Check?
Essentials	Airline tickets			
	Passports			
	Other documents			
Day clothes	Set of clothes			
	Cardigan			
	Shoes			
Underwear	Undershirts			
	Socks			
Sleepwear	Pajamas			
Outerwear	Fleece jacket			
	Bunting bag			
	Gloves			
	Toque			
	Shoes			
	Sun hat			
Eating	Portable chair			
	Cereal			
	Vegetables			
	Fruit			
	Meat/alternatives			
	Bibs			
	Bowls			
	Spoons			
Toiletries	Box of tissues			
	Sunscreen			
	Shampoo/soap			
	Moisturizer			
	Bath thermometer			
	Face cloths			
	Towel			
Toys	Books			
	Toys for the car/plane/etc.			
	Toys to use at destination			

Category	Item	Number/day	Total Number	Check?
Breast/bottle	Cooler – small			
	Frozen ice packs			
	Sterile bottles with nipples			
	Sterile pump and bottle with lid			
	Breastfeeding pillow			
	Sterilizer			
	Thermos with hot water			
	Cup for defrosting			
	Water for mom			
	Snacks for mom			
	Receiving blanket			
Diapering	Diapers			
	Hand sanitizer			
	Diaper cream			
	Wipes			
	Change pads			
	Diaper bag			
Teething	Frozen face cloths			
	Teething gel			
	Teething ring			
	Bibs			
Sleeping	Blanket			
	Sheet			
	Bassinet/playpen			
Transportation	Baby carrier			
	Stroller			
	Blanket for stroller			
	Baby backpack			
Medical	Baby Tylenol			
	Any other medications			
	Thermometer			
	Doctor's phone number			
	Insurance information			
Other	Umbrella			
	Sunglasses			
	Baby monitor and receiver			
	Spare batteries			
	Laundry soap			

DIAPER BAG CHECKLIST

Item	Quantity	Check
Baby Guide to Calgary	1	
Diapers	4 per child	
Wipes/cloths	10 per child	
Diaper cream	1	
Plastic bags	4	
Change pad	1	
Set of clothes	2 per child	
Receiving blanket	2	
Facial tissues	Pack	
Hand sanitizer	1	
Hat and gloves	1	
Medication	?	
Pacifier	1	
Snack for baby	1	
Snack for mom	1	
Toys	2	
Disposable camera	1	
Bottle of water	1	
Clean shirt for parent	1	
Breast pads	2	
Nursing apron/blanket	1	

APPENDIX 2:
EVEN MORE ORGANIZATIONS AND PUBLICATIONS

ORGANIZATIONS

Families Matter
Phone: 205-5178
Website: www.familiesmatter.ca

Families Matter offers a wide range of programs for parents and children in Calgary, including:

- Family Life Education – Designed to facilitate understanding and skill development on the various ages and stages of child development as well as specific parenting challenges.
- Postpartum Support Program (205-5177) – Includes consultations with trained staff, weekly support groups, volunteer telephone support, couple's night and community presentations.
- Dads Are Parents Too – Designed for fathers and their child between ages two to six.
- L.E.A.P. – (Literacy - Education - Attachment Parenting – Play) – A combination program of education, forum for meeting other parents, playtime for children, and resources to help you with your parenting.
- Parent-Child Mother Goose Program – (See "Chapter Twelve: Activities" – "Drop-in Playcentres")
- In-Home Parent Support Program – Weekly home visits for families with children under six years.
- Healthy Families Program – For northeast Calgary families with a baby under three months old. This program requires a referral from a Public Health Nurse.
- Parents as Teachers (PAT) – (For families with children zero to six) Provides parents with access to quality parenting education at a low cost.
- Moving Forward – For moms and dads under twenty-three years of age with children under six years of age
- Parent Resource Phone Line (205-5189) – Weekdays 9 a.m. to 3 p.m.
- Family Resource Centres – Families Matter operates two resource centres in Calgary located in Keeler Elementary School and the Bowness Resource Centre. They have drop-in play and education programming, access to resources and child education facilitators.

Children's Cottage Society
Phone: 283–4200 or 233–2273 (Crisis Nursery 24-hour line)
Website: www.childrenscottage.ab.ca

The Children's Cottage provides a number of crisis, respite and support programs to families. See "Chapter Three: Parenting Help" – "Children's Cottage Society" for more information.

Calgary Attachment Parenting Group
Phone: 253-3954
Website: www.naturalfamilyfair.com (Click on "AP Group")

The Calgary Attachment Parenting Group provides support for parents who are interested in this style of parenting. In attachment parenting, the child is the infallible instruction manual. Attachment parenting teaches parents to read that manual. For more information, check the website.

Women in Need Society
Phone: 255-5102
Website: www.womeninneed.net

The Women In Need Society of Calgary (WINS) helps women coming out of shelters, single mothers and their children in crisis situations, women in transition and in need of support, new Canadians and others. Among other things, WINS operates three Family Resources Centres, whose mission is to help women help themselves. Women and their families receive help to connect with resources, services, and support in their local community.

COMMUNITY RESOURCE CENTRES AND FAMILY RESOURCE CENTRES

Community Resource Centres (CRCs) are places where people can obtain help and learn about what services are available to them in their local community. The CRCs can help with a wide range of social issues including counseling, needs around housing or food, parenting, or other concerns. They also work with a wide variety of other services, so they can help you find a program or service that you need. Contact your local community association to see if there is a CRC in your area. To contact your community association, look in the Yellow Pages under "Associations, Societies and Foundations" or check out the Federation of Calgary Communities' website at www.calgarycommunities.com.

Some CRCs house family resource centres, which provide services for families with children. Here's some information on two such family resource centres:

West Central Community and Family Resource Centre

Address: 3507A 17 Avenue S.W.
Phone: 543-0555
Website: http://members.shaw.ca/westcentralcrc
Serves: Spruce Cliff, Glendale, Coach Hill/Patterson, Rosscarrock, West Springs, Wildwood, Strathcona/Christie, Glendale Meadows, Glenbrook, Westgate, Killarney/Glengarry, Discovery Ridge, Signal Hill, Glamorgan, Shaganappi, Springbank Hill

Family programs at the resource centre include Nobody's Perfect Parenting Program (see "Chapter Three: Parenting Help" – "Parenting Courses"), toy lending (see "Chapter Twelve: Toys, Books and Games" – "Toys"), Mother Goose Program (see "Chapter Twelve: Activities" – "Playgroups") and Parent Talk. Parent Talk provides a place where parents can meet each other in a casual environment to gain insight and ideas on parenting. Contact the centre for details.

Millican-Ogden Community Association's Family Resource Centre

Address: 6901 20A Street S.E.
Phone: 720-3322
Website: www.moca-frc.org
Serves: Southeast communities within these boundaries: North – CNR tracks; East – CPR Mainline; South – Glenmore Trail, 24 Street, 90 Avenue; West – Bow River

This Family Resource Centre offers parenting courses, Mother Goose and other programs. Contact the centre for details.

PUBLICATIONS

The following is a list of publications relevant to parents of infants and toddlers.

Alberta Parent Quarterly

Website: www.albertaparentquarterly.com (Under construction) as of September 2007

This free magazine contains interesting articles about all aspects of being a parent or child caregiver. It is self-described as being "the only full glossy magazine for parents in Alberta". You can pick up your free copy at Sobeys, Second Cup, some schools, community centres, libraries and other locations. See the website under "Distribution" for a complete list of locations. Annual subscriptions are available for $16. This magazine does not have a lot of information about infants but you may find it interesting nonetheless.

Birth of a Mother

Website: www.birthofamother.com

Self-described as "Calgary's magazine for healthy pregnancy, baby and family lifestyle", this magazine is published by bo bébé and is available free in bo bébé stores and at many other locations around the city. The articles are on issues of interest to new parents and contain relevant advertising.

Calgary's Child

Website: www.calgaryschild.com

This is a great publication for Calgary families. It is a free sixty-page bimonthly paper that can be picked up at about six hundred locations in Calgary. Well worth your time to do it! Annual subscriptions are also available for about $15 so you can get it delivered to your home. Calgary's Child contains articles on safety, parenting, health and wellness, a calendar of family-oriented events in the city and lots of advertising from children's stores, photographers, educational and recreational companies. You can find out about things to do or where to buy the things you are looking for.

Pick-up locations include Safeway, Co-op, all City of Calgary Parks and Recreation facilities, many elementary schools, public libraries and stands at restaurants and coffee shops. Calgary's Child also has a very good website.

Got My Kids
Website: www.gotmykids.com

This magazine describes itself as the "ultimate parent resource." There is a separate version for each quadrant of the city, listing local service providers within that quadrant. The listings are advertising-based. The website features a free classified section, parents' forum and local event listings. The magazine sells a savings card for $20 which provides you discounts at a number of child-focused businesses.

The Hybrid Mom
Website: www.hybridmom.com

The Hybrid Mom is a quarterly U.S.-based magazine distributed by Gymboree. It defines the hybrid mom as a woman who has discarded outdated and unrealistic concepts of motherhood. The magazine contains some interesting articles and the website features a chat room.

The Mompreneur
Website: www.themompreneur.com

The Mompreneur magazine is a free monthly national magazine. It focuses on women who are balancing motherhood with being an entrepreneur. The publisher also provides seminars, extensive networking opportunities and an online forum.

Today's Parent
Website: www.todaysparent.com

This Canadian magazine contains a lot of interesting information for new parents. Some content will be relevant to you as a parent of a new baby and the rest will give you a good preview of the years to come. Their website is definitely worth visiting and has a separate "Baby" section. At the time of writing a one-year subscription was about $17.

The Western Parent
Phone: 543-3775
Website: www.western-parent.com

This free bi-monthly paper often features articles on parenting babies with special needs and contains articles on general parenting as well. It can be picked up at over a hundred locations including major grocery stores (Safeway, Co-op, and IGA), public libraries, leisure centres, and some schools and shops.

USEFUL WEBSITES

Here is a list of some useful websites not otherwise mentioned in this book:

Baby Centre
Website: www.babycenter.com

There are many articles of interest on this website, to new and expecting parents, including articles on health and safety topics.

Calgary Babyzone
Website: www.babyzone.com (Find Calgary in "Local Events and Resources")

This website features a directory of what is going on around Calgary. The database can be searched by age group, so you can find events suitable for your child.

Canadian Parents
Website: www.canadianparents.com

It calls itself "Canada's Parenting Community". The site provides a lot of information relevant to parents. Check out the "Babies" link for articles on health, feeding, sleep, safety, child care, and more. There are also message boards for peer support.

Caring for Kids by the Canadian Paediatric Society
Website: www.caringforkids.cps.ca

This site provides information on matters such as caring for your new baby (e.g. jaundice in newborns, colic and pacifiers), nutrition (e.g. breastfeeding, cows' milk and babies' iron needs) and common illnesses.

Child & Family Canada
Website: www.cfc-efc.ca

This is a partnership of "fifty Canadian non-profit organizations [that] have come together under the banner of Child & Family Canada to provide quality, credible resources on children and families on an easy-to-navigate website." You will find links to the websites of the partner organizations, along with a very large library of articles.

e-Parenting Network
Website: www.eparentingnetwork.ca

This website features interactive web TV segments covering a variety of topics important to parents. Topics include safety in the home, car and neighbourhood, breastfeeding, nutrition and effective parenting strategies.

Invest in Kids
Website: www.investinkids.ca

This website is maintained by a Canadian non-profit charity. It aims to strengthen parenting knowledge skills and confidence.

Health Canada
Website: www.hc-sc.gc.ca (go to "Healthy Living", then "Children & Adolescents", then "Parenting")

This site contains information on official guidelines for infant nutrition, as well as articles on safety and parent-child relationships.

iVillage
Website: www.ivillage.com
               (go to "Pregnancy & Parenting", then "Baby")

This website contains a lot of advertising and pop-ups, but its "Babies" section contains interesting articles on topics such as sleep, health, development, safety and feeding.

The National Parenting Center
Website: www.tnpc.com

This U.S.-based site contains general parenting articles and also offers consumer information on products.

Zero to Three
Website: www.zerotothree.org

The "Parenting" section of this American website has many articles of interest to new parents. Topics include attachment, babysitting, crying, development, infant massage, and reading your baby's signals and routines, just to name a few.

APPENDIX 3:
ACTIVITY TIMELINE AND REMINDERS FOR THE FIRST AND SECOND YEARS

This list is intended to help you plan and enjoy your baby's first two years. Please note that it is not comprehensive and some things on this list can be done earlier or later.

BEFORE OR SOON AFTER BIRTH

- If you are planning to work after your parental leave, start considering child care options and put yourself on the waiting list of any child care establishments that you are interested in. See "Chapter Sixteen: Child Care Options" – "Looking for Child Care after Parental Leave".
- Determine what type of equipment and products you are going to buy for your baby. See "Chapter Seven: Clothing, Accessories and other Sundry" – "Baby Product Advice".
- Sign up for the free car seat installation course by CHR. See "Chapter Seven: Clothing, Accessories and Other Sundry" – "Car Seats".
- Consider whether you will use cloth or disposable diapers. See "Chapter Seven: Clothing, Accessories and Other Sundry" – "Diapers".
- Take a free breastfeeding course. See "Chapter Two: Surviving the First Six Weeks" – "Breastfeeding".
- Have a look to see how popular the names you are considering for baby have been. See "Chapter One: Administration" – "Baby Naming".
- If appropriate, take the CHR course Helping Your Child Adjust to a New Baby. See "Chapter Three: Parenting Help" – "Calgary Health Region".

MONTH 1

- Read "Chapter Two: Surviving the First Six Weeks".
- Read "Chapter Three: Parenting Help".
- Register your baby for her two-month immunizations. See "Chapter Four: Health of Baby and Mom" – "Immunizations".
- Fill out your employment insurance application within four weeks of stopping working. See "Chapter One: Administration" – "Employment Insurance".
- Add your baby to your work benefit plan. See "Chapter One: Administration" – "Adding Baby to Work Benefit Plan".

- Buy yourself a nursing bra if you are breastfeeding. See "Chapter Two: Surviving the First Six Weeks" – "Nursing Bras".
- Make Mom's six week appointment with her physician.
- Get all your paperwork done or at least get it started. See "Chapter One: Administrative Issues".
- If you are breastfeeding and need assistance, contact a breastfeeding clinic. See "Chapter Two: Surviving the First Six Weeks" – "Breastfeeding".
- Send out birth announcements and start a time capsule box. See "Chapter Fifteen: Mementos".

MONTH 2

- Take your baby for his two-month immunizations and register for his four-month immunizations. See "Chapter Four: Health of Baby and Mom" – "Immunizations".
- Start thinking about acquiring more clothes for your baby, new or used, as well as equipment. Have a look at sales and start planning your strategy for acquiring clothing and equipment. See "Chapter Seven: Clothing, Accessories and Other Sundry".
- Consider setting up a Parents' Club. See "Chapter Twelve: Activities" – "Organizing Your Parent's Club."
- Think about using a babysitter occasionally so that your baby gets used to another caregiver and you get a night out once in a while. See "Chapter Sixteen: Child Care Options" – "Babysitting".
- Consider registering with the CHR for Baby & You or for Daddies & Babies. See "Chapter Fourteen: Courses" – "Calgary Health Region's Courses".
- Keep going on your paper work. See "Chapter One: Administrative Issues".
- At the very least, fill out the Canada Child Tax Benefit form. See "Chapter One: Administrative Issues".
- If you are ready to go for a few walks or start exercising, read "Chapter Eleven: Fitness and Getting Back Into Shape".

MONTH 3

- Start looking at a Registered Education Savings Plan for your baby. See "Chapter One: Administrative Issues" – "Registered Education Savings Plan".
- Consider taking yoga classes! See "Chapter Eleven: Fitness and Getting Back Into Shape" – "Fitness Classes and Working Out".

MONTH 4

- Take your baby for her four-month immunizations and register for her six-month immunizations. See "Chapter Four: Health of Baby and Mom" – "Immunizations".
- Start shopping for high chairs. Your baby should be ready for solids in another couple of months.
- Consider registering for the CHR's "Feeding Your Baby" course. See "Chapter Fourteen: Courses" – "Calgary Health Region's Courses".

MONTH 5

- Start babyproofing to prepare for your baby's mobile stage. See "Chapter Six: Baby Safety" – "Babyproofing".
- You may need to start shopping for your next car seat. Some car seats take four to six weeks to order, so start shopping ahead of time. See "Chapter Seven: Clothing, Accessories and Other Sundry" – "Car Seats".

MONTH 6

- Take your baby for his six-month immunizations. See "Chapter Four: Health of Baby and Mom" – "Immunizations".
- Take baby in for an eye exam by an eye care specialist (optometrist or ophthalmologist). See "Chapter Four: Health of Baby and Mom" – "Eye Check Ups for your Baby".
- If you are planning to work after your parental leave, actively start looking for child care. See "Chapter Sixteen: Child Care Options" – "Looking for Child Care after your Parental Leave".

MONTH 7

- Register for Baby Story Time at the Calgary Public Library. See "Chapter Fourteen: Courses" – "Calgary Public Library".

MONTH 8

- Consider attending weekly playgroups to give your baby plenty of interesting play and to give yourself an opportunity to socialize. See "Chapter Twelve: Activities" – "Playgroups".
- Don't forget to schedule your own dentist appointment.
- Consider signing up for a music class. See "Chapter Fourteen: Courses" – "Music Classes".

MONTH 9

- Register your baby for her twelve-month immunizations. See "Chapter Four: Health of Baby and Mom" – "Immunizations".
- Consider signing up for a swimming class. See "Chapter Fourteen: Courses" – "Swimming with Your Baby".

MONTH 10

- If you are planning to return to work after your parental leave, contact your employer about returning to work.
- Complete your time capsule box for your baby. See "Chapter Twelve: Mementos" – "Time Capsule".

MONTH 11

- If you are returning to work, introduce your baby to his future caregiver or daycare facility.
- Time to buy a new car seat for your little one. See "Chapter Seven: Clothing, Accessories and Other Sundry" – "Car Seats".

MONTH 12

- First birthday! Congratulations on the close of an exciting year.
- Take your baby for his twelve-month immunizations. See "Chapter Four: Health of Baby and Mom" – "Immunizations".
- Take your baby for her one-year physical exam by the family doctor or paediatrician.

MONTH 13

- Start doing additional babyproofing as your baby becomes more mobile.
- Look into switching your baby from formula to homogenized milk.
- If you are returning to work, give yourself some time to adjust to the new routine.
- Install a new car seat if your baby is over twenty pounds.
- Apply for the Alberta Child Care Subsidy if your child is attending daycare, home care or being cared for by a nanny.

MONTH 14

- Consider picking up some stacking cups for your baby to play with.
- Time for Mom's annual appointment with her physician.

MONTH 14

- Sign up for the Calgary Health Region's free "Picky Eaters" course for children between one to three years old. See "Chapter Five: Healthy Eating for Baby and Toddler" – "Calgary Health Region" – "Feeding Your Toddler".

MONTH 15

- Start looking for a paediatric dentist or family dentist and make an appointment for your child to have an assessment. See "Chapter Four: Health of Baby and Mom" – "Caring for Your New Baby's Teeth".

MONTH 16

- Consider what you are going to do with your toddler's outgrown clothing and equipment. See "Chapter Ten: Just for You" – "Outgrown Clothing and Equipment".

MONTH 17

- Consider attending a refresher course of Infant CPR or Safety First through the CHR. See "Chapter Fourteen: Courses" – "Calgary Health Region's Courses".

MONTH 18

- Take your baby for his eighteen-month immunizations.
- Don't forget your own dentist appointment.

MONTH 19 TO MONTH 24

- Start doing additional babyproofing as your baby becomes taller.
- Determine whether your child's speech is within the range for appropriate development. See "Chapter Four: Health of Baby and Mom" – "Speech Therapy and Language Development".
- Start getting used to your baby's newest word: "No!"
- Second birthday! Congratulations on the close of another exciting year.

APPENDIX 4:
FREE AND INEXPENSIVE ACTIVITIES AND COURSES

FREE ACTIVITIES AND COURSES

- Enjoy a short walk in your area.
- Try some of the walks suggested in "Chapter Eleven: Fitness and Getting Back Into Shape" – "Walks".
- Start exercising once you have had the all-clear from your physician. Read "Chapter Eleven: Fitness and Getting Back Into Shape".
- Try a hike or two. Some suggestions are listed in "Chapter Eleven: Fitness and Getting Back Into Shape" – "Hiking".
- Check the library for some of the recommended books in the section "Chapter Twelve: Toys, Books and Games" – "Games to Play with Your Little One", and try some of the games suggested.
- Head into Airdrie Family Services for a free playgroup. See "Chapter Twelve: Activities" – "Drop-in Playcentres".
- Enjoy a trip to a pet store to view the fish, birds and mammals. Babies and toddlers love this.
- Meet up with some of your friends for a weekly Parents' Club meeting or play dates. See "Chapter Twelve: Activities" – "Organizing Your Parent's Club".
- Review VRRI's schedule to find out when there is no charge for entry into their pool or gym.
- Sign up for the BP BirthPlace Forest. See "Chapter Fifteen: Mementos" – "BP BirthPlace Forest".
- Head to Wild Rose United Church on a Thursday for a free playgroup with the Attachment Parenting Playgroup. See "Chapter Twelve: Activities" – "Playgroups" – "Attachment Parenting Playgroup".
- Drop by one of the Parent Link Alberta centres to access resources and have a chat with other parents. See "Chapter Three: Parenting Help" – "Parent Link Alberta Centres".
- Sign up to attend the Parent-Child Mother-Goose Program. See "Chapter Twelve: Activities" – "Playgroups".
- Join Laughing Families on the first Thursday of each month. See "Chapter Three: Parenting Help".

- Attend the CHR's car seat installation course. See "Chapter Seven: Clothing, Accessories and Other Sundry" – "Car Seats" – "General Information".
- Sign up for the Feeding Your Baby course offered by the CHR. See "Chapter Fourteen: Courses" – "Calgary Health Region's Courses".
- Sign up for Baby Story Time at your local Calgary Public Library. See "Chapter Fourteen: Courses" – "Calgary Public Library Children's Programs".
- Put together a time capsule box for your baby. See "Chapter Fifteen: Mementos" – "Time Capsule".
- Attend a CBC Learn at Lunch. See "Chapter Twelve: Activities" – "Keeping Your Mind Active During Your Parental Leave" – "CBC Learn at Lunch".
- Try the Baby & You course offered to moms or the Daddies & Babies course for dads by the CHR. See "Chapter Fourteen: Courses" – "Calgary Health Region's Courses".
- Check out Calgary's Child annual free family Fun Fair. See "Chapter Twelve: Activities" – "Festivals and Special Events" – "Calgary's Child Annual Free Family Fun Fair".
- Attend the Calgary Health Region's Baby Care Fair. See "Chapter Three: Parenting Help".
- Head down to the Devonian Gardens for a wander. See "Chapter Twelve: Activities" – "Calgary Sites" – "Devonian Gardens".
- Check out the Airdrie Festival of Lights. See "Chapter Twelve: Activities" – "Festivals and Special Events" – "Airdrie Festival of Lights".
- Register for the free Picky Eaters course at the Calgary Health Region. See "Chapter Five: Healthy Eating for Baby and Toddler" – "Calgary Health Region" – "Feeding your Toddler".
- Take a tour of the Bernard Callebaut chocolate factory. See "Chapter Twelve: Activities" – "Calgary Sites" – "Bernard Callebaut".
- Enjoy one of the many story times hosted in bookstores and toy stores around Calgary. See "Chapter Twelve: Toys, Books and Games" – "Calgary and Area Toy Stores".
- Go for a walk through the Inglewood Bird Sanctuary. See "Chapter Twelve: Activities" – "Calgary Sites" – "Inglewood Bird Sanctuary".
- During the Calgary Stampede, attend a Stampede breakfast with other parents and babies. See "Chapter Twelve: Activities" – "Calgary Sites" – "Calgary Stampede".
- In the summer, go to a City of Calgary wading pool and let your baby splash in the water.
- Head to Market Mall for a free thirty-minute playtime at "Kids at Play". See "Chapter Twelve: Activities" – "Drop-in Playcentres".
- Go for a walk around Market Mall when the weather is poor.
- Visit your local playground or park. See "Chapter Twelve: Activities"– "Calgary Sites" – "Calgary Parks".
- Relax at home with your baby and cuddle.

ACTIVITIES AND COURSES UNDER $16 PER SESSION

- Head out to an afternoon movie. See "Chapter Twelve: Activities" – "Movies".
- Attend the Calgary International Children's Festival. See "Chapter Twelve: Activities" – "Calgary Children's Festival".
- Hang out at the Calgary Tower and enjoy a 360-degree view of Calgary. See "Chapter Twelve: Activities" – "Calgary Sites" – "Calgary Tower".
- Head to Heritage Park for the day; get there before 10 a.m. for a free "Stampede-style" breakfast for the family. See "Chapter Twelve: Activities" – "Calgary Sites" – "Heritage Park".
- Go to the Calgary Stampede grounds for the day. See "Chapter Twelve: Activities" – "Calgary Sites" – "Calgary Stampede".
- Wander around the Calgary Zoo, Botanical Garden and Prehistoric Park. You can get 50% off admission if the weather is poor. See "Chapter Twelve: Activities" – "Calgary Sites" – "Calgary Zoo".
- Check out the Family-A-Fair (formerly the Mom and Tots' Fair). See "Chapter Twelve: Activities" – "Festivals and Special Events" – "Family-A-Fair".
- Sign up for the Cardel Place Babies in Toyland playgroup. It works out to about $7 per session. See "Chapter Twelve: Activities" – "Playgroups" – "Cardel Place".
- Head to Canada Olympic Park with your baby for a self-guided tour. See "Chapter Twelve: Activities" – "Calgary Sites" – "Canada Olympic Park".
- Head to IKEA for breakfast or lunch.
- Spend an afternoon at Aggie days. See "Chapter Twelve: Activities" – "Festivals and Special Events" – "Aggie Days".
- Head to the Olympic Oval for a skate.
- Head to Calaway Park after 2 p.m. when adult entry is only $15 and children under twenty-four months are free. See "Chapter Twelve: Activities" – "Calgary Sites".
- Have a wander around Fort Calgary. See "Chapter Twelve: Activities" – "Calgary Sites" – "Fort Calgary".
- Try the St. David's Time Out program to give your baby to some time to play while you have a chat. See "Chapter Twelve: Activities" – "Playgroups" – "St. David's Time Out".
- Head south to The Saskatoon Farm for some saskatoon berry picking. See "Chapter Twelve: Activities" – "Calgary Sites".
- Take your baby to a weekly Salsa Baby or Salsa Tots class. See "Chapter Ten: Just for You" – "Salsa Baby!"
- Sign up for a membership at the Calgary Public Library. See "Chapter Fourteen: Courses" – "Calgary Public Library Children's Programs".

- Head to the airport with your kids. Let them watch the planes take off. You will only have to pay for parking at $3.75 per hour. Pack a lunch since airport food is pricey! See "Chapter Twelve: Activities" – "Calgary Sites".
- Drop in at an indoor playcentre. See "Chapter Twelve: Activities" – "Drop-In Playcentres".
- Rent a Chariot bike trailer or cross-country ski trailer and head out cross-country skiing or biking with your baby. See "Chapter Eleven: Fitness and Getting Back Into Shape".
- Head to the Telus World of Science for the day. Bring your lunch. See "Chapter Twelve: Activities" – "Calgary Sites".
- Go for a swim at your local pool and take advantage of any available babysitting services. Or take your baby to an indoor wading pool at one of the City of Calgary aquatic and fitness facilities or leisure centres. Take advantage of special admission deals on certain days. Check the City's Recreation in the City Program Guide. See "Chapter Fourteen: Courses" – "Swimming with your Baby".
- Drop into a music class at bo bébé's Music and Play, space permitting. See "Chapter Fourteen: Courses" – "Music Courses".
- Consider signing up for a playgroup program: a Gymboree program, the Inquiring Minds Playgroup, YMCA's Reading, Rocking, Running and Kangaroo & Climbers or St. David's Time Out. See "Chapter Twelve: Activities" – "Playgroups".
- Try a parenting course at Parents and Children Together. See "Chapter Three: Parenting Help" – "Parenting Courses" – "Parents and Children Together".

APPENDIX 5:
ACTIVITIES AND COURSES SUITABLE TO BABY'S AGE

ANY TIME IN THE FIRST TWENTY-FOUR MONTHS

- Tour the Bernard Callebaut chocolate factory. See "Chapter Twelve: Activities" – "Calgary Sites".
- Visit the Calgary Tower. See "Chapter Twelve: Activities" – "Calgary Sites".
- Visit Heritage Park. See "Chapter Twelve: Activities" – "Calgary Sites".
- Attend the Calgary Health Region's Baby Care Fair. See "Chapter Three: Parenting Help".
- Start your Saturday morning at the symphony (SMATS). See "Chapter Twelve: Activities" – "Festivals and Special Events".
- During the Calgary Stampede, spend a day at the Stampede grounds. See "Chapter Twelve: Activities" – "Calgary Sites".
- Spend a few hours during July or August picking saskatoon berries at The Saskatoon Farm. See "Chapter Twelve: Activities" – "Calgary Sites".
- Visit the Calgary Zoo, Botanical Garden and Prehistoric Park. See "Chapter Twelve: Activities" – "Calgary Sites".
- Head to Heritage Park for the Twelve Days of Christmas. "Chapter Twelve: Activities" – "Festivals and Special Events".
- Join Laughing Families on the first Thursday of each month. See "Chapter Three: Parenting Help".
- Enjoy one of the many story times hosted in bookstores and toy stores around Calgary. See "Chapter Twelve: Toys, Books and Games" – "Calgary and Area Toy Stores".
- Walk through the Devonian Gardens. See "Chapter Twelve: Activities" – "Calgary Sites".
- Go for a self-guided tour of Canada Olympic Park. See "Chapter Twelve: Activities" – "Calgary Sites".
- Sign up for a parenting course. See "Chapter Three: Parenting Help" - "Parenting Courses".
- Picnic in your backyard or in the local park.
- Visit the Calgary Maple Festival in mid-March to early April. See "Chapter Twelve: Activities" – "Festivals and Special Events".
- Visit Fort Calgary. See "Chapter Twelve: Activities" – "Calgary Sites".
- Attend an Infant CPR or Safety First course through the CHR. See

"Chapter Fourteen: Courses" – "Calgary Health Region's Courses".

- Go to the Family-A-Fair (formerly Mom and Tots' Fair) in March. See "Chapter Twelve: Activities" – "Festivals and Special Events".
- Enjoy an evening at the Airdrie Festival of Lights. See "Chapter Twelve: Activities" – "Festivals and Special Events".
- Sing along with the carolers at the Calgary Zoo Lights. See "Chapter Twelve: Activities" – "Festivals and Special Events".
- Work out or swim while your baby is being looked after by the babysitting service at the City of Calgary facilities, Talisman Centre or YMCA. See "Chapter Eleven: Fitness and Getting Back Into Shape" – "Fitness Classes and Working Out".
- Attend the Calgary Child's annual free family fun fair. See "Chapter Twelve: Activities" – "Festivals and Special Events".
- Work on your baby's time capsule box or first year scrapbook. See "Chapter Fifteen: Mementos" – "Time Capsule".
- Go for a walk or a get-together with your Parents' Club.
- Head to the airport and enjoy watching the planes take off and land. See "Chapter Twelve: Activities" – "Calgary Sites" – "Calgary International Airport".
- Hike in the mountains with your baby or toddler in a carrier.
- Attend St. David's Time Out Program. See "Chapter Twelve: Activities" – "Playgroups" – "St. David's Time Out".
- Attend music classes with your baby: at Mount Royal College, at Creative Kids, with a Kindermusik teacher or through the Suzuki Talent Education Society. See "Chapter Fourteen: Courses" – "Music Classes".
- Head to a playgroup: Mother Goose Program, Brilliant Beginnings Educational Centre, Les Copains de Jeux, Gymboree, Inquiring Minds Playgroup, Parents and Children Together, or the TTMAC. See "Chapter Twelve: Activities" – "Playgroups".

UNDER THREE MONTHS

- Bring your baby along to a baby-friendly movie (Stars and Strollers at Cineplex Odeon or Reel Babies at Empire Theatres). See "Chapter Twelve: Activities" – "Movies".
- Sign up for the programs at Gymboree. See "Chapter Twelve: Activities" – "Playgroups".
- Register for a Bright Babies class with Brilliant Beginnings. See "Chapter Twelve: Activities" – "Playgroups"
- Register for Baby & You or Daddies & Babies, Infant Massage or Playtime with Dad through the CHR. See "Chapter Fourteen: Courses" – "Calgary Health Region's Courses".
- Attend a post-natal yoga course with your baby at the City of Calgary facilities, at the YWCA, at the Yoga Studio or through the CHR. See "Chapter Eleven: Fitness and Getting Back Into Shape" – "Fitness Classes and Working Out".

- Attend a fitness class for moms or dads and babies at the City of Calgary facilities or VRRI. See "Chapter Eleven: Fitness and Getting Back Into Shape" – "Fitness Classes and Working Out".
- Enroll in a class at bo bébé. See "Chapter Fourteen: Courses" – "Music Classes".
- Attend a CBC Learn at Lunch discussion. See "Chapter Twelve: Activities" – "Keeping Your Mind Active During Your Parental Leave" – "CBC Learn at Lunch".

FROM THREE TO SIX MONTHS

- Head to a movie at Cineplex Odeon or Empire Theatres. See "Chapter Twelve: Activities" – "Movies".
- Consider signing up for the Child and Infant Learning and Development Research Group at the University of Calgary. See "Chapter Four: Health of Baby and Mom" – "Child and Infant Learning and Development Research Group".
- Sign up for Gymboree. See "Chapter Twelve: Activities" – "Playgroups".
- Try the classes at bo bébé. See "Chapter Fourteen: Courses" – "Music Classes".
- Participate in a fitness class for moms or dads and babies at the City of Calgary facilities or VRRI. See "Chapter Eleven: Fitness and Getting Back Into Shape" – "Fitness Classes and Working Out".
- Enroll in a post-natal yoga course with your baby at the City of Calgary facilities, at the Yoga Studio or through the CHR at the Talisman Centre. See "Chapter Eleven: Fitness and Getting Back Into Shape" – "Fitness Classes and Working Out".
- Join a swimming class with your baby at the YMCA.

FROM SIX TO NINE MONTHS

- Sign up for the Feeding Your Baby, Baby Talk or Sleep Workshop for Tired Parents courses offered by the CHR. See "Chapter Fourteen: Courses" – "Calgary Health Region's Courses".
- Go to your local park and check out the swings if your baby's neck is strong enough.
- Once your baby is mobile, enjoy a drop-in playcentre.
- Register for Babies in Toyland at Cardel Place. See "Chapter Twelve: Activities" – "Playgroups".
- Sign up for Baby Story Time at the Calgary Public Library. See "Chapter Fourteen: Courses" – "Calgary Public Library Children's Programs".
- Enroll in swimming classes at the City of Calgary facilities, Talisman Centre, the University of Calgary, the YMCA or VRRI. See "Chapter Fourteen: Courses" – "Swimming with your Baby".
- Register for music classes. See "Chapter Fourteen: Courses" – "Music Classes".

FROM NINE TO TWELVE MONTHS

- Visit your local park playground.
- Register for the YMCA's Gym and Stories course (after ten months and walking). See "Chapter Twelve: Activities" – "Playgroups".
- Sign up for Baby Story Time at the Calgary Public Library. See "Chapter Fourteen: Courses" – "Calgary Public Library Children's Programs".
- Head to a drop-in playcentre. See "Chapter Twelve: Activities" – "Drop-In Playcentres".
- Sign up for the playgroup program at Gymboree. See "Chapter Twelve: Activities" – "Playgroups".
- Attend swimming classes at the City of Calgary facilities, Talisman Centre, the University of Calgary, the YMCA or VRRI. See "Chapter Fourteen: Courses" – "Swimming with your Baby".
- Register for music classes. See "Chapter Fourteen: Courses" – "Music Classes".
- Attend the YMCA courses for toddlers, Reading, Rocking, Running and Kangaroos & Climbers. See "Chapter Twelve: Activities" – "Playgroups".

FROM TWELVE TO EIGHTEEN MONTHS

- Register for the free Picky Eaters course at the Calgary Health Region. See "Chapter Five: Healthy Eating for Baby and Toddler" – "Calgary Health Region" – "Feeding your Toddler".
- Consider heading to Calaway Park to enjoy the day. See "Chapter Twelve: Activities" – "Calgary Sites" – "Calaway Park".
- Register for the Inquisitive Toddlers class with Brilliant Beginnings. See "Chapter Twelve: Activities" – "Playgroups"
- Attend the Calgary Children's Festival held in late May or early June. See "Chapter Twelve: Activities" – "Calgary Children's Festival".

FROM EIGHTEEN TO TWENTY-FOUR MONTHS

- Consider heading to Butterfield Acres Farm with your toddler. See "Chapter Twelve: Activities" – "Calgary Sites" – "Butterfield Acres Farm".
- Spend some time at the Telus World of Science. See "Chapter Twelve: Activities" – "Calgary Sites" – "Telus World of Science".

APPENDIX 6:
ACTIVITIES BY SEASON

SPRING

- Registration for preschool starts in February through March.
- Family-A-Fair (Formerly Mom and Tots' Fair) holds a show over a weekend in March.
- Calgary Maple Festival takes place in mid-March or early April.
- Aggie days are held during April.
- Community sales can save you lots of money. Check out www.babyguidetocalgary.com for a listing.
- Butterfield Acres Easter Egg Hunt is on!
- Calaway Park is open on weekends only starting in late May.
- Some farmers' markets start to open in May.
- Butterfield Acres opens in May.
- Start heading out for walks when the weather gets warm enough.

SUMMER

- Ultimate Trains in Nanton is open.
- Heritage Park is open daily from May to September.
- Calgary Child's annual free Family Fun fair runs the first Saturday of May.
- Calgary Children's Festival runs in late May or early June.
- Yeehaw! The Calgary Stampede runs for ten days in July.
- Late July to early August, saskatoon berries are ripe for the picking at The Saskatoon Farm.
- Enjoy Calgary's spray pools.
- Head out for walks.
- Time to go hiking.
- Enjoy the farmers' markets

AUTUMN

- Calaway Park is open on weekends only.
- Butterfield Acres runs Harvest Pumpkin Hunts.
- Community sales can save you lots of money. Check out www.babyguidetocalgary.com for a listing.
- Heritage Park is open on weekends only during September and October.
- Heritage Park offers free rides on Thanksgiving Monday.
- Farmer's markets start to close.
- Flu vaccinations are available through the Community Health Units.

WINTER

- Airdrie Festival of Lights is held from late November to December 31.
- Calgary Zoo Lights festival is held.
- Twelve days of Christmas runs on weekends at Heritage Park.
- Ski season comes.

ALL YEAR ROUND

- Calgary's farmers' markets
- Calgary International Airport
- Bernard Callebaut
- Calgary Tower
- Your local park
- Indoor swimming pools and gyms
- Calgary Zoo
- Devonian Gardens
- Canada Olympic Park
- Inglewood Bird Sanctuary and Nature Centre
- Fort Calgary
- The Saskatoon Farm
- Telus World of Science
- Drop-in playcentres

APPENDIX 7:
TIME AND MONEY SAVING TIPS

MONEY SAVING TIPS

- Check out "Appendix 4: Free and Inexpensive Activities and Courses"
- Try using the non-brand name diapers available at grocery and drug stores. Many of them offer the same features as brand name diapers (stretch, leak protection, etc.) but cost substantially less.
- Visit community sales for used clothing, toys and equipment.
- Check out second-hand stores for baby clothing and toys.
- Consign your maternity clothing at a maternity store.
- Put your favourite DVD on hold at the library and pick it up for a movie night at home.
- Buy clothes for your baby a year ahead during the end-of-season sales.
- Add some spice to your children's toy collection by checking out the toy lending libraries in Calgary. See "Chapter Twelve: Toys, Books and Games" – "Toy Libraries and Toy Banks".
- Shop at garage sales and consignment stores.
- Head to Chic Mama for your haircut and bring your baby. No need to pay a babysitter. "Chapter Ten: Just for You" – "Have Baby Will Travel (to Spa)!"
- Exchange hand-me-downs with other families.
- Use toy libraries or swap toys with other families.
- Carefully consider what you really need and what you don't.
- Use fewer paper products by switching to cloths that can be washed and reused for household cleanup.
- Use facecloths and water instead of commercial baby wipes.
- Plan your vacation during the low season.
- Have a picnic instead of eating out.
- Make some or all of your baby's food.
- Log on to www.calgaryattractions.com and print coupons for discounted entry to Calgary's attractions.
- Prepare a weekly menu and shop specifically for that menu to eliminate impulse buying.

- Take advantage of discounts on customer appreciation days at your grocery store. You can bulk up your shopping list for this day to lower your overall costs per month. For example, at Safeway on the first Tuesday of every month customers receive 10% off on their purchases with the Safeway Club Card.
- Instead of buying gifts, give homemade gifts such as cookies or banana bread.
- Swap babysitting services with your friends or join a babysitting co-op.
- Take advantage of the free activities and activities under $16 listed in "Appendix 3".

TIME SAVING TIPS

- Make enough dinner for two or more nights. Freeze the rest or serve it the following evening.
- Hire a local teenager to mow your lawn and shovel your walks.
- Make your meals in bulk.
- Consider telephone or online banking for automatic bill payment.
- Sign up for quick passes at your favourite gas stations. These are convenient when it is really cold outside and you never have to go inside to pay.
- Use your answering machine. Don't worry about trying to get to the phone every time it rings; save up the messages and get back to people when you have time.
- Use a speaker phone or headset on a cordless phone so that you can go about your chores while you listen to your messages or make a phone call.
- Keep your diaper bag ready to go at all times and keep an emergency toy and snacks in the bottom.
- When you are shopping ask store personnel for help.
- Order your groceries online.
- Maintain a safe, entertaining spot for the baby in most rooms. Keeping a bouncer in the bathroom or an ExerSaucer in the living room will allow you to take a quick bathroom break or make yourself some lunch while keeping your baby safe and entertained.
- Whenever you leave a room, take a moment and pick up any objects that don't belong there.
- Open, read and sort your mail as soon as you bring it inside.
- Take fifteen minutes at the end of each day to clean the kitchen and living room. This will help reduce the build-up of clutter.
- Consider utilizing a BBQ to its full potential in the warmer months. Not only can you make fresh, quick and healthy meals, but without pots and pans the clean-up is minimal.

INDEX

211 Calgary, 42, 259
22TEETH, 67

A

Aboriginal Parent Link Centre, 43
Aggie Days, 205
Airdrie Family Services, 44, 198, 199, 215
Airdrie Festival of Lights, 206
Airdriemommas, 130, 131
Airport; see Calgary International Airport
Alberta Association for Family Day Home
   Services, 258
Alberta Association of Optometrists, 69
Alberta Centennial Education Savings Plan, 8
Alberta Child Care Subsidy Program, 14,
   260
Alberta Child Health Benefit, 67
Alberta Children's Services (ACS), 12, 13,
   14, 15, 43, 257, 258, 276, 278
Alberta Children's Hospital, 19, 48, 57, 71
Alberta Family Employment Tax Credit
   (AFETC), 8, 9
Alberta Health and Wellness, 3, 4, 70, 74, 75,
   76, 82
Alberta Health Care, 3, 67, 72, 265
Alberta Medical Association, 25
Alberta Parent Quarterly, 296
Alberta Poison Control Centre, see Poison
   and Drug Information Centre
Alberta Speech-Language Association, 68
Amaranth Whole Foods Market, 77
Annie the Nanny, 50
Aquatic and Fitness Centres (AFCs), 168,
   172, 173
art classes, 238
Ask Dr. Sears website, 57
Attachment Parenting, 54, 192, 293, 294
Awo Taan Family Wellness - Parent Link
   Centre, 43

B

Babies "R" Us, 93, 218
Baby & You for Moms, 51, 129
baby announcements, 246
baby blues. see postpartum depression
   support
Baby Care Fair, 45
Baby Gourmet, 76
Baby Love Products/Kidalog, 94
Baby Marketplace, the, 94
Baby Story Time, 234
Baby Talk, 229

BabyCentre website, 298
babyproofing, 80–88, 91, 136, 138, 144
babyScoop™, 89
babysitting certification courses, 253
babysitting co-ops, 254
Babyvibe, 130, 131
Banff, 144, 160, 165, 167
Barclay Mall, 189
Bay, the, 31, 90
Beaners Fun Cuts for Kids, 108
Bellies & Babies by Nicole, 250
Bellies, Babies and Beyond, 175
benefit plan, 4, 35, 68, 72
Bernard Callebaut, 178
Bethany Chapel Toy Lending Library, 214,
   215
Bikini Bootcamp, 176
Birth Certificate, 45
Birth of a Mother, 296
birthday cake, 272
birthday parties, 267
bo bebe Fine Baby Products, 31, 90
bo bebe's Music and Play, 235
Bobobaby, 77
Books and Babes, 53
Bow River Valley Walk, 147
Bowes Photography, 250
Bowness Park Walk, 151
BP Birthplace forest, 251
Bra Lady, the, 31
bras, 30–31, 161
breastfeeding clinics, 23, 26, 27, 28
breastfeeding, 19–28, 30, 47, 56, 74, 76, 115,
   139, 149, 154, 167, 183, 200, 205, 283
breast pumps, 28
Brenda Castonguay Photography, 250
Brilliant Beginnings Educational Centre, 50,
   75, 192
Budgeting for Baby, 2, 10
Busy Family, 259
Butterfield Acres Farm, 179

C

Café Mom, 131
Cakes, 216, 268, 269–273
Cakeworks, 273
Calaway Park, 180–181
Calgary Adventure Bootcamp, 176
Calgary Babies, 131
Calgary Babyzone website, 298
Calgary Child's Annual Free Family Fun
   Fare, 207
Calgary Children's Festival, 206
Calgary Co-op, 40, 109, 181, 273
Calgary Family Services, 52, 260

Calgary Health Region, 52, 56, 60, 67–70, 74–75, 81, 103, 129, 134, 227, 229, 233, 232, 230, 251, 257
Calgary International Airport, 142, 180
Calgary Maple Festival, 207
Calgary Moms, 96, 131
Calgary parks, 168, 181–182, 251, 296
Calgary Pathway and Bikeway Map, 146, 161
Calgary Police Service, 104
Calgary Pregnancy Care Centre, 124
Calgary Public Library, 181, 212, 222, 223, 225, 234, 247
Calgary Science Centre (Telus World of Science), 271
Calgary Stampede, the, 182
Calgary Tower, 183
Calgary Urban Project Society, 67
Calgary Youth Physiotherapy, 72
Calgary Zoo Lights, 207
Calgary Zoo, the, 180, 184, 207
Calgary's Child, 196, 250, 252, 278, 279, 296
Canada Child Tax Benefit (CCTB), 2, 7, 8–10
Canada Education Savings Grant, 6
Canada Learning Bond, 7, 9;
Canada Olympic Park, 163, 185
Canada Revenue Agency (CRA), 8
Canada Safety Council, 104
Canadian Association of Optometry, 69
Canadian Dental Association, 64, 66, 285
Canadian Paediatric Society, 57, 106, 298
Canadian Parents website, 298
Canadian Toy Testing Council, 211
canadiannanny.ca, 264
canadiansitter.ca, 253
Canmore Park, 189;
car seat, 16, 85, 89, 90, 93, 97, 103–106, 109, 115, 136, 137, 140
car seat/booster seat education class, 16
Cardel Place, 167, 172, 173, 193, 235, 237, 239, 240, 241
Caring for Kids, 57, 298
carriers, baby, 91, 96, 145, 159, 161, 162, 163
Castle Toys, 218
Cater Tot Consignment, 97
Centennial Education Savings Plan, 6, 8
Chapters, 223
Chariot Carriers Inc., 161, 162, 163
Chef Services, 39
Chic Mama, 123
Child & Family Canada, 298
Child and Family Services Authority (CFSA), 255, 258
Child and Infant Learning and Development Research Group (Ch.I.L.D.), 62
Child at Heart Children's Store, 221

Child Care Online, 259
Child Care Subsidy Program. see Alberta Child Care Subsidy Program
child care, 9, 10, 12–15
Child Find Alberta, 85–6
Child Save Canada, 87
Child Tax Benefit, 2, 7, 9, 10
Childcare SOLUTIONS, 259
Childproofing. see babyproofing
Children's Fitness Tax Credit, 8
Children's Hospital of Alberta. see Alberta Children's Hospital
Children's Cottage Society, 46, 292
Children's Festival. see International Children's Festival
Children's Link Website, 42
Children's Place, the, 90
Children's Program Guide, 234
Children's Safety Association of Canada, 85, 210
Chrysalis Education, 233, 232
Cineplex, 203
City of Calgary, 42, 66, 118, 146, 161, 168, 172, 173, 181, 182, 189, 239, 240, 241–242, 274, 297
Claudia's Choices, 94
cloth diapers, 101–102
Cocoon Baby, 95
Coffee & S'cream, 134, 198, 199, 268
community association, 101, 191, 247, 254, 257, 261, 267
concierge services, 36
consignment stores. see second-hand stores
Consular Affairs Bureau, 10
Consumer Reports, 89
cookingforyou.ca, 38
co-operative child care, 266
Copains de Jeux, les, 195
CopperPot Creations, 38–39, 78
counselling, 34
CPR, 81, 232, 253
crash test results, 106
Creative kids Active Music, 235
Creative Kids Hands-On Art Classes, 238
Creative Kids, 12, 13, 189, 235, 238, 268, 270
Crisis Nursery. see Children's Cottage Society
cross-country skiing, 90, 160, 163, 185
CUPS. see Calgary Urban Project Society
Curbside Recycling Association of Southern Alberta, 118
cycling, 145, 160, 161–162, 182

D

Daddies & Babies, 51, 134
Dads Can, 48, 135
daycare and day homes, 14, 43, 46, 123,
    163–167, 252–253, 255–258, 260,
    266, 276
dental care, 62–67
dentist, 62, 64, 65, 66, 67, 285
Devonian Gardens, 111, 181, 185
Diaper Depot, 102
diapers, 21, 91, 92, 93, 94, 95, 101–103, 114,
    127, 129, 137, 138, 139, 141, 142, 160,
    163, 189, 190, 239, 240, 241, 242, 244,
    245
dietitian, 74, 75, 76
dining out, 204–205
Discovery Toys, 219
doctor, 17–18, 19, 22, 23, 24, 25, 26, 27, 34,
    46, 56, 69, 71
downhill skiing, 163–167
Dr. Toy, 211, 212
drop-in centre, 252, 255
duct tape, 83, 84, 138

E

Early Start Drop-In Service, 17
Early Start Parent Information Line, 17, 56
East Lake Recreation and Wellness Centre,
    169, 174, 239, 242
East Region 3 – Parent Link Centre, 44
eBay, 95, 109
E-Children, 90
Empire Theatres, 203
Employment Insurance, 1–3
Entrees Express, 39, 117
Environmental Health Program, 257
Especially for Fathers, 134
eye checkup, 69

F

Families Matter Resource Centre, 216
Families Matter Society, 36, 43, 195
family coaching, 53
family day home. see daycares and day
    homes
Family Fun Fair, Calgary's child, 207
Family of Men Support Society, 135
Family Pride – Parent Link Centre, 44
Family Resource Centres, 216
Family Travel Files, 144
Family-a-Fair (formerly Mom's and Tot's
    Fair), 208
Farmers' markets, 78–79
Federation of Calgary Communities, 100,
    191, 267

Feeding Baby Solid Foods booklet, 75
feeding your baby, 24, 33, 74–79, 231
Fernie Alpine Resort, 164, 166, 167
festivals, 205–208
First-Aid course, 138
FITMOM Calgary, 176
fitness, 175–7, 181, 197, 239–245
flu shots. see immunizations
footwear, 106
Foreign Affairs Canada, 10, 144
formula, 23, 33, 74, 76, 93, 139, 163
Fort Calgary, 188
Fun with math, 53
games, 51, 73, 98, 134, 195, 209, 213, 214,
    224, 225, 236, 245, 268, 270

G

Gap Kids, 90
Going back to work, 126
Golly Geez Baby, 95
Got My Kids, 297
Gracie and Gruff, 219
Grand River Toys, 220
Great Outdoors Junior Outfitters, 91
Great Things in Store, 97
Greenway Recycling Inc., 118,
Griffith Woods Walk, 148–149
gross motor development, 70–73
Growing Up Organic, 95
growth charts, 57
Gym and Swim, 240, 241, 245
Gymaniacs, 14
Gymboree, 72, 91, 193–194, 225, 235, 236,
    238, 267, 297
Gymtastics, 194, 270
GymTots, 194

H

haircut, 107–8
Hand in Hand – Parent Link Centre, 44
Hands First Baby Sign, 229
Happy Nappy Diaper Service, 102
Happyland Children's Shoes, 107
Health Canada, 209, 210,
Health Care Insurance Plan, 3, 4, 265
Health Link Line, 18, 56, 60, 75
Healthy Families Calgary and Area, 46
helping your child adjust to a new baby, 51
Heritage Park to South Glenmore Park
    Walk, 150
Heritage Park, 150, 180, 186, 208
High Steppers for Children, 107
Hiking, 145, 159–160, 182
Hipmama, 130, 131
Huckleberry Kids, 98

CHAPTER 1 - ADMINITRATIVE ISSUES

Human Resources and Skills Development
Canada (HRSDC), 262
Hybrid Mom, 297

I

Ice-skating, 162
IKEA, 110, 114, 162
immunization, 56, 59–60, 70, 138, 165, 275
infant CPR, 232, 253
infant massage, 50, 193, 233
information sessions, 19, 199
Inglewood Bird Sanctuary and Nature
Centre, 187
In-home Infant Respite Program. see
Children's Cottage Society
Inquiring Minds Playgroup, 195
Insurance Corporation of British Columbia
(ICBC), 105
In-Sync, 52
International Children's Festival, 206
international nanny. see nannies
iVillage website, 299

J

jaundice, 24
jogging stroller, 160–161, 162, 163
Julie Marwood Photography, 250
Jump'N'Java, 198, 200, 268

K

Kacz's Kids, 84, 91, 159, 161
Kicking Horse Resort, 166
Kids at Play. see Market Mall's Kids at Play
Kids Photo, 249
Kidsource, 219
Kidz Printz, The Identification Kit Company,
86
Kimberly Alpine Resort, 165, 166
Kin Child Care Program, 260
Kindermusik Village, 235, 236–237
Kristen Shima Photography, 250

L

La Léché League, 24
lactation consultants, 26, 27
Lake Louise, 160, 164, 167
language development, 67
Laughing Families, 48
Learn at Lunch, 120
Learn to Swim, 239
leisure centre, 168, 172, 173, 241
Les Copains de Jeux, 195
Let's Play, 198, 201, 268
Liberated Cook, the, 39, 117
Library Children's Programs, 234

Life Assistants, 36
Little Beanstalks Clothing, 95
Little Tigers Childproofing Services, 81
Little Traveller, 137
Lollipop Children's Fashions, 98
Lower Income Services. see Services for
Lower Income Albertans
Lullaby Lane Children's Consignment, 98

M

M&M Meat Shops, 37
Make or Take Meals, 117
Makeovers of Moms (M.O.M.), 176
malls, 110, 158
Marda Loop Walk, 154
Market Mall's Kids at Play, 198, 201
Massage Medics, 123
massage, 123
Maternity Cupboard, 125
McNally Robinson Booksellers for Kids, 224
meal plans, 116
meetup.com, 130, 131, 132
MegaMood Baby Boutique, 96
mementos, 246
Millican-Ogden Community Association's
Family Resource Centre, 295
Mom & Baby Fit Together, 168
Mom Store, the, 91
Mom2Boys Productions, 251
Mommy Buzz, 142
Mommy Chats, 130, 132
Mommy Club, 130, 132
Mommy Mode, 129
Mompreneur, the, 297
Moms in Motion, 177
Momsandtots.ca, 130, 132
Monkeyshines Children's Books, 221, 224
Montessori, 12, 277
Mother Goose program, 134, 195, 293, 295
Motherisk, 25
Mother's Day Run and Walk, 159
Mount Engadine Lodge, 143
Mount Royal College, 237
Mountain Baby, 96
Mountain Equipment Co-op (MEC), 91
movies, 203
Moxie Moms, 130, 132
Mt. Royal College Conservatory – Music
with your baby, 237
Multiples. see Twins or Multiples
music classes, 234–237
Mustard, Betsy, 72

N

nannies, 252, 260–266
National Child Benefit, 7, 8, 9
National Swimming Program, 239, 240, 245
New Family Place – Parent Link Centre, 44
Nobody's Perfect Parenting, 52, 296
North Central Family Connections –
    Parent Link Centre, 44
North Glenmore Park Walk, 156
North Rocky View Community Resource
    Centre, 44
Numina Counseling Inc., 34
nursing bras. see bras
nutrition, 63, 74, 75

O

Okotoks Healthy Family Resource Centre,
    45
Okotoks Toy Library, 214, 215, 272
Old Navy, 92
Olympic Plaza, 189, 206
Once Upon a Child, 99, 125
One Tiny Suitcase, 137
online forums, 130
online store, 94–96
Oppenheim Toy Portfolio, 212
Optometrists, Alberta College of, 69
Outdoor Resource Centre, 182
Owl's Nest Bookstore, 224

P

pacifier, 64, 65
paediatrician, 17–18, 33, 57, 69, 70, 71
Panorama Mountain Village, 167
Parent & Baby Fit Together, 168
Parent Link Alberta Centres, 43–45
Parent Link Corridor – Parent Link Centre,
    44
parenting courses, 50–55
Parenting Power, 52, 53
Parenting Resource line, 36
parenting style, 53, 121,
Parents and Children Together (PACT), 12,
    53, 196
Parents as Teachers (PAT), 53, 294
Parents' Choice Awards, 211–212
Parents' Club, 83, 120, 121
passport, 10–12
Peas in a Pod, 50
Pedipeds, 107
Pelvic Floor Clinic, 59
perinatal education, 45, 47, 50, 74, 81
personal chef, 39
pharmacy, 18
photography, 249–250

physiotherapy, 59, 71, 72, 73
Pic'N'Del, 40
placement agencies, 264
Planet Organic, 77
playgroups, 191–197
Playtime Toy and Party Rentals, 214, 216
Playtime with Dad, 51
Please Mum, 92
Poison and Drug Information Centre, 87, 88
Portrait Studios, 249–250
Positive Parenting, 53
Post Natal Helpers Ltd., 254
postnatal yoga, 168, 170, 230
Postpartum Community Services, 16
postpartum depression, 22, 34–36
Prairie Winds Park, 189
Prepared Meals, 37–39
preschool, 68, 71, 82, 274–281
product advice, 89
Professional Parenting, 52, 54
Pumps. see breastpumps

R

Rapid Rent a Ski, 162
Raymond Parenting, 52, 54, 227
Real Canadian Superstore, 92
recalls, 97, 104, 210–211
Recreation in the City Program Guide, 168,
    173, 181, 242
Reel babies, 203
Reggio, Emilio, 277
Registered Education Savings Plan (RESP),
    6–7
Riley Park, 180, 182, 189,
River Park Walk, 152
Robeez, 107
Rockadry Baby, 103
Rotary Park, 189
Running, 160

S

Safe and Sound Babyproofing Ltd., 81
Safe Kids Canada, 85
Safety First Course, 253
safety products, 81, 82, 83, 90, 92, 93
Safeway, 102, 109, 158
Salsa, 120
Saskatoon Farm, the, 188
Saturday Morning at the Symphony
    (SMATS), 208
Savvy Mom, 130, 132
Scholar's Choice, 220
science centre, 271
scrapbooking, 247
SEARS I Can Swim, 239, 240, 243,

Sears Portrait Studios, 249
Sears, 92
second-hand stores, 96–98
Service Canada, 2, 5, 6, 8
Services for Lower Income Albertans, 2, 15, 252
Shaw Millennium Park, 189
Shoe Company, 107
Shriners Hospitals for Children, 85
sign language, 228–229
single parent, 49, 141
Single Parent Tours, 141
Sip'N'Safari, 198, 202, 269
skiing daycare, 164, 165
sleep courses, 226, 227
Sleep Workshop for Tired Parents, 227
slope-side accommodation, 166–167
Small Potatoes Urban Delivery, 41
Social Insurance Number, 5
South Glenmore Park, 150
Southland Leisure Centre, 173, 180, 242
Spa, 123
Spagoes, 123
speech therapy, 67
Sports Rent, 162
SportsBras, 31
Spray Parks, 189
Sproutz Kidz Inc., 99
Sproutz Kidz Metro, 92, 96,
St. David's Time Out, 196
Stampede, the, 182
Stanley Park to Talisman Centre walk, 157
Stanley Park, 189
Stars and Strollers, 203
Statement of Live Birth, 4
Stay-at-Home Parent Child Care Subsidy, 12
sterilizer, 29
Sugar Shack Cakes, 272
Sunshine Village, 167
Sunterra Quality Food Markets, 37, 38, 40
Superstore see Real Canadian Superstore,
Suzuki Talent Education Society, 237
Swanky Moms, 130, 132
Sweet Pea Baby Food, 77
Swim for Life, 239, 240, 241, 244
swimming classes, 239
Synergy in Motion, 123

T

Talisman Centre, 157, 169, 172, 174, 176, 232, 239, 240, 243, 253
teeth, 62–67
Telus World of Science, 189–190, 271
Thrive Fitness, 177
thumb-sucking, 65
time capsule, 248
Time is Money Executive Concierge Inc., 37
TimeOut Solutions Inc., 37
Tiny Gem Baby Solutions, 96
Tiny Talk and Walk, 72, 229
Today's Parent, 297
Toxic Plants, 88
Toy libraries/banks, 214
toy recalls, 210
Toy safety, 209
ToyDreams Inc., 220
Toylend Inc., 214
Toys "R" Us, 93
Traditional Learning Programs, 277
travelling with baby, 136
Twelve Days of Christmas, 208
Twice Upon a Time, 93
Twins and Triplets and More Association of Calgary (TTMAC), 48, 49, 196

U

Ultimate Trains, 191
Universal Child Care Benefit (UCCB), 10
University of Calgary Gymnastics Centre, 271
University of Calgary Kinesiology, 243, 253
University of Calgary Outdoor Program Centre, 162
University of Calgary, 62, 162, 243, 253, 271, 279
UrbanMoms, 130, 133
Urban Therapeutics, 123
Urban Treehouse Playcentres Inc., 198, 202, 269
Usborne Baby Books, 225
UsedCalgary.com, 99

V

Valleyview Park, 189
Value Village, 100
Village Square Leisure Centre, 173
Vocational Rehabilitation Research Institute (VRRI), 170, 198, 203, 237, 239, 240, 244, 270

W

wading parks, 189
Waiters en Route, 39
Wal-Mart Portrait Studio, 249
Wal-Mart, 93
Wee Feed Inc., 28
Wee Hands, 229
Wee Sign, 229
West Central Community and Family
    Resource Centre, 214
Western Parent, 298
Western Rocky View PLC – Parent Link
    Centre, 45
Westside Recreation Centre, 174, 244
Women in Need Society, 125, 129, 294
Women's Health Centre, 55, 59
Wovenfare, 116

Y

YMCA, 13, 170, 171, 172, 175, 197, 231, 230,
    239, 240, 245, 253, 270
yoga, 230
Yoga Shala, 230
Yoga Studio, 230
You & Me Baby Workout, 169,
Yummy Mummy, 130, 133

Z

Zellers, 93
Zero to Three, 299
Zoo, the Calgary, 180, 184, 207

Baby Notes

QUICK REFERENCE CONTACT DETAILS

Poison Control Centre 944-1414
    Open 24 hours

Emergency 911
    Open 24 hours

Calgary Police 266-1234
    Open 24 hours

Early Start Line 244-8351
    Babies up to two months old.

Health Link 943-5465

Children's Cottage Crisis Nursery 233-2273

La Leche League 242-0277

Distress Centre 266-1605

Postpartum Support Line 205-5177
    Monday to Friday: 9 a.m. – 4 p.m.

Women's Emergency Shelter 234-7233

Telecare 266-0700

Contact in case of emergency
    Name: Phone:

Family Doctor
    Name: Phone:

Dentist
    Name: Phone:

Babysitter #1
    Name: Phone:

Babysitter #2
    Name: Phone:

Babysitter #3
    Name: Phone:

Community sales   Spring and Fall
    www.babyguidetocalgary.com